FLANDERS IN THE FIFTEENTH CENTURY:
ART AND CIVILIZATION

FLANDERS IN THE FIFTEENTH CENTURY: ART AND CIVILIZATION

Catalogue of the Exhibition

MASTERPIECES OF FLEMISH ART: VAN EYCK TO BOSCH

Organized by

THE DETROIT INSTITUTE OF ARTS

and

THE CITY OF BRUGES

The Detroit Institute of Arts

October — December

1960

THIS CATALOGUE IS PUBLISHED JOINTLY BY
THE DETROIT INSTITUTE OF ARTS, DETROIT, MICHIGAN, AND
THE CENTRE NATIONAL DE RECHERCHES PRIMITIFS FLAMANDS,
BRUSSELS, BELGIUM

The special expenses of this
exhibition and of the publication of this catalogue have
been contributed by The Detroit
Museum of Art Founders Society

The Honorable Dwight D. Eisenhower

President of the United States

and

His Majesty Baudouin

King of the Belgians

have graciously accorded their High Patronage

to this Belgian-American Exhibition

HONORARY COMMITTEE

The Hon. Christian A. Herter, Secretary of State of the United States
The Hon. Thomas S. Gates, Jr., Secretary of Defence of the United States
The Hon. Arthur S. Flemming, Secretary of Health, Education and Welfare of
the United States
The Hon. William B. Franke, Secretary of the Navy, Department of the Navy of
the United States
The Hon. Wilber M. Brucker, Secretary of the Army of the United States
The Hon. William A.M. Burden, Ambassador of the United States to Belgium
The Hon. G. Mennen Williams, Governor of the State of Michigan
The Hon. Louis C. Miriani, Mayor of the City of Detroit
Mr. K.T. Keller, President of the Arts Commission of the City of Detroit
Mr. Alvan Macauley, Jr., President of The Detroit Museum of Art Founders
Society
Mrs. Edsel B. Ford, Detroit, Michigan

Son Em. le Cardinal Joseph E. Van Roey, Archevêque de Malines
M. Gaston Eyskens, Premier Ministre de Belgique
M. René Lefebvre, Vice-Président du Conseil et Ministre de l'Intérieur de
Belgique
M. Jean Van Houtte, Ministre des Finances de Belgique
M. Albert Lilar, Ministre de la Justice de Belgique
M. Pierre Wigny, Ministre des Affaires Etrangères de Belgique
M. P.W. Segers, Ministre des Communications de Belgique
M. Pierre Harmel, Ministre de la Fonction Publique de Belgique
M. Omer Vanaudenhove, Ministre des Travaux Publics et de la Reconstruction
de Belgique
M. Charles Moureaux, Ministre de l'Instruction Publique de Belgique
M. Louis Scheyven, Ambassadeur de Belgique à Washington
M. Walter Loridan, Ambassadeur de Belgique auprès des Nations-Unies
Le Chevalier Pierre van Outryve d'Ydewalle, Gouverneur de la Flandre
Occidentale
Leurs Exc. les Evêques de Belgique
M. Pierre Vandamme, Bourgmestre de Bruges
M. Jan-Albert Goris, Ministre Plénipotentiaire, Commissaire à l'Information,
Belgian Government Information Center, New York

COMMITTEE OF ORGANIZATION

Joseph Bernolet, Secrétaire Communal de la Ville de Bruges

William A. Bostick, Executive Secretary, The Arts Commission of the City of Detroit, The Detroit Institute of Arts, Detroit, Michigan

Paul Coremans, Directeur, Centre National de Recherches Primitifs Flamands et Institut Royal du Patrimoine Artistique, Brussels

Melle Jacqueline Folie, Attaché, Institut Royal du Patrimoine Artistique, Brussels

Alin Janssens de Bisthoven, Directeur, Musées Communaux de la Ville de Bruges

Melle Lucie Ninane, Conservateur - Adjoint, Musées Royaux des Beaux-Arts, Brussels

Edgar P. Richardson, Director, The Detroit Institute of Arts, Detroit, Michigan

Francis W. Robinson, Curator of Ancient and Medieval Art, The Detroit Institute of Arts, Detroit, Michigan

Carl Tiedeman, Executive Secretary, The Detroit Museum of Art Founders Society, Detroit, Michigan

Fernand Vanden Broele, Echevin des Finances et des Affaires Culturelles de la Ville de Bruges

Frans Van Molle, Chef du Service des Archives Iconographiques, Institut Royal du Patrimoine Artistique, Brussels

Melle Nicole Verhaegen, Secrétaire Scientifique, Centre National de Recherches Primitifs Flamands, Brussels

Michael Weyl, Cultural Affairs Officer of the Foreign Service of the United States, American Embassy, Brussels

Publicity :   Julien Blontrock, Bruges
                 John D. Morse, Detroit
                 John L. Oliver, Detroit
                 Peter Pollack, New York

Insurance :   Detroit Insurance Agency, Detroit
                 L. Eeckman, Brussels

Transportation : La Continentale Menkés, Brussels
                 Schumm Traffic Agency, New York
                 United States Navy, Military Sea Transportation Service

ACKNOWLEDGMENTS

The organizers of this exhibition are very grateful to the following persons, and to the institutions which they represent, for the generous assistance and cooperation which have made the exhibition possible:

Nicholas M. Acquavella Galleries, New York, N.Y.

Frederick B. Adams, Jr., Director, The Pierpont Morgan Library, New York, N.Y.

Philip R. Adams, Director, The Cincinnati Art Museum, Cincinnati, Ohio

Maurice-A. Arnould, Conservateur Honoraire de la Bibliothèque Publique, Mons

Mme Betty Barzin, Brussels

Warren Beach, Director, The Fine Arts Gallery of San Diego, San Diego, California

Miss Mary V. Beck, President of the Common Council of the City of Detroit, Detroit, Michigan

Mme Suzanne Berger, Attaché, Musée Royal du Congo, Tervueren, Brussels

Melle Simone Bergmans, Brussels

Julien Blontrock, Directeur du Service du Tourisme de la Ville de Bruges

Ruth and Leopold Blumka, New York, N.Y.

Julien Boes, Archiviste de la Ville de Gand

Paul Bonenfant, Professeur à l'Université Libre de Bruxelles, Membre du Centre National de Recherches Primitifs Flamands, Brussels

Karel Borgers, Curé de l'Eglise Sainte-Dymphne, Geel

Chanoine Carlos Botte, Curé de la Cathédrale Saint-Sauveur, Bruges

Richard F. Brown, Chief Curator of Art, Los Angeles County Museum, Los Angeles, California

Richard D. Buck, Director, Intermuseum Laboratory, Oberlin, Ohio

Melle Marguerite Calberg, Conservateur, Musées Royaux d'Art et d'Histoire, Brussels

Raphaël Calliauw, Directeur à l'Administration Communale, Bruges

Giovanni Carandente, Ispettore, Galleria Nazionale d'Arte Moderna, Rome

Ed. Carey, Member of the Common Council of the City of Detroit, Detroit, Michigan

Chanoine Jean Cassart, Conservateur du Trésor Diocésain de la Cathédrale Notre-Dame, Tournai

A. Castermans, Président du Conseil de Fabrique de l'Eglise Saint-Jacques, Bruges

Adolph S. Cavallo, Curator of Textiles, Museum of Fine Arts, Boston, Massachusetts

Gilbert Chase, Former Cultural Affairs Officer of the Foreign Service of the United States, American Embassy, Brussels

James Chillman, Jr., Interim Director, The Museum of Fine Arts of Houston, Houston, Texas

Emiel Claeys, Bourgmestre de la Ville de Gand

Allen W. Clowes, Vice-President, The Clowes Fund, Indianapolis, Indiana

Ralph T. Coe, Curator of Paintings and Sculpture, William Rockhill Nelson Gallery of Art, Kansas City, Missouri

Edward Connor, Member of the Common Council of the City of Detroit, Detroit, Michigan

John Coolidge, Director, Fogg Art Museum, Harvard University, Cambridge, Massachusetts

Lode Craeybeckx, Bourgmestre de la Ville d'Anvers

Chanoine Juul Creten, Curé-Doyen de l'Eglise Saint-Pierre, Louvain

Mme Marthe Crick-Kuntziger, Conservateur Honoraire, Musées Royaux d'Art et d'Histoire, Brussels

Miss Nancy Curtis, Assistant Librarian, The Solomon R. Guggenheim Museum, New York, N.Y.

Ch. Dael, Ghent

Martin Davies, Keeper, The National Gallery, London

S.A.S. le Prince de Croy-Roeulx, Le Roeulx

Le Rév. Père Baudouin de Gaiffier d'Hestroy, S.J., Brussels

Gustaaf Dehulster, Secrétaire à la Direction des Musées de la Ville de Bruges

A. De Jaeger, Président des Amis des Musées Communaux, Membre de la Commission des Musées, Bruges

Chanoine Leo De Kesel, Président du Grand Séminaire, Ghent

Jean Delacour, Director, Los Angeles County Museum, Los Angeles, California

J. Delacroix, Tirlemont

Comte de Limburg Stirum, Brussels

Louis De Man, Archiviste de la Ville, Louvain

Cyriel De Meester, Echevin de la Ville de Bruges

J. Demeter, Brussels

Raymond De Mey, Conseiller Communal, Membre de la Commission des Musées, Bruges

Melle Isabelle de Ramaix, Brussels

A. de Schietere de Lophem, Bruges

Antoine De Schryver, Conservateur des Musées d'Archéologie, Ghent

J. De Smet, Archiviste de l'Etat, Membre de la Commission des Musées, Bruges

Léon Dewez, Conservateur du Musée Diocésain, Liège

L. De Winter, Président de la Section de Peinture, Commission des Musées, Bruges

Robert Didier, Collaborateur Scientifique, Institut Royal du Patrimoine Artistique, Brussels
Duveen Brothers, Inc., New York, N.Y.
Gérard Eneman, Membre de la Chambre des Représentants, Echevin de la Ville de Bruges
Miss Eleanor Ferry, Registrar, The Detroit Institute of Arts, Detroit, Michigan
J. Fontier, Membre de la Commission des Musées, Bruges
William H. Forsyth, Associate Curator of Medieval Art, The Metropolitan Museum of Art, New York, N.Y.
Henry S. Francis, Curator of Paintings and Prints, The Cleveland Museum of Art, Cleveland, Ohio
Perrin C. Galpin, President, Belgian American Educational Foundation, New York, N.Y.
Horst Gerson, Director, Rijksbureau voor Kunsthistorische Documentatie, The Hague
John Gilissen, Professeur à l'Université Libre de Bruxelles
H. Gombert, Museumsdirektor, Augustinermuseum, Freiburg im-Breisgau
William Harry Gothard, Conservator, The Cincinnati Art Museum, Cincinnati, Ohio
Gerard Hanssen, Bourgmestre de la Ville de Diest
Walter Heil, Director, M.H. de Young Memorial Museum, San Francisco, California
Rudolf J. Heinemann, New York, N.Y.
Chanoine Arthur Hodüm, Curé-Doyen de l'Eglise Saint-Jacques, Bruges
Albert Hoegaerts, Curé de l'Eglise Saint-Sauveur, Hakendover
James Humphrey III, Chief Librarian, Metropolitan Museum of Art, New York, N.Y.
Sam Hunter, Acting Director, The Minneapolis Institute of Arts, Minneapolis, Minnesota
Adolf Jansen, Conservateur-Adjoint, Musées Royaux d'Art et d'Histoire, Brussels
Melle Claire Janson, Conservateur en Chef Honoraire, Musées Royaux des Beaux-Arts de Belgique, Brussels
Albert-Edouard Janssen, Ministre d'Etat, Président de l'Association Belgo-Américaine, Brussels
Bob Jones, President of Bob Jones University and Director, University Museum and Art Gallery, Greenville, South Carolina
A. Joos de ter Beerst, Conservateur du Musée du Saint-Sang, Bruges
F. Joos de ter Beerst, Secrétaire de la Commission d'Assistance Publique, Bruges
Alan W. Joslyn, Trustee of The Detroit Museum of Art Founders Society, Detroit, Michigan

Richard Kay, Research Associate, Department of History, University of Wisconsin, Madison, Wisconsin

Sheldon Keck, Conservator, Brooklyn Museum, Brooklyn, N.Y.

G. Kelly, Secretary to the Director, The Art Gallery of San Diego, San Diego, California

David W. Kendall, Special Consultant to the President of the United States, Washington, D.C.

Charles Kerremans, Attaché au Cabinet de S.M. le Roi, Brussels

Herman Kerremans, Drukkerij L. Blondé, Antwerp

J.M. Kervyn de Marcke ten Driessche, Conseiller Communal, Membre de la Commission des Musées, Bruges

Edward S. King, Director, The Walters Art Gallery, Baltimore, Maryland

M. Knoedler and Company, Inc., New York, N.Y.

Chanoine Leo Kortleven, Curé-Doyen de l'Eglise Notre-Dame, Tongres

Baron Kronacker, Brussels

Emile Langui, Directeur Général des Arts et des Lettres, Ministère de l'Instruction Publique, Brussels

Chanoine Valère Laridon, Curé-Doyen de l'Eglise Notre-Dame, Bruges

Jacques Lavalleye, Directeur de l'Institut Supérieur d'Archéologie et d'Histoire de l'Art, Université Catholique de Louvain et Président du Centre National de Recherches Primitifs Flamands, Brussels

Sherman E. Lee, Director, The Cleveland Museum of Art, Cleveland, Ohio

Jaap L. Leeuwenberg, Conservateur, Rijksmuseum, Amsterdam

René Lefebure, Chef du Cabinet de S.M. le Roi, Brussels

Raymond M. Lemaire, Professeur à l'Université Catholique de Louvain

William D. Lemoine, Chercheur, Centre National d'Histoire des Sciences, Brussels

Albert Leyssens, Sacristain de l'Eglise Saint-Léonard, Léau

Chanoine André Lobet, Président du Petit Séminaire de Bonne-Espérance, Vellereille-lez-Brayeux

Lawrence F. Loffman, Detroit Insurance Agency, Detroit, Michigan

Chanoine Joseph Loncke, Curé-Doyen de l'Eglise Saint-Roch, Blankenberge

Louis Loose, Attaché, Institut Royal du Patrimoine Artistique, Brussels

Miss Carol Macht, Curator of Decorative Arts, The Cincinnati Art Museum, Cincinnati, Ohio

Georges Marlier, Brussels

L.-C. Marshall, Brussels

Lucien Massart, Professeur à l'Université de Gand, Président du Conseil National de la Politique Scientifique, Brussels

Thomas N. Maythem, Assistant, Department of Paintings, Museum of Fine Arts, Boston, Massachusetts

J. Meulemans, Président du Conseil de Fabrique de l'Eglise Saint-Pierre, Louvain

Henri Michel, Brussels

Miss Dorothy E. Miner, Librarian and Keeper of Manuscripts, The Walters Art Gallery, Baltimore, Maryland

Henry Moens, Trésorier du Conseil de Fabrique de l'Eglise Saint-Sauveur, Hakendover

André Molitor, Professeur à l'Université Catholique de Louvain, Secrétaire Général du Conseil National de la Politique Scientifique, Brussels

Miss Alice Mongan, Assistant Director and Curator of Drawings, Fogg Art Museum, Harvard University, Cambridge, Massachusetts

Miss Elizabeth Mongan, Curator of Graphic Arts, National Gallery of Art, Washington, D.C.

Mrs. Dorothy Moore-Deflandre, Executive Officer, The United States Educational Foundation, Brussels

Gérard Neels, Sénateur, Echevin de la Ville de Bruges

Edmund B. Nielsen, Research Associate, The Museum of Fine Arts of Houston, Houston, Texas

René Oversteyns, Curé-Doyen de l'Eglise Saint-Léonard, Léau

Miss Elizabeth Packard, Director of the Department of Conservation, The Walters Art Gallery, Baltimore, Maryland

Robert O. Parks, Director, Smith College Museum of Art, Northampton, Massachusetts

William T. Patrick, Member of the Common Council of the City of Detroit, Detroit, Michigan

Henri Pauwels, Attaché, Musées Royaux d'Art et d'Histoire, Brussels

J. Peemans, Attaché au Cabinet de S.M. le Roi, Brussels

K.C. Peeters, Professeur à l'Université Catholique de Louvain, Secrétaire de la Ville d'Anvers

Le Personnel Scientifique et Administratif du Centre National de Recherches Primitifs Flamands, Brussels

Le Personnel Scientifique, Technique et Administratif de l'Institut Royal du Patrimoine Artistique, Brussels

The Personnel of the Military Sea Transportation Service of The United States Navy

Joseph Philippe, Conservateur des Musées Curtius et d'Ansembourg, Liège

Joseph Philippen, Archiviste de l'Eglise Saint-Sulpice, Diest

Melle C. Piérard, Conservateur de la Bibliothèque Publique, Mons

Constant Pirlot, Conseiller-Chef de Division au Ministère de l'Instruction Publique, Brussels

John H. Plummer, Curator of Medieval and Renaissance Manuscripts, The Pierpont Morgan Library, New York, N.Y.

Richard H. Randall, Jr., Assistant Curator of Decorative Arts, Museum of Fine Arts, Boston, Massachusetts

Perry T. Rathbone, Director, Museum of Fine Arts, Boston, Massachusetts

Andrew C. Ritchie, Director, Yale University Art Gallery, New Haven, Connecticut

Philippe Roberts-Jones, Attaché au Cabinet du Ministre de l'Instruction Publique, Brussels

William G. Rogell, Member of the Common Council of the City of Detroit, Detroit, Michigan

James J. Rorimer, Director, The Metropolitan Museum of Art, New York, N.Y.

Rosenberg and Stiebel, Inc., New York, N.Y.

Theodore Rousseau, Curator of European Paintings, The Metropolitan Museum of Art, New York, N.Y.

Jørn Rubow, Director, Statens Museum for Kunst, Copenhagen

Miss Pauline Rupp, Secretary to the Director, Bob Jones University, Museum and Art Gallery, Greenville, South Carolina

Etienne Sabbe, Archiviste Général du Royaume, Brussels

Hanns Schaeffer, New York, N.Y.

Albert Schouteet, Conservateur f.f. des Archives de la Ville, Bruges

Miss Henrietta M. Schumm, Schumm Traffic Agency, New York, N.Y.

Ed. P. Seeldrayers, Secrétaire Général du Ministère de l'Instruction Publique, Brussels

Laurence Sickman, Director, William Rockhill Nelson Gallery of Art, Kansas City, Missouri

Mrs. Bente Skovgaard, Associate Curator, Statens Museum for Kunst, Copenhagen

Frans Smekens, Conservateur des Musées d'Archéologie, Antwerp

Alfons Smets, Bourgmestre de la Ville de Louvain

Del A. Smith, Member of the Common Council of the City of Detroit, Detroit, Michigan

Frank Smolar, Brussels

D. Somerlinck, Membre de la Commission des Musées, Bruges

Jean Squilbeck, Conservateur-Adjoint, Musées Royaux d'Art et d'Histoire, Brussels

Miss Felice Stampfle, Curator of Prints and Drawings, The Pierpont Morgan Library, New York, N.Y.

Richard M. Stein, Brussels

E. Clark Stillman, Secretary, Belgian American Educational Foundation, New York, N.Y.

Egide Strubbe, Professeur à l'Université de Gand, Membre de la Commission des Musées, Bruges

Hanns Swarzenski, Curator of Decorative Arts, Museum of Fine Arts, Boston, Massachusetts

Miss Barbara Sweeney, Associate Curator, John G. Johnson Collection, The Philadelphia Museum of Art, Philadelphia, Pennsylvania

James Johnson Sweeney, Director, The Solomon R. Guggenheim Museum, New York, N.Y.

Chanoine Raphaël Tambuyser, Secrétaire de l'Archevêché de Malines

Robert H. Thayer, Special Assistant to the Secretary of State of the United States, Washington, D.C.

W.A. Thorpe, Deputy Keeper, Department of Woodwork, Victoria and Albert Museum, London

Frans Tits, Secrétaire du Conseil de Fabrique de l'Eglise Saint-Pierre, Louvain

Elie Traen, Echevin de la Ville de Bruges

Evan H .Turner, Director, The Montreal Museum of Fine Arts, Montreal, Quebec, Canada

Mrs. Elizabeth Usher, Assistant Librarian, The Metropolitan Museum of Art, New York, N.Y.

Miss Ninfa Valvo, Associate Curator of Painting, M.H. de Young Memorial Museum, San Francisco, California

Eugene I. Van Antwerp, Member of the Common Council of the City of Detroit, Detroit, Michigan

Walter Vanbeselaere, Conservateur en Chef du Musée Royal des Beaux-Arts, Antwerp

R. Van Biesebroeck, Membre de la Commission des Musées, Bruges

Albert Van den Brouck, Curé de l'Eglise Sainte-Gertrude, Etterbeek

Frans Vanden Eynde, Curé de l'Eglise Sainte-Gertrude, Louvain

Roger Van den Hauten, La Continentale Menkés, Brussels

Maurice Vanden Stock, Secrétaire Comptable, Centre National de Recherches Primitifs Flamands, Brussels

Jacques van der Belen, Secretary in Belgium, Belgian American Educational Foundation, Brussels

Frans Vanderborght, Curé de l'Eglise Saint-Jacques, Louvain

Gilbert Van der Linden, Archiviste de la Ville, Diest

C. van de Walle de Ghelcke, Président de la Section d'Archéologie, Commission des Musées, Bruges

Chanoine Louis Van de Walle, Membre de la Commission des Musées, Bruges

H. Van de Wijer, Attaché au Cabinet du Premier Ministre, Brussels

L. Van Haecht, Président du Conseil de Fabrique de l'Eglise Saint-Sulpice, Diest

J. Van Hee, Bourgmestre de Furnes

Jan Van Herck, Antwerp

Jozef Van Herck, Curé-Doyen de l'Eglise Saint-Martin, Kontich

Melle D. Vanhoutte, Membre de la Commission des Musées, Bruges

Jan Van Lerberghe, Conseiller à la Propagande Artistique, Ministère de l'Instruction Publique, Brussels

Arthur van Schendel, Director, Rijksmuseum, Amsterdam

Léopold Van Uytven, Curé-Doyen de l'Eglise Saint-Sulpice, Diest

Son Exc. Mgr Honoré Van Wayenbergh, Recteur Magnifique de l'Université Catholique de Louvain

Son Exc. Mgr Guillaume van Zuylen, Evêque Coadjuteur de Liège

Pieter Verdroncken, Curé-Doyen de l'Eglise Saint-Germain, Tirlemont

Philippe Verdier, Curator of Decorative Arts, The Walters Art Gallery, Baltimore, Maryland

Gaspard Verecken, Conseiller Chef de Service aux Relations Extérieures, Ministère de l'Instruction Publique, Brussels

Melle Violette Verhoogen, Conservateur-Délégué, Musées Royaux d'Art et d'Histoire, Brussels

Roger Versteegen, Chef de l'Atelier Photographique, Institut Royal du Patrimoine Artistique, Brussels

L. Viérin, Membre de la Commission des Musées, Bruges

R. Waes, Président de la Commission d'Assistance Publique, Bruges

John Walker, Director, The National Gallery of Art, Washington, D.C.

Julius H. Weitzner, New York and London

Wildenstein and Co., Inc., New York and Paris

Jean Willems, Vice-Président et Directeur, Fonds National de la Recherche Scientifique, Brussels

Mrs. Blanche Parent Wise, Member of the Common Council of the City of Detroit, Detroit, Michigan

Mrs. Nancy Coe Wixom, Assistant Curator of Painting, The Cleveland Museum of Art, Cleveland, Ohio

William D. Wixom, Assistant Curator of Decorative Arts, The Cleveland Museum of Art, Cleveland, Ohio

18

ADMINISTRATIVE AND CURATORIAL STAFF

Edgar P. Richardson, *Director and Curator of Western Art*

Paul L. Grigaut, *Assistant to the Director, Chief Art Curator, Curator of Oriental Art*

William A. Bostick, *Secretary and Business Manager*

Francis W. Robinson, *Curator of Ancient and Medieval Art*

Elizabeth H. Payne, *Associate Curator of Western Art*

A. Franklin Page, *Curator of Contemporary Art*

Gil Oden, *Curator of Theatre Arts*

William E. Woolfenden, *Curator in Charge of Education*

Virginia Harriman, *Associate Curator in Education*

Nicholas Snow, Patricia Slattery, Ralph Glowacki, Jerome Pryor, Curtis Coley, *Junior Curators in Education*

Carol Selby, *Librarian;* F. Warren Peters, *Associate Librarian;* Elisabeth Fischer, *Cataloguer*

Joseph Klima, *Photographer*

Eleanor Ferry, *Registrar*

Harold T. Shaw, *Superintendent*

CENTRE NATIONAL DE RECHERCHES PRIMITIFS FLAMANDS

MEMBRES DU CONSEIL

Jacques Lavalleye, *Président*

Paul Coremans, *Directeur*

Paul Bonenfant, *Membre*

Louis Lebeer, *Membre*

Melle Nicole Verhaegen, *Secrétaire Scientifique*

Maurice Vanden Stock, *Secrétaire-Comptable*

PRELIMINARY REMARKS

The *classification* of the objects in this catalogue is arranged in a systematic order according to the different categories of works and documents. The categories are: painting, drawing and woodcut, sculpture, metalwork, goldsmith's work, arms and armor, textiles, furniture, glass and stained-glass, historical documents, and illuminated manuscripts. Within each of these categories, the works are classified, as far as possible, in chronological order.

The *basic data* for all the items from America is that given by the lenders. This information has been completed by the documentation of the Centre National de Recherches Primitifs Flamands and the Institut Royal du Patrimoine Artistique, Brussels.

The *attributions* are those of the lenders. They have occasionally been amended in the entry.

The *entries* begin with a general presentation of the object within the frame of the 15th century. Next is the factual data: physical data, history of the work, and exhibitions in which it has been shown. This is followed by the body of the entry which presents the *status quaestionis* and a discussion relative to the origin, attribution, dating, and iconography of the work. This information is supported by references which provide a basic bibliography.

An *illustration* accompanies each entry. Consequently, purely descriptive information has been held to a minimum. Where not otherwise indicated, the terms right and left are given from the position of the viewer as he faces the object.

The *dimensions* of the paintings are given for the total surface of the panel whenever these measurements could be obtained. Where it was impossible to remove the frame, the dimensions correspond to the surface visible within the frame (sight measurement). The absence of an indication of the basis on which the measurements were calculated signifies that this information was not available. For all works the measurements are presented in the following order: height, width, thickness or depth.

The *history* of each work is made up from the documentation of the Centre National de Recherches Primitifs Flamands and the Institut Royal du Patrimoine Artistique, and is completed by the data furnished by the lenders.

20

The *exhibitions* section of each entry briefly indicates the place and year of the exhibition and the catalogue number which was assigned to the work. These exhibitions are given in the bibliography at the end of the volume.

The *discussion* furnishes an indication of the bibliographical sources, also in brief form, for each element of the *status quaestionis*. These references are also given in the bibliography.

The *bibliography,* at the end of the catalogue, lists all references cited in the entries. It is classified alphabetically by author, and chronologically for each author. Next, the catalogues of museums, exhibitions, and sales referred to in the entries are listed in chronological order. The abbreviation, R.K.D., refers to the Rijksbureau voor Kunsthistorische Documentatie, The Hague.

AUTHORS OF THE ENTRIES

Paintings from Belgian collections, drawings, sculpture, metalwork, goldsmith's work, arms and armor, textiles, furniture and glass from Belgian and American collections: *Melle Lucie Ninane,* Conservateur-Adjoint, Musées Royaux des Beaux-Arts, Brussels.

Paintings from American collections: *Melle Jacqueline Folie,* Attaché, Institut Royal du Patrimoine Artistique, Brussels.

Illuminated manuscripts from The Walters Art Gallery, Baltimore: *Miss Dorothy E. Miner,* Librarian and Curator of Manuscripts, The Walters Art Gallery, Baltimore, Maryland.

Illuminated manuscripts from The Pierpont Morgan Library, New York: *Francis W. Robinson,* Curator of Ancient and Medieval Art, The Detroit Institute of Arts, Detroit, Michigan.

Historical documents: *Albert Schouteet,* Conservateur f.f. des Archives de la Ville de Bruges. Introductory note: *Richard Kay,* Research Associate, Department of History, University of Wisconsin, Madison, Wisconsin.

This catalogue has been translated by *Richard M. Stein,* the section on historical documents by *Frank Smolar,* and some entries by *Mrs. Robert Shepherd.*

21

FOREWORD

It has been the privilege of the Centre National de Recherches Primitifs Flamands in Brussels to assume the task of preparing the American catalogue for the Exhibition "Masterpieces of Flemish Art: Van Eyck to Bosch", organized by the City of Bruges and The Detroit Institute of Arts, Detroit, Michigan.

The Center recalls, first, that this exhibition was realized through the initiative of Dr. Edgar P. Richardson, Director of The Detroit Institute of Arts, who, in the very heart of a region to which many Belgians have immigrated, has been able to assemble one of the most beautiful Flemish collections that can be found in America. It is truly encouraging to witness this collaboration between Detroit, which has become one of the principal depositories of Flemish art in the United States, and Bruges, the birthplace of the art which was, in the 15th century, one of the most influential centers of European civilization north of the Alps.

The Center is keenly aware that more 15th century Flemish paintings, by far, are preserved in the United States than in any other country. In 1956, of the approximately 4500 works inventoried in the world up until then, some 450 were in the United States. Thanks to the complete and gratifying cooperation displayed by the American universities and museums which shelter early Flemish paintings, the Center was able to undertake the immense task of research and publication which it proposed to achieve in the United States. First and foremost is the *Corpus of Painting in the former Southern Netherlands in the 15th Century,* in which each of the 450 paintings will be analyzed from an iconographic, historic, and stylistic point of view, in addition to a complete photographic documentation in both color and black-and-white. The first volume of the American Corpus, that of New England, will be published soon. It will include fourteen works from six museums: Museum of Fine Arts, Boston, Massachusetts; Fogg Art Museum, Harvard University, Cambridge, Massachusetts; Wadsworth Atheneum, Hartford, Connecticut; Yale University Art Gallery, New Haven, Connecticut; Sterling and Francine Clark Art Institute, Williamstown, Massachusetts; and the Worcester Art Museum, Worcester, Massachusetts. The author is Dr. Colin Eisler, Professor at the Institute of Fine Arts, New York University, who was able to benefit from the assistance of Dr. Millard Meiss, Professor at the Institute for Advanced Study, Princeton, New Jersey. The Center is especially pleased that the United States wishes to associate itself in this activity, as have many other countries such as Australia, Belgium, France, Germany, Great Britain, Italy, Poland, Spain, the U.S.S.R., and Yugoslavia.

By actively participating in this Belgian-American exhibition, the Center is trying to encourage in various countries a systematic and objective research in a field where much more specialized study could be done. In Belgium, its work is greatly facilitated through the continuous collaboration of the Institut Royal du Patrimoine Artistique in Brussels, its art historians and technicians as well as its chemists and physicists, whose new working techniques have been placed at the service of art and archaeology.

The present catalogue begins with a captivating chapter which Dr. Edgar P. Richardson entitles "Flemish Primitives in American Collections". He traces the history of the formation and development of the principal Flemish art collections in the United States, from the purchase made by Thomas Jefferson in 1784 up to the present time. This is followed by "Flanders in the 15th Century" which is based on documentation collected by Miss Lucie Ninane, Assistant Curator at the Musées Royaux des Beaux-Arts in Brussels, whom the Belgian Minister of Public Instruction generously attached to the Center for the preparation of this catalogue, and by Mr. Robert Didier, Scientific Assistant at the Institut Royal du Patrimoine Artistique. These notes are intended for the American reader, less familiar with the geographical, historical, political, social, and cultural environment of Flanders and the Burgundian provinces in the 15th century. The entries on paintings loaned by Belgium and almost all art treasures coming from both the United States and Belgium were written by Miss Lucie Ninane, assisted by Miss Isabelle de Ramaix. Those relative to paintings from American collections were prepared by Miss Jacqueline Folie, Junior Curator at the Institut Royal du Patrimoine Artistique. All are based on the documentation of the Center. Certain of the painting notices were revised by Miss Nicole Verhaegen, Scientific Secretary of the Center, and the majority, especially those dealing with the objects of art, by Dr. Frans Van Molle, Head of the Department of Iconographic Archives of the Institute. The entries concerning the illuminated manuscripts which belong to The Walters Art Gallery, Baltimore, Maryland, were prepared by its Librarian and Curator of Manuscripts, Miss Dorothy E. Miner. The entries for those loaned by The Pierpont Morgan Library in New York, N.Y., are from Mr. Francis Waring Robinson, Curator of Ancient and Medieval Art of The Detroit Institute of Arts. Mr. Albert Schouteet, Acting Curator of the Archives of the City of Bruges, wrote the entries on historical documents.

The Center wishes to express its most sincere thanks to all who have assisted it in this task. We beg the Honorable William A.M. Burden, United States Ambassador to Belgium, His Excellency Mr. Charles Moureaux, Minister of Public Instruction of Belgium, and Mr. Pierre Vandamme, Burgomaster of the City of Bruges, to accept our gratitude for their encouragement. We thank Dr. Edgar P. Richardson and his associates of The Detroit Institute of Arts, especially Mr. Francis Waring Robinson, as well as Dr. Alin Janssens de Bisthoven, Director of the Museums of the City of Bruges. We also wish to express our recognition of the contributions made by the lenders and correspondents who did so much to complete the data already possessed by the Center. For their special efforts in the production of this catalogue we thank Miss Jacqueline Folie, who assumed the responsibility of its editing, and also the technicians and photographers of the Institute in Brussels, as well as the L. Blondé and De Schutter firms of Antwerp, printer and engraver, respectively, of the catalogue.

The exhibition is placed under the High Patronage of the President of the United States and the King of the Belgians. In consenting to support the present exhibition, the two Heads of State have clearly shown their desire to underline the prime importance of culture in international relations between the Old and the New World. It is their privilege to encourage such enterprises in a field where identical joys of the mind and the heart can be shared without restriction.

PAUL COREMANS

*Director, Centre National de Recherches
Primitifs Flamands, Brussels*

There are today more than two hundred and fifty Flemish Primitive pictures in the museums of the United States. Many others are in private collections. This is an extraordinary cultural treasure.

The taste for Flemish painting is as old as serious collecting in this country; but at first it was limited to the masters of the seventeenth century, with an occasional excursion into the art of the sixteenth. The earliest collector to buy a work of the Flemish Renaissance was Thomas Jefferson, who bought an *Ecce Homo* by Jan Gossaert at a sale in Paris in October, 1784, while serving as United States Minister to France. The picture now belongs to the New-York Historical Society, to which it came as the bequest of Louis Durr in 1882; but today it is again in Jefferson's home, Monticello, at Charlottesville, Virginia, on indefinite loan.

The taste for pictures of the fifteenth century did not come until a century later. Its beginnings, and the collectors responsible for creating the principal groups of Flemish Primitives in our museums, are interesting and worth remembering.

The first fifteenth century painting of great quality and unchanged attribution to come to the United States, was, so far as I know, Roger van der Weyden's *St. Luke Drawing a Portrait of the Virgin* (cat. no. 7) which was sold in New York in the sale of pictures belonging to Don Pedro de Bórbon, Duque de Dúrcal, in 1889. It was purchased by Mr. Henry Lee Higginson of Boston (whose personal taste was for music and for Barbizon pictures) with the intention of giving it to the Boston Museum of Fine Arts.

The Metropolitan Museum of Art was incorporated in 1870 and made its first purchases of European paintings in 1871. These include an *Adoration of the Magi* attributed to Gerard van der Meire, now recognized as a late fifteenth century copy after Hugo van der Goes. In 1889 Mr. Henry Marquand of New York City bought a *Lamentation over the Dead Christ* by Petrus Christus, and gave it to the museum in 1890. This initiated the magnificent series of donations by Benjamin Altman, Theodore M. Davis, J. Pierpont Morgan, Michael Dreicer, H.O. Havemeyer, Michael Friedsam, Jules Bache, George Blumenthal, Mrs. Edward S. Harkness and John D. Rockefeller, Jr., which, together with the museum's own purchases, like the two van Eyck wings, bought from the Hermitage in 1933, have given The Metropolitan Museum of Art and The Cloisters the most important group of Flemish Primitives in America.

Between 1884 and 1888 Mr. James E. Scripps of Detroit formed a collection of European paintings to give to the museum of his city. The Flemish pictures were

27

chosen to represent the development of three centuries of painting: with two fifteenth century panels (now attributed to the Master of the St. Catherine Legend and to a follower of Dieric Bouts), and paintings by the Master of Frankfort, Jan Provost (one of the best works of the master), Quentin Metsys, Pieter Neefs, Hendrik van Steenwyck, and a major Rubens, which were given to the museum in 1889. In the 1920's the museum bought the *St. Jerome* (cat. no. 5) by Jan van Eyck (which in its overpainted state was then attributed to Petrus Christus), the *Virgin of the Rose Garden* (cat. no. 41) by the Master of the St. Lucy Legend, and the Gerard David *Annunciation* (cat. no. 46). Paintings by Roger van der Weyden (cat. no. 9), Master Michiel (cat. nos. 52 and 53), the Master of the St. Ursula Legend (cat. no. 40) have subsequently been added through the generous aid of Mr. and Mrs. Edgar B. Whitcomb and Mr. and Mrs. Henry Ford II. An important set of four Brussels tapestries was the gift of the Hearst Foundation in 1955 and a pair of Tournai tapestries were presented by Mrs. Edsel B. Ford, Mr. K.T. Keller and Mr. and Mrs. Douglas F. Roby in 1959 and 1960.

In 1894 Mr. John G. Johnson of Philadelphia bought his first Flemish Primitive, the *St. Francis Receiving the Stigmata* by Jan van Eyck. He purchased it from Lord Heytesbury, whose ancestor, Sir William à Court, had been British Ambassador to Portugal from 1824 to 1828 and had there bought the picture (then called Dürer) for forty dollars. This was the beginning of his noble group of fifteenth century Flemish paintings now in the Philadelphia Museum of Art, of which the other high point is the *Crucifixion* with the *Virgin and St. John* by Roger van der Weyden.

The casual attributions to Dürer or some other vaguely remembered name belong to the era before the great exhibition of 1902 in Bruges. This exhibition stimulated and inspired the first generation of specialists in early Flemish art, to whose work we owe the creation of the serious art history of the period. The enthusiasm of American collectors was awakened by this exhibition, also, and the great age of collecting Flemish Primitives began.

Three outstanding groups of paintings remain to be mentioned. One is the collection of Mr. Martin A. Ryerson of Chicago, who left it, on his death in 1932, to The Art Institute of Chicago. The beautiful group of paintings ranging from Roger van der Weyden to Joos van Cleve was only a part, but a notable part, of Mr. Ryerson's enormous and discerning collecting, which gives so much distinction to the museum in Chicago.

Mr. Henry Walters of Baltimore acquired, between 1910 and 1925, a number of Flemish fifteenth century paintings (cat. nos. 2 and 22), objects of art (cat. nos. 109-112), textiles and miniatures (cat. nos. 68-69, 74-76, 80 and 85. Though only a small part of his omnivorous collecting, they form a distinguished and important group.

Mr. Andrew W. Mellon bought in 1930-31 from the Hermitage, through Knoedler's, the famous *Annunciation* by Jan van Eyck, whose history can be traced back to Dijon, where it was probably part of an altar made for Duke Philip the Good of Burgundy. It passed with the *Adoration of the Christ Child* by Petrus Christus and Roger's *Portrait of a Lady* to the National Gallery in Washington which Mr. Mellon created by his will. Mr. Mellon's benefactions were followed by those of Mr. Samuel Kress and the Kress Foundation, so that Washington, latest comer of great museums, has also a group of Flemish Primitives of which to be proud.

The related pictorial arts, tapestry, in the monumental scale, and illumination, in miniature scale, are also richly represented in the United States. Some of the finest fifteenth century tapestries are in New York (cat. no. 150) and Minneapolis (cat. nos. 149 and 151), Washington (at the Corcoran Gallery, Dumbarton Oaks and the National Gallery of Art), Boston (the Museum of Fine Arts, cat. no. 153, and the Gardner Museum), Worcester, Detroit (cat. nos. 154-155) and San Francisco. The chief American collections of illuminated manuscripts are in The Pierpont Morgan Library in New York and The Walters Art Gallery in Baltimore (cat. nos. 196-213).

Only sculpture and metalwork, of the great arts of the fifteenth century Netherlands, are represented in the United States by few important examples, (cat. nos. 96, 109-112). The American student must visit Belgium to learn to what heights these arts were developed there.

A museum collection means nothing until it enters into people's minds, until it is interpreted, known, and loved. Seventy-five years of collecting have given us in the United States some 500 or more works of art of all kinds to represent the creative genius of Flanders in the fifteenth century. These works of art are popular with the public of our museums. Their glowing color, their intensity of vision, their magical reality of detail, cast their spell over the people of the United States today as they cast it over all Europe in their own time.

Yet we must confess, as American art historians, that the study of these works of art is relatively neglected by us today, always with the notable exception of Professor Erwin Panofsky, whose writings and teaching have inspired a new generation of students. This is the scientific reason why we have made such great efforts, my colleagues in Belgium and myself, to overcome the extremely numerous and extremely difficult obstacles in the way of an exhibition of fifteenth century Flemish art.

Some of the key works for the study of the fascinating intellectual problems of fifteenth century painting are now in America: the problems of the transition from miniature to panel painting; of the van Eyck atelier, both in its beginning and its close; of the Robert Campin - Roger van der Weyden workshops; of the great mass of anonymous masters between 1460 and 1520; of the question of Bosch and his followers and his copyists. These questions stare at us from our collections in America as well as from those of Belgium and other European countries. We have work to do.

That is also the reason why we have extended the period shown in this exhibition beyond the strict limits of the fifteenth century. We begin with the pre-Eyckian painting of the time of Broederlam and the *Calvaire des Tanneurs* (cat. no. 1) in the 1390's, and continue to the end of the development of the Gothic style in Bosch and Gerard David, who died in 1516 and 1523 respectively. It is easy to draw the stylistic frontier between David and the painters of the Flemish Renaissance, more difficult to draw it between Bosch and the tradition which he founded; yet the period forms an entity which we all recognize.

Flanders in the fifteenth century was a cultural complex of far larger significance than even the educated American public realizes. In the great cities of Flanders and Brabant, as in those of fifteenth century Italy, the Middle Ages came to an end and the modern world began. It is difficult for us in the new world to grasp their ancient outlines and comprehend their importance as a focal point of western civilization. To give, therefore, some sense of Flanders in the fifteenth century as a civilization is the cultural aim of our exhibition. We hope that it may lead to a wider interest in the history and create a more vivid image of the splendor, variety and profound originality of the culture of the Southern Netherlands under the Dukes of Burgundy.

EDGAR P. RICHARDSON

Director,
The Detroit Institute of Arts

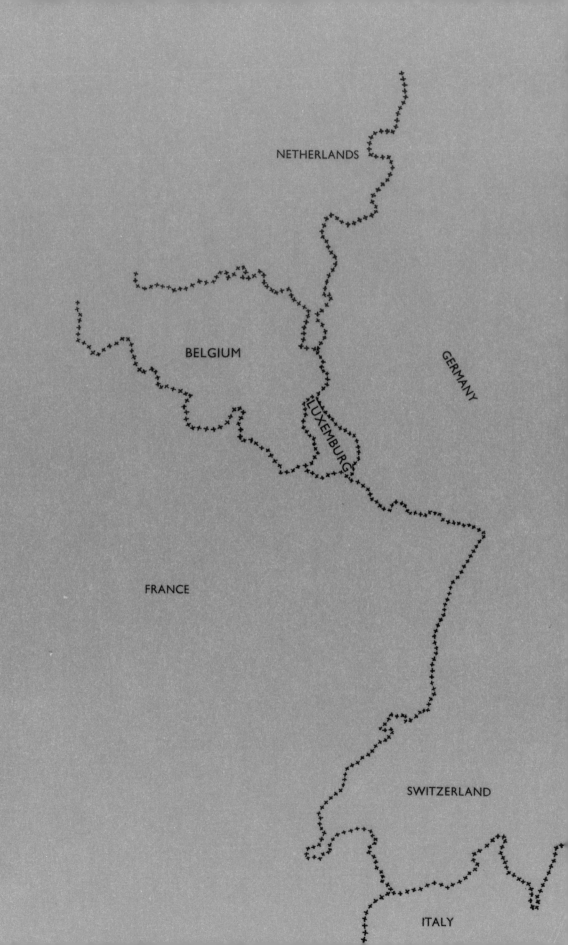

NETHERLANDS

BELGIUM

GERMANY

LUXEMBURG

FRANCE

SWITZERLAND

ITALY

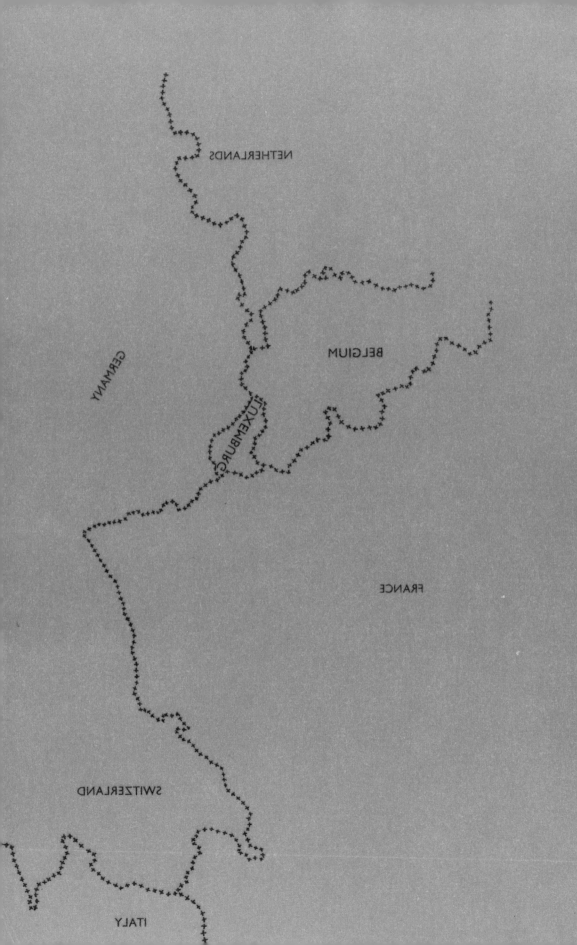

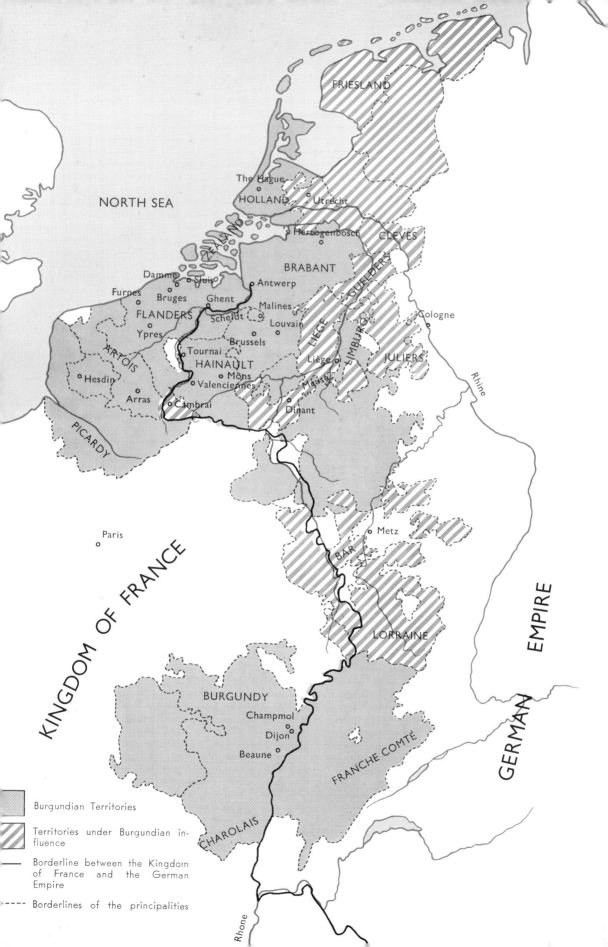

FRIESLAND

NORTH SEA

The Hague
HOLLAND
Utrecht

Hertogenbosch
CLEVES

Damme
Sluis
Antwerp
BRABANT
GUELDERS

Furnes
Bruges
Ghent
Malines
LIÈGE
Cologne

FLANDERS
Scheldt
Louvain
LIMBURG

Ypres
Brussels
JULIERS

ARTOIS
Tournai
Liège
Mons
HAINAULT
Maas
Hesdin
Valenciennes
Dinant

Arras
Cambrai

PICARDY

Rhine

Paris

Metz

KINGDOM OF FRANCE

BAR

LORRAINE

BURGUNDY

GERMAN EMPIRE

Champmol
Dijon

Beaune
FRANCHE COMTÉ

Rhone

CHAROLAIS

Burgundian Territories

Territories under Burgundian influence

Borderline between the Kingdom
of France and the German
Empire

Borderlines of the principalities

Rhone

FLANDERS IN THE FIFTEENTH CENTURY

Belgium of today, a tiny country (11,800 sq. mi.) in Western Europe, is approximately five times smaller than the State of Michigan (58,216 sq. mi.) with a population (9,2 million) a little greater than this state (approximately 7½ million). It includes nine provinces whose names correspond to those of former principalities, such as the County of Flanders. Its territory is inhabited by people called the Flemish and the Walloons; the former live in the North and speak Flemish (or Dutch) and the latter live in the South and speak French. A country without natural frontiers, a buffer-state as well, its geographic situation has always left it exposed to invasions and foreign occupations. The latter, the religious troubles of the 16th century, and destructions of every kind have considerably reduced its historical and cultural patrimony. Today, only a small part remains.

In the 15th century, this region was joined to the northern part of France and to part of the present Netherlands. Although it was sometimes practiced by artists of French expression in cities like Arras and Tournai, its art is qualified as *Flemish art* because the great centers of activity were in Flanders: Ypres, Ghent and Bruges, later Brussels and Louvain, and finally Antwerp and Malines. However, the main reason for it is that, in the 16th century, the whole Netherlands was called Flanders by the French, by the Italians (Fiandra) and by the Spanish (Flandes). Flemish art spread into numerous European countries, especially Germany, Scandinavia, the Baltic Countries, France, Italy, Spain, and Portugal.

On the *political scene* it is important to recall that in the 14th century, the country was divided into many principalities which were more or less

A landscape in Flanders (Damme)

independent. The main ones were the County of Flanders, that of Hainault, the Duchy of Brabant, which was united to that of Limburg and to the Marquisate of Antwerp, and the ecclesiastical Principality of Liège. The first two counties were dependent on the King of France and the others on the German Empire. However, this control had already been only nominal for a long time. France had been ravaged by the Black Death (1348) and the Hundred Years War (1337-1453) was still in progress, the Empire was divided to the point where the central power was ineffective, while the Western Schism (1378-1429) split apart the Church between Rome and Avignon. The country, however, was partially saved from these shaking events with the consequence that, at the end of the 14th century, its situation was favorable to the flourishing of the arts.

By the marriage in 1369 of Philip the Bold (d. 1404), Duke of *Burgundy,* to Margaret, only daughter of Louis de Male, Count of Flanders, the House of Burgundy was given the opportunity to obtain a foothold in Flanders and then in the adjoining principalities. By a clever policy of inheritances, acquisitions, and sometimes conquests, Philip the Good (d. 1467), son of John the Fearless (d. 1419), succeeded in grouping the different neighboring principalities of Flanders under his rule or protection. He also much enlarged his heritage in the North, the " Pays de par-deçà ", and is to be considered as the founder of the Netherlands ("Pays-Bas"), as this country was called since the end of the 15th century. Thinking back on his provinces it could almost be referred to as the Burgundian "United States" or the Burgundian "Commonwealth". The ambition of Charles the Bold (d. 1477) brought about ill-fated wars which endangered the Burgundian power. Its final objective was to try to unite the "pays de par-deçà" to Burgundy itself, a few hundred miles away. It was, in the end, this final attempt which caused the downfall of the Duke, whose ever-increasing power became very troublesome to the King of France and the Emperor. It was only through the marriage in 1477 of Mary of Burgundy to Maximilian of Habsburg, son of the Emperor, that the core of the Burgundian states was not dismembered. The death of Mary of Burgundy in 1482 marked the beginning of the reign of the Habsburgs who, in spite of numerous vicissitudes, retained their dominance over the Netherlands until 1794. It marked also the entry of that dynasty into the international scene and with it, the beginning of the Franco-Habsburg wars. Philip the Handsome (d. 1506), son of Mary of Burgundy and Maximilian of

Philip the Good

32

Habsburg, married in 1496 Joan of Castile, called Joan the Mad, daughter of the King of Spain. This marriage resulted in the birth in Ghent in 1500 of the future Emperor, Charles V. Under his successors, above all kings of Spain, the Netherlands began gradually to lose its former importance. It soon became no more than a pawn on the political chessboard of Europe where the game was henceforth directed sometimes by Spain, sometimes by the Empire, and finally by France, while England gradually prepared for its role as arbiter.

During almost a century, the House of Burgundy had succeeded in making the Netherlands one of the European centers of gravity. By a harmonious synthesis of unification, without which the modern states which began to form at the end of the Middle Ages would have been thrown into anarchy, and through respect for the regionalism of their provinces, the Dukes of Burgundy succeeded in generally establishing order and security in their states. Adding to this a still relatively favorable economic situation, the growing importance of the "bourgeoisie" and the class of functionaries and, finally, the taste for ostentation and art shown by the Dukes of Burgundy, the conclusion seems clear that the conditions were fulfilled for the creation of a favorable

Charles the Bold

climate enabling the arts to make a brilliant triumph whose influence was felt over a large part of Europe.

The *administration* of the "Commonwealth" of Burgundy may be characterized by its respect for local traditions and customs. This was accomplished thanks to the maintenance, unification, and existence of regional institutions. At the same time the Dukes increased their power through solid central institutions. This centralization was manifested by the creation of the post of chancellor, a position much like that of a prime minister with very broad powers. From 1422 to 1462, it was Nicolas Rolin who continuously exercised this important function. Like his master, Philip the Good, he was a great patron of the arts whose principal beneficiary was the city of Beaune. Thus it was he who engaged Roger van der Weyden to do a painting of the Last Judgment for the hospital he had constructed in that city. He was also the donor of The Virgin with Chancellor Rolin by Jan van Eyck (Paris, Louvre). The Duke also made the Grand Council permanent as from 1434, to aid him further in the exercise of his powers. In 1464, the Duke called the first meeting of the Estates General of the northern provinces, which brought together the representatives of the provincial assemblies. This Parliament did not have any powers of its own and could only be convened by order of the sovereign. The Estates retained as their basic task the voting of subsidies to the Duke.

The ducal *finances* were controlled by the Chambers of Accounts which met in Lille and in Brussels. The archives of these chambers of accounts provide an unending source of information for historians and art historians. In the field of finances the Dukes were careful to create a stable currency, strong and unified in the sense that the money of one province could be spent in all the others. Nevertheless, the Netherlands being more prosperous than Burgundy, the former used gold currency while the latter had only silver money.

On the provincial level of administration, the former magistrates ("baillis") were subordinated to governors. The councils were gradually transformed into high courts of *justice* composed of professional judges who were appointed for life.

Thanks to the prosperity of the Burgundian States, the fine arts were able to develop. In the Netherlands this prosperity was partially the result of the fertility of the soil, but came, especially, from still flourishing *industries*. Nevertheless, some of these industries had to be converted in the face of serious problems, when they were not already in full decadence, as was the cloth industry in Flanders. In the country, however, the recession seemed to have less effect.

It was *commerce* which was the true source of the wealth of the Netherlands. In this respect its geographic position was ideal. The ports of Bruges (with its outer ports of Damme and Sluis) and Antwerp, opening onto the North Sea, provided easy contact with England and the Baltic Countries, where the northern German cities grouped in the Hansa occupied a privileged position. The Atlantic established liaison with France, Spain, and Portugal. In the Mediterranean, the Flemish navigators reached Italy and the Near East. Moreover, good roads facilitated relations not only within the Netherlands itself, but also with Champagne, the Rhône Valley, Switzerland, Central Europe, the south of Germany and through it, Northern Italy. These lines of sea and land communication made Bruges, and later Antwerp, the pivotal points of European commerce next to Venice, Genoa, and Lübeck. It was, above all, a commerce of transit, with numerous banks where, thanks to the commissions granted to brockers, important Flemish (Vijdt, Moreel), Italian (Arnolfini, de Villa, Portinari, Tani), and other merchants and financiers rapidly became opulent bourgeois who could contribute to the economic and artistic wealth of the cities where they lived. Good evidence that the Netherlands was a center for a large part of European commercial activity of the period is demonstrated by the origin of the French word for stock exchange, "bourse", which comes from the name of the van der Beurse family, whose residence in Bruges served as the meeting place for Italian merchants.

It was in Antwerp, in 1460, that the first international commercial "bourse" was created. In Malines, in 1489, the first international postal service was born, and it was also in Flanders that the first insurance companies were formed. Capital was abundant and the cities loaned money to princes, issued bonds, and organized lotteries. Commercial activity reigned in the Netherlands, and, in fact, the bourgeois merchants and the cities became as rich as the princes, and sometimes even richer. It was thus that they possessed the means to become important patrons of the arts, and they contributed to the construction of civic and religious buildings which they decorated, through devotion or a desire for prestige, with works of art.

Crane at a port

Medieval Western European *society* was divided into three classes: the nobility, the clergy, and the third estate ("tiers état"). In the beginning, the nobility possessed all the power and their revenues came basically from their estates. The deep belief of the faithful formed the base of the influence of the clergy, whose revenues came from numerous donations of property or money by the nobility as well as by the bourgeois and the lower classes. A significant evolution occurred within the sphere of the clergy as a result of the growth of the cities and this had an influence on artistic life. While the abbeys played a leading role in the beginning of the Middle Ages, starting in the 13th century the new mendicant religious orders made considerable inroads in the cities, where numerous Dominican and Franciscan monasteries were built. Moreover, the Beguines, institutions peculiar to the Netherlands, also found much support. The "third estate" saw its influence grow through the wealth and power of a bourgeois class whose role became increasingly more important in the conduct of urban affairs and later influenced those of the state. Next to this third estate there was still the class of craftsmen whose number increased with the industrialization of the Flemish cities. These craftsmen, by grouping together, succeeded in seizing power in many cities. The conflicts which broke out first between the princes and the bourgeois merchants, and then between the latter and the professional associations of craftsmen, are an important part of the historical picture of the Netherlands during the Middle Ages.

The *cities* of the Netherlands are of remote origin. Some, like Tongres and Tournai, go back to the Roman period, whose vestiges they still retain. Others were born between the 7th and 9th centuries. However, most of them were

35

founded by the beginning of the 10th century, seemingly earliest in the Meuse region. This region experienced an awakening of economic activity and, with Liège, had the advantage of possessing an important cultural center. Thus, metalwork, especially brass, was for a long time a specialty of the Meuse area, notably in Huy and Dinant. Flanders and Brabant did not stay out of the economic activity. Their cloth industry made a particularly spectacular ascent and was the source of a very active exportation trade. Industry, the corollary of trade, quickly served to enrich the bourgeois merchants, and in consequence was to assure the growth and power of the cities. The obvious political result was an increasing conflict between the princes and the bourgeois of the cities. In fact, since the feudal regime with its domanial privileges was a rural economy based on landed wealth, it could only have the effect of slowing down the expansion of the cities. This is the phase of the political, economic, and social history of the Netherlands which is characterized by the upsurge of the cities. The object of the latter, led by merchants grouped in guilds, was to limit the power of the princes and obtain from them liberties for the cities, guaranteed by Charters granted first in the Meuse region (Huy, 1066), then in Flanders (Saint-Omer, 1127), and finally, Brabant (Tirlemont, 1168). By these charters, the princes accorded personal, commercial and land-owning freedom to the bourgeois, and recognized the cities as having a certain autonomy and judicial personality, for example, the right to levy taxes or contract alliances. This permitted them to have the attributes of their power: to surround themselves by walls, construct city halls, build belfries, maintain a militia, and possess seals. The upsurge of the cities led to the installation of an aristocratic regime in the sense that the city governments were held by the merchants who, not content just to monopolize commercial activities, also monopolized the public offices. In fact, although all the bourgeois of the city enjoyed civic rights, only the aristocrats had political rights. Such a situation led directly to a plutocratic and then to an oligarchic system with all the abuses it brings. The inevitable result was a new series of conflicts. Thus came the second phase in the history of the cities of the Netherlands, the Democratic Revolutions, which burst out in the most industrialized regions: Flanders, Brabant, and the Meuse area. The lower class of the cities, that is, the craftsmen, were grouped together in professional organizations ("métiers", "corporations") for all those exercising the same profession, whether owner, worker, or apprentice. The "métiers" were manifestly powerful in 1302, at the time of the battle of the Golden Spurs, when the Flemish trades inflicted a resounding defeat on the French knighthood. They were conscious of their power and did not hesitate to enter the struggle against the aristocracy. The conflict between capital and labor does not date from the 19th century! These struggles were rather complex because in most cities the social conflicts between aristocracy and the trades overflowed into the political field and often served national objectives. In general, their aim was to take the power away from the aristocrats. The results of these struggles, often long and violent depending on the city and region, were rather varied. The end of that period marked the high point of the cities which, as was the case in Flanders, exercised a veritable dictatorship over the countryside. The entire country

36

15th century Bruges

became regulated by urban law. From a political point of view, the autonomy of the cities was established, and vestiges of this can still be found in the Belgium of today. The weakened position of the nobility opened the way to the absolutism of the princes, an absolutism which appeared at the end of the Middle Ages and which characterized the modern period. From a social viewpoint, all these conflicts enabled the bourgeois to form and to assume an ever more important role as a balancing factor.

In the 15th century, the power of the large Flemish cities was attenuated by the Dukes of Burgundy, who restrained, sometimes by force, the individualism of some cities who wanted to retain their former independence, which was incompatible with the exercise of a strong and effective central power. Moreover, the cities underwent the effects of an economic regression, although it was somewhat counterbalanced by industrial reconversion. At the end of the 15th century, Monetarius observed that the perimeter of Ghent was no smaller than that of Paris. A few years earlier, Bruges could be considered one of the most important business centers in the world. Malines and Louvain, although less populated (the estimated population of the Netherlands in the 15th century was about two million inhabitants), were very active centers also. Louvain, thanks to its University founded in 1425, attracted numerous students, which made it the pre-eminent cultural center of the Netherlands. During the 15th century, Brussels and Antwerp soon began to play for themselves the role occupied until then by the cities of the County of Flanders. Toward the East was the Principality of Liège which, in law, depended on the Empire but, in fact, was politically very closely allied to the Dukes of Burgundy. This city experienced a rebirth of activity due to the growth of coal mining, which had as its consequence the development

37

of the iron industry in that region. These circumstances served to encourage economic and artistic exchanges between the Principality and the other cities of the Netherlands. On the occasion of the Joyous Entry of their princes or a visit of an ambassador, all these cities organized colorful celebrations. In the cities literary societies called "Chambres de rhétorique" emerged and were cultural centers for the development of the art of poetry. With their imposing sets, the religious mystery plays, whose mysticism and spectacular character appealed to the crowds, attracted them to the cities in great numbers. Many foreign merchants were also drawn there to trade their goods and participate in commercial or financial transactions. The most important among them retained permanent agents there and the large Italian banks installed branches in these cities. For example, the Medici had a bank in Bruges which was directed by men such as Tommaso Portinari and Pierantonio Bandini Baroncelli. The Flemish cities offered outstanding comforts to the travellers of that period: the main streets were paved, the distribution of drinking water was assured at numerous intersections through a system of subterranean canals, stone and brick were common in buildings, and, finally, luxury merchandise and products were abundant and, by their quality, pleased even the most discriminating customers.

Brussels, Sainte-Gudule

The *"métiers"*, whose political activity has already been described, had an important influence on the arts through their professional strength. It should be recalled that the corporations were based on the principle of grouping together all those who engaged in the same type of work. These associations did not restrict themselves to political and social objectives alone. The concern for self-protection shown by the craftsmen being one of the reasons for their creation, these associations envisioned a rather strict regulation of the economy of the cities. In following moral principles, taking inspiration from political and social considerations, and implying protectionist principles, the object of these regulations was the strengthening of the political and social structure of medieval urban society. These, then, were the general principles. In practice, these regulations, granted by the princes or the cities, concerned the producer, the worker and, indirectly, the consumer. These regulations were applied most rapidly in the regions where the "métiers" were most powerful, well organized, and composed of active memberships. The producers had to be assured that they would have the ability to purchase the raw materials, transform them, and, finally, be able to sell their products. With this in mind, supplies were subject to quotas, competition strangled, and advertising prohibited. The working class was protected by the fixing of salaries, working hours, and other conditions. The consumer himself was also protected against mal-practices. The regulations contained clauses assuring the training of craftsmen and the quality of the products used, quality which, in the case of weavers, goldsmiths and sculptors, for example, was guaranteed by marks.

These associations were not only professional, they were also made up of religious groups. Thanks to their solidarity and charity, they also looked after the needs of their members when it was necessary.

Beginning in the 14th century, the regulations of certain artists' corporations had an influence on art which it is important to understand. Works of art were often done in workshops where, by a long and carefully regulated apprenticeship, young artists were trained in their craft under the guidance of experienced masters. These artists could, in turn, become masters through the execution, under certain conditions, of a "masterpiece". By setting the quality of the materials, establishing the techniques to be used, and assuring the training of artists, these rules made a clear contribution to the good reputation of Flemish art. This organization of artistic work, well established in the Netherlands, survived, in part, until the end of the Old Regime. In other countries like Italy, it disappeared more quickly.

Everywhere in Europe, until the 14th century, the role of the *patrons of the arts* was restricted to the royal and princely courts, ecclesiastical circles, and the nobility. Starting at that time, however, art patrons began to come from the newly emerging lower classes and they had an important influence during the following century. Just as in Italy and Germany, perhaps even more, the development of art in the Netherlands is due in a large part to the numerous orders placed with artists by cities, the bourgeois, corporations, and religious confraternities. However, the role played by the clergy, especially in the cities, and by the nobility, and more particularly by the new class of important administrators, conscious of their importance and prestige, cannot be underestimated. The Dukes of Burgundy, by their interest in art and the numerous works which they ordered, also made a very special contribution to artistic life in the Netherlands.

The patronage of the clergy is demonstrated by the painting by Jan van Eyck in which the donor, Canon van der Paele, is shown kneeling before the Virgin (Bruges, Stedelijk Museum). Canon Toussaint Prier gave a set of tapestries dedicated to the life of Saint Piat to the Cathedral of Tournai (cat. no. 148). It was the nuns who ordered from Memlinc the altarpiece of the Mystic Marriage of Saint Catherine for Saint John's Hospital in Bruges. A monk, Jan Floreins, commissioned the small triptych of the Adoration of the Magi in the same gallery (cat. no. 30).

Still more brilliant was the patronage coming from the clergymen who owed their fortunes to ducal favor as a result of the large administrations created

Philip the Good and his counsellors

by Philip the Good. In a certain sense, therefore, this patronage can be considered a part of that exercised by the Great Duke of the West. It was Bishop Jean Chevrot who ordered from Roger van der Weyden the Altarpiece of the Seven Sacraments (Antwerp, Musée Royal des Beaux-Arts); Guillaume Fillastre was responsible for the richly illuminated History of the Order of the Golden Fleece (Brussels, Bibliothèque Royale), and Ferry de Clugny ordered the making of several tapestries (cat. no. 153).

The older nobility, when it benefited from ducal favor, also participated in this movement. The miniaturists received orders from the Lalaing and Croy families. Philippe de Croy engaged Roger van der Weyden to paint his portrait (Antwerp, Musée des Beaux-Arts).

There was no field of art that failed to benefit from the patronage of the Dukes of Burgundy. Philip the Bold ordered for the Carthusian Monastery of Champmol two carved altarpieces by Jacques de Baerze, the wings of which were painted by Melchior Broederlam (Dijon, Musée des Beaux-Arts). He maintained, in addition, an entire workshop of sculptors, directed by Claus Sluter. John the Fearless, although less interested in the arts, still continued to support the same workshop, under the leadership of Claus de Werve. The most important patronage for the Netherlands was, however, that of Philip the Good. He relieved the artists of many worries by paying them pensions as, for example, that which Jan van Eyck received. Painters were given many orders. The portrait of Philip the Good painted by Roger van der Weyden is known to us through its many replicas (Paris, Louvre; Lille, Musée des Beaux-Arts; Bruges, Stedelijk Museum, cat. no. 13). The Duke was equally interested in tapestries, and the workshops supported by him in Tournai produced important sets of tapestries with mythological subjects. Philip the Good was also a great book-lover and collected a large number of illuminated manuscripts for his library. Part of these

40

are now in the Bibliothèque Royale in Brussels and make up the richest and most important part of the Manuscript Department. Music also profited from ducal patronage. Minstrels were engaged to brighten the lavish celebrations organized by Philip the Good who, in addition, maintained a ducal chapel to enhance the musical part of religious services. Charles the Bold followed this tradition to a lesser degree but he did order, for example, the precious reliquary for the Cathedral of Saint-Lambert in Liège (cat. no. 133) from the goldsmith Gérard Loyet.

Gravitating around the Dukes of Burgundy were the jurists and financiers who were the leaders in the great ducal administrations from which emerged a new nobility. They displayed their wealth by becoming patrons of the arts. For example, the works ordered by Chancellor Rolin have made his name known to posterity (The Virgin with Chancellor Rolin by Jan van Eyck, Paris, Louvre; The Last Judgment by Roger van der Weyden, Beaune, Hôtel-Dieu; the tapestry of the Woodcutters ordered from the Tournai artist Pasquier Grenier, Paris, Musée des Arts Décoratifs). Hippolyte de Berthoz, who directed the financial administration, gave the triptych of the Martyrdom of Saint Hippolytus (cat. no. 19) to the Church of Saint-Sauveur in Bruges. Pierre Bladelin who was both a businessman and a member of the ducal administration, ordered the Triptych of the Nativity (Berlin, Gemäldegalerie) from Roger van der Weyden, built a beautiful house in Bruges, and contributed his money and influence to the founding of the city of Middelburg in Flanders. Laurent de Maech, a financier who also entered the service of Philip the Good, gave the Calvary attributed to Joos van Gent to the Cathedral of Ghent.

The patronage of the bourgeois was also important, and conditions in Flanders at that time can be compared with what took place in the United States at the end of the 19th century, when many great fortunes were founded. Josse Vijdt gave the celebrated Polyptych of the Mystic Lamb to the Cathedral in Ghent. Guillaume Moreel, who directed the Bruges branch of the Bank of Rome and was burgomaster of the city, ordered a triptych from Memlinc for the Church of Saint-Jacques (Bruges, Stedelijk Museum). Another bourgeois of Bruges, Martin van Nieuwenhove, had Memlinc paint a portrait of him with the Virgin (Bruges, Saint John's Hospital). Numerous carved tombstones were also ordered by the bourgeois and this was, very probably, one of the causes for the great development of Tournai workshops in the 15th century. Foreign diplomats and businessmen passing through Flanders or living in one of the large cities of the Netherlands were also attracted by the vogue for Flemish art. Edward Grimston, an English diplomat, ordered Petrus Christus to paint his portrait (Earl of Verulam Collection). The agents of the large Italian firms in Bruges did the same: the Arnolfini had Jan van Eyck do their marriage portrait (London, National Gallery); the Tani family ordered a triptych of the Last Judgment (Danzig, National Museum) from Memlinc; Tommaso Portinari, an Italian ship-owner living in Bruges, decorated his family chapel in a Florentine church with a large triptych of the Adoration of the Shepherds painted by Hugo van der Goes (Florence, Uffizi). Claude de Villa and his wife were shown as the

41

donors in a carved altarpiece (Brussels, Musées Royaux d'Art et d'Histoire), and in a painted polyptych (Cologne, Wallraf-Richartz Museum). These are only some examples of the importance of the bourgeois patronage.

The many orders given by the corporations and religious confraternities provided another source of support for artistic activity. In Bruges, the Corporation of Tanners had a Calvary painted (cat. no. 1). In 1453, the Grand Oath of Crossbowmen of Louvain ordered Roger van der Weyden to paint a Descent from the Cross (Madrid, Prado) and, in 1493, that organization paid the sculptor Jan Borman to do the Altarpiece of Saint George (Brussels, Musées Royaux d'Art et d'Histoire). In Louvain, in 1464, Dieric Bouts painted the Altarpiece of the Last Supper (cat. no. 17) for the Brotherhood of the Blessed Sacrament.

No less important was ecclesiastical patronage. Examples of this are the Altarpiece of Saint Léonard, the paschal candlestick in Léau (cat. nos. 73 and 103-104), the choir-stalls in Diest (cat. no. 81-84), the rood-screen and the Calvary in the Church of Saint-Pierre in Louvain (cat. no. 74-77).

Finally, the great resources of the cities enabled them also to offer an important patronage. To encourage judges to remain impartial, the cities decorated their tribunals with works of the Last Judgment and pictures of Justice. The latter were scenes illustrating legendary subjects such as the condemnation of dishonest judges. The Justice of Herkenbald and the Justice of Trajan, painted by Roger van der Weyden for the Brussels City Hall, are now lost. In 1468, the City of Louvain contracted with Dieric Bouts for the Justice of Otto (Brussels, Musées Royaux des Beaux-Arts) and a Last Judgment from which only the wings remain (Lille, Musée des Beaux-Arts). In Bruges, the judges of the time held court before the Justice of Cambyses, painted by Gerard David (cat. no. 44). The tribunal of the City Hall of Diest was decorated with a Last Judgment (Brussels, Musées Royaux des Beaux-Arts).

These few examples among so many others can do no more than give a faint idea of the widely spread patronage which existed in the Netherlands in the 15th century. Great numbers of works have disappeared, but enough remain throughout the world to illustrate the greatness of what Flemish art was in that period and to retrace its evolution.

Before presenting a *brief survey of 15th century Flemish art,* it is important to note that Gothic art originated in France where, in the 13th century, it found some of its most beautiful expressions. It was, moreover, the period at which medieval France was at its height. In the 14th century, when the Netherlands was enjoying a better economy than its neighbors to the South, the Flemish, Brabantine, Mosan and Hainault artists often frequented the royal and princely courts of France. The art which was most in vogue at the end of the 14th and beginning of the 15th centuries is conventionally qualified by the term "international" and more precisely, for France and the Netherlands, by the expression "Franco-Flemish". It was at the same time French, because of the always present influence of Parisian circles, and Flemish, because the contributions by artists who came from the Netherlands were always on the increase. Among these artists were people such as Jean Bandol (died after 1381, author of the cartoons of the tapestries of the Apocalypse of Angers), Jean Beaumetz (d. 1396, worked for Philip the Bold), and André Beauneveu of Valenciennes (died after 1403, sculptor and miniaturist who was active in the Netherlands, France and England). There were others like the sculptor Jacques de Baerze from Termonde and the painter Melchior Broederlam from Ypres (d. ca. 1409), the authors of two altarpieces for the Carthusian Monastery of Champmol, Jacques Coene of Bruges (d. after 1411), and the brothers Limbourg (one of whom, Pol, died after 1416). An important transitory period came to a close with the last mentioned painters when the first characteristics of truly Flemish art began to appear.

In attaching to their court a sculptor like Claus Sluter and painters like Broederlam and van Eyck, the Dukes of Burgundy revealed themselves as eclectic patrons. They were, furthermore, especially interested in *literature:* they subsidized poets and historians (Monstrelet, Georges Chastellain, Olivier de la Marche), and chronicles and illuminated books of hours were abundant in their library. Next to the French literature of the court, there began to develop a Flemish literature aimed at the masses, after having produced some of the earliest literary masterpieces of the Middle Ages (Hendrik van Veldeken, d. 1189). Popular Flemish literature flourished in the 15th century with the literary societies called "Chambres de Rhétorique". They were found in all cities and emphasized poetry and prose in the form of long dissertations with a didactic and moralizing tendency. They gave theatrical pieces also, often of a religious character ("Elckerlijk", literally "Everyman", and "Mariken van Nieumeghen"), and were especially active at public festivities organized in honor of distinguished visitors. There still exist today in Belgium several chambers of rhetoric dating from the Middle Ages. They can be seen nowadays in annual processions ("Ommegang") which originated at that same period.

The Dukes were also interested in *music* and they were responsible for the birth, soon after 1450, of a polyphonic school headed by Jan van Ockeghem (d. 1496) who had a strong influence on the music of the princely courts. His student Josquin des Prez (d. 1521) successfully continued his work.

Flemish *manuscript illumination,* as said by L.M.J. Delaissé in his catalogue of Flemish miniatures (Brussels, 1959), did not produce very original works between 1420 and 1445. Nevertheless, the famous manuscript known as the Turin-Milan Hours (the major part of what remains is in the Museo Civico in Turin) left the Duke of Berry's library in 1413 and was continued by Flemish artists such as van Eyck. Thanks to the patronage of Philip the Good and Charles the Bold, illumination was very popular until around 1475. Important centers were Mons (Jean Wauquelin, Jacquemart Pilavaine), Valenciennes (Jean Mansel, Simon Marmion), Hesdin (Loyset Liédet), Lille (Master of Wavrin, Jean Miélot), Oudenaarde (Jean le Tavernier), Bruges (Loyset Liédet, Guillaume

Vrelant, and Philippe de Mazerolles), Ghent (David Aubert and the Master of Mary of Burgundy), and Brussels (Jean Dreux). It was the bourgeois-supported Ghent-Bruges School which dominated from 1475 to 1500. These miniaturists were influenced by local painters such as Joos van Gent, Hugo van der Goes, Memlinc, and Gerard David.

The richest collections of 15th century Flemish miniatures in the United States are those of The Pierpont Morgan Library in New York and The Walters Art Gallery in Baltimore, Maryland. They have both lent examples to the current exhibition (cat. nos. 196-213).

Jan van Eyck's signature

Flemish *painting* in the 15th century found its origin in miniatures. From the very beginning the painters of the Netherlands met with so great a success and their works found their way into foreign countries in such numbers that it is worth examining the basic reason for the renown of the "Flemish Primitives". In the 16th century Vasari had already pointed out that the Flemish painters had been the first to apply the oil medium to easel painting. This opinion has been subsequently supported by art historians and technicians. But technique alone is not enough; it must be put to use by creative genius if it is to produce masterpieces.

Flemish painting reached one of its summits with Jan van Eyck (d. 1441) who, in transcending every technical means, introduced into painting a new realistic vision of man and nature. He greatly surpassed his northern contemporaries as well as those in the South. When more is known about the masters who were active at the beginning of the 15th century, it will become possible to understand more fully the origins of Flemish painting and to determine the contribution made by the genius of Jan van Eyck.

The spirit of van Eyck was especially reflected in the art of Petrus Christus (d. 1472), about whom little is known. The work of Roger van der Weyden

44

(d. 1464), who worked in Brussels, was considerable even without including that which some art historians attribute to the Master of Flémalle. His paintings, all of an extreme sensibility, enjoyed such a prodigious success that they were imitated and exported and even other techniques, such as sculpture or tapestry, took their inspiration from them. Along with Jan van Eyck and Hugo van der Goes, he must be considered one of the greatest masters of 15th century Flanders.

Dieric Bouts (d. 1475), who worked mostly in Louvain, created figures whose impassiveness conceals deep inner tension. Moreover, he introduced the Brabantine countryside into Flemish painting. Joos van Gent (Joos van Wassenhove ?, active between 1460 and 1480) worked in Urbino, Italy. Here was a Flemish artist who had to adapt himself to another circle, that of an Italian court influenced by humanism. The Ghent School is further illustrated by Hugo van der Goes who experimented with new pictorial solutions. Well before his death in 1482, he showed indications, through the anxiety of the human emotions of his figures, of a mind close to madness, just as is seen much later in the works of Van Gogh.

Two painters of great renown began fruitful careers in Bruges at the end of the century: Hans Memlinc (d. 1494) and Gerard David (d. 1523). The former was very mindful of balanced composition and the rendering of space. He took his inspiration from Roger van der Weyden but is more conservative and less emotional. David is sometimes reminiscent of van Eyck, but his paintings, although always colorful, give an impression of coldness. His workshop, as well as other Bruges workshops of the same period, produced paintings of a greatly varying quality.

A unique role was played by the astonishing Hieronymus Bosch (d. 1516). Here was the devil turned painter, but a devil whose skilled handling of the brush produced a grimacing humanity which was always at the cross-roads of Heaven, Purgatory, and Hell. He was, to some extent, a forerunner of Pieter Bruegel, the great 16th century Flemish painter.

There were other artists who deserve mention, even if less important and less original. Among them are many anonymous masters some of whom have been provisionally assigned a conventional name. There are also the painters whose names appear on the rolls of the guilds, but of whom nothing is known.

At the beginning of the 16th century the art of the Northern European countries was affected by the Renaissance. The economy of Bruges fell into inactivity and its artistic role ended. Antwerp took its place as the business and artistic center. Many painters worked there but only one of them resisted the Italian vogue and retained his individuality: Pieter Bruegel. It was not until the 17th century that Flemish painting, with Pieter-Paul Rubens, knew another golden age.

Sculpture in the Netherlands of the 15th century experienced a success in some ways comparable to painting, although it was eclipsed by the latter. Art historians agree generally that realism was first manifested in sculpture. This new tendency was illustrated especially by Claus Sluter of Haarlem (d. 1406). It is known that this sculptor spent some time in Brussels, where he is said to have received his training. Sluter went to Dijon where he succeeded Jean de Marville as head of the workshop maintained by Philip the Bold. Because of the quality of Sluter's work he is often credited with the rebirth of sculpture north of the Alps at the end of the 14th century. The portal of the Carthusian Monastery of Champmol, the Wells of Moses, and the Mourning Procession on the Tomb of Philip the Bold (Dijon, Musée des Beaux-Arts) could confirm this judgment. Nevertheless, at approximately the same period in the Netherlands, there were works in which rather similar stylistic characters could be seen as, for example, in the corbels of the Bruges City Hall (cat. no. 68), the prophets and corbels of the portal of the Brussels City Hall, or the statues of the apostles in the Church of Notre-Dame in Hal. Through the influence of the Brabantine workshops of the middle of the 15th century, the Netherlands developed its own style which had a certain affinity with painting. This style had already begun to manifest itself in the stone carvings decorating the city halls of Brussels and Louvain. Other examples are found in Nivelles, Hal, Mons, and Soignies. In the field of stone carving the Tournai workshops became specialized in the production of bas-relief tombstones.

Apostle in Hal

It was especially in the field of woodcarving that the workshops of the Netherlands, particularly those of Brabant, were very active, beginning in the second half of the 15th century. Activity was so great that the sculptors' corporations created identification marks to guarantee the works against bad workmanship: the mallet was the mark of Brussels while that of Antwerp was a hand. Some of these works were of a very high quality, such as those in Etterbeek, Louvain, and Léau (cat. nos. 85, 78-79 and 92). The workshops of Brussels, Antwerp, and Malines were renowned for carved altarpieces, often polychromed, generally in wood, and rarely in stone. Very few of those which date from the end of the 14th and the beginning of the 15th century are preserved. Brabantine altarpieces were very much in vogue although their quality was sometimes inferior because their production was almost industrial. The proof of their success is demonstrated by the fact that they were exported in great numbers to Germany, Scandinavia, France, Spain, and even the Canary Islands. Among the altarpieces which escaped ordinary production and are on a level almost comparable to the best paintings are, from the beginning of the 15th century, the altarpiece of Hakendover (cat. nos. 69-70), and, from the second half of the 15th and the beginning of the 16th century, the Altarpiece of Saint George by Jan

46

Borman (Brussels, Musées Royaux d'Art et d'Histoire), the Altarpiece of Saint Léonard in Léau (cat. no. 73), that of the Passion in Geel (cat. no. 74-77), and the one of the Life of the Virgin in the Church of Notre-Dame in Lombeek.

It appears that sculptors often worked from models done by painters: documents in the archives such as contracts ordering works are evidence of this. No drawing is known, however, which can be said with certainty to have been a model of this kind. Nevertheless, the drawing of Men Shovelling Chairs in the Lehman Collection in New York may very well have served such a purpose. If so, it would have been the model for the sculptor of a capital for the Brussels City Hall. It is certain that painters and sculptors collaborated in polychrome work. For example, it is known by documents that Jan van Eyck was charged with the polychromy of the statues which formerly decorated the façade of the Bruges City Hall.

Domestic and religious *furniture* in the Netherlands during the 15th century reflects the intense activity which existed at that time in all the arts. Religious furniture provided the opportunity for a close collaboration between architects, sculptors, and carpenters or stone cutters. In addition to the altarpieces already mentioned, other works were produced which were of remarkable quality. Stone rood-screens, whose decoration has often been compared to lace, enclosed the choirs of numerous churches, as is still the case in Saint-Pierre in Louvain (1488), in Aarschot (1510-1525), and in Walcourt (1531). These rood-screens were frequently topped by a triumphal cross with the Virgin on one side and Saint John on the other, as is the case in the Church of Saint-Pierre in Louvain (cat. nos. 78-79). The turrets of the Blessed Sacrament which are monumental tabernacles isolated from the altars, were much in favor in the Netherlands (Louvain, Church of Saint-Pierre, 1450; replica dating from 1537-1539 in the Church of Saint-Jacques). Carpenters and sculptors were able to demonstrate their abilities in church stalls. Those of Saint-Pierre in Louvain (1438-1442), Diest (1493), and Aarschot (1510-1525), although mutilated, are still outstanding on account of the imaginative quality of their misericords (cat. nos. 81-84). The cradles known as "Repos de l'Enfant Jésus" were a type of furniture peculiar to the Netherlands, and scarcely any still exist. The example being shown in this exhibition (cat. no. 161) may be considered one of the best. Domestic furniture, including chairs, chests, and trunks, is less known. These was not as monumental as religious furniture but of equal quality and they were more rarely decorated in carved bas-relief. These furnishings and the interior decorations of private homes are mostly known indirectly through the faithful reproductions in early Flemish painting and sculpture.

Artistic life found a most impressive expression in *architecture*. There was great construction activity in the Netherlands from the 13th to 16th centuries, as can be seen from the number of private and public buildings (city halls, covered markets, and corporation houses) as well as religious edifices (churches, abbeys, monasteries, and convents) constructed in that period. Large public works were also undertaken by the cities: locks, dikes, bridges, and fortifications. From the end of the 12th century and particularly in the following century the influence of the great French Gothic cathedrals was felt in the architecture of the Netherlands (Tournai, Chapel of the Bishopric and choir of the Cathedral; Abbey of Villers; Ghent, Saint-Bavon; Brussels, choir of Sainte-Gudule, and others). The architecture of the Netherlands developed forms which, although inspired by French patterns, had an autonomous development which gave rise to several schools. The earliest (13th and 14th centuries) was the Scheldt School, so named because, beginning at Tournai on the Scheldt, it spread into the Scheldt basin (Tournai, Saint-Jacques, Saint-Nicolas, Saint-Quentin; Bruges, Notre-Dame, in the nave). To this same group may be attached numerous churches of maritime Flanders which had, however, certain special features: they were constructed in brick, the naves had the same height and width (the "Hallekirche" type), and the west façade was emphasized by a powerful tower dominating the surrounding countryside (Bruges, Notre-Dame; Damme; Lisseweghe). The churches of the Meuse region (Dinant; Huy; Liège, Sainte-Croix, Saint-Denis, Saint-Jacques; Tongres, Notre-Dame) and the Hainault area (Ath, Chimay) also formed more or less characteristic groups. But, in the 15th century, the Brabantine School deserves the most attention. This school began to form in the second third of the 14th century through the influence of Jean d'Oisy (Malines, choir of the cathedral, ca. 1340; Tirlemont, Notre-Dame-au-Lac, 1350) and, benefiting from the economic growth in Brabant and the presence of an excellent building material (sandstone), it dominated all the architectural activity in the Netherlands during the 15th and the beginning of the 16th centuries. Numerous churches were constructed, finished, or enlarged during that period in Brabant: Antwerp, cathedral (14th - 16th centuries); Brussels, Sainte-Gudule (14th - 16th centuries) and Notre-Dame-du-Sablon (15th-16th centuries); Louvain, Saint-Pierre (1425 - 1479); Anderlecht (1470 - 1525); Diest (1417 - 1534); and many others. Because of its success this school spread beyond the borders of the Duchy of Brabant. Thus manifestations or influences of the Brabantine School are found in other provinces of the Netherlands (Flanders: Ghent, nave and transept of Saint-Bavon (1533-1569); Hainault: Mons, Sainte-Waudru (1450 - 1621); Holland: Haarlem, Saint-Bavon) as well as in France, Spain, and Germany. The expansion of this school can be

Louvain, City Hall

48

partially explained by the classicism and technical perfection of Brabantine architecture itself and by the fame of the architects working in Brabant. There were men such as Jan de Ruysbroeck (tower of the Brussels City Hall, 1449-1455), Sulpice van Vorst (Church of Diest; Saint-Pierre of Louvain), Mathieu de Layens (Louvain, City Hall, 1445-1463), and especially the Keldermans dynasty (14th-16th centuries) whose members directed construction in Antwerp, Ghent, Malines, Louvain, and elsewhere. The boldness of these architects was manifested particularly in the towers which they built to express the belief of the faithful (church towers) or to magnify the power of the cities (belfries, towers of city halls). Those of the Cathedral of Antwerp (15th-16th centuries, 413 ft. 5 in.) and the Brussels City Hall (1449-1455, 377 ft. 5 in.) are among the most beautiful. Most of them stand unfinished (Malines, among others) but, by their elegance or robustness emphasized by buttresses, they are all eloquent evidence of the good taste, mastery, and ambition of the Brabantine architects (the tower of the Cathedral of Malines was supposed to have been built up to 547 ft. 3 in.).

Just as important is the civil architecture which reflects the same tendencies. The cities themselves, the corporations, and the bourgeois, all contributed to the growth of this architecture. Commercial activity brought about the construction of covered market places: Ypres (1201-1304), Louvain (work begun in 1317). Local security required belfries: Tournai (ca. 1200-1294), Ghent (1314-1380), Bruges (14th-15th centuries). The wealth of the cities manifested itself in aldermen's houses (Malines, 14th century) and city halls, many of which derived from the Brabantine School: Brussels (1402-1455), Louvain (1445-1463), Mons (1479), Ghent (1518), Oudenaarde (1527), and others. The ornate façades of these city halls provided the opportunity for sculptors to exercise their talents. Private homes with their gables, sometimes tiered, gave the cities of the Netherlands the picturesque and prosperous character which can be seen in great detail in the paintings of the early Flemish artists.

The study of monuments is facilitated by plans and architectural drawings. Only a few examples have survived. This, then, gives special value to the plan of the Castle of Courtrai (cat. no. 170) and the drawing of the façade for the Church of Saint-Pierre (cat. no. 171). The latter church is fortunate in possessing a stone model of the upper part of its façade, which was never completed. There also exist drawings for the façade of the Ghent City Hall (Ghent, Museum voor Oudheden) and the tower of Sainte-Waudru in Mons (Brussels, Bibliothèque Royale).

Flemish *tapestry* enjoyed a reputation comparable to that of painting and sculpture. Evidence of this is the number of works still preserved in various countries. Arras, in Artois, was the earliest and most active center from the end of the 14th century (cat. no. 148). There were other workshops in Brabant, Flanders, and Hainault, but their production is barely known except by records. Around the middle of the 15th century, the Tournai workshops took over the leadership and it is not surprising that it was with them that Philip the Good placed his orders. The tapestry work of Tournai was dominated by the strong personality of Pasquier Grenier, manufacturer and merchant. It was he who received an order from Philip the Good, in 1462, to do the story of the Knight and the Swan (Vienna, Österr. Museum für Kunst und Industrie; Cracow, Wawel Castle). Many products of these workshops are still preserved: Brussels, Musées Royaux d'Art et d'Histoire; New York, Metropolitan Museum; Paris, Musée des Arts Décoratifs, and elsewhere. During the second half of the 15th century the Brussels workshops were extremely active. Their reputation led Philip the Good to order a series of the Story of Hannibal which is now lost. In some instances the Brussels tapestries reflected the works of painters. Roger van der Weyden's Saint Luke Painting the Virgin (cat. no. 7) was the model for, or at least strongly inspired, the author of a tapestry of the same subject (Paris, Louvre). There were sometimes such close relationships between Brussels painting and tapestry that certain art historians have theorized that Roger van der Weyden may have done some cartoons of tapestries. The same hypothesis, but more probable in these cases, has been proposed for Vrancke van der Stockt and the Master of the View of Sainte-Gudule. It is suggested that the former did the cartoons for the tapestries of the Annunciation and the Adoration of the Magi (Paris, Louvre) and that the latter drew the cartoon for the tapestry of the Adoration of the Magi in the Cathedral in Sens. The Brussels workshops reached their peak at the end of the 15th and the beginning of the 16th centuries. The great number of gold threads mixed into the silk gave such a splendor to the richest of these tapestries that they were called the "cloths of gold". This is the period and style reflected in the Glorification of Christ (New York, Metropolitan Museum) and its replicas. The preponderant importance of the workshops of Arras, Tournai, and Brussels should not overshadow the existence of other centers like Bruges where tapestries of equally fine quality were woven (cat. no. 153).

In the other textile arts such as *embroidery* there was as great an activity and the same concern for lavishness through the use of gold or silver thread. There were numerous embroidery workshops whose production cannot be determined with certainty. It is known that the Bruges ateliers made works destined for export to Scandinavia and the Baltic Countries. The most prodigious series still preserved is certainly the one from the former Chapel of the Treasure of the Golden Fleece (Vienna, Kunsthistorisches Museum) whose embroidery sometimes appears to have drawn its stylistic and iconographic inspiration from the works of Roger van der Weyden. The treasuries of certain churches such as in Bruges (cat. no. 157) or Léau (cat. no. 160) also contain liturgical vestments with embroidery which evidence the skill and decorative sense of the craftsmen who made them.

The *dinanderie,* a generic term which includes brass and copper objects, was embedded in a secular tradition because it had long been developed as a specialty of the Meuse region; from there it was exported to England, Germany, Scandinavia, France, and Italy. The brass founders and beaters of the city of Dinant must have acquired a special reputation for the quality of their products because the French word for metalwork ("dinanderie") was derived from the name of the city of Dinant. In the 14th century, Dinant and its rival Bouvignes were practically the only cities of the Meuse region which still had very active workshops. Already at that time the Meuse area had lost its monopoly over brass work and it is known that Tournai, Brussels, Malines, Louvain, Bruges, and Ghent possessed workshops. Certain of these, as in Bruges and Ghent, were sending their products to Germany, Scandinavia, and Spain. The sacking of Dinant, in 1466, put a sudden end to the workshops' activity there for some years and they were never again able to recover their former splendor. The result was an exodus of Dinant craftsmen to other centers like Namur, Huy, Tournai, Bruges, or Middelburg. Metalwork experienced considerable progress in the 15th century and achieved some of its most beautiful examples in, among others, lecterns (cat. no. 105), baptismal fonts, paschal candelabra (cat. nos. 103-104), and fountains (Huy, the Bassinia, 1406). Other works, although less monumental, are noteworthy; they are objects like utensils (plates and tableware: cat. nos. 117-120), or numerous objects for church use: crosses, censers, light brackets (cat. no. 106), and chandeliers (cat. no. 107) which were often introduced into their works by painters. An example of this is the chandelier shown by Jan van Eyck in the wedding chamber of the Arnolfinis (London, National Gallery). There were also great masters of metalwork among the numerous anonymous artists and those of whom little is known. In Tournai there was Guillaume Le Febvre, who did the baptismal fonts ornamented with statuettes in Hal (1464) and the paschal candlestick from Saint-Ghislain (1442) (Brussels, Musées Royaux d'Art et d'Histoire). In Brussels there were Jacques de Gérines and Renier van Thienen, the latter of whom did the particularly imposing paschal candelabrum in Léau (1482-1483) (18 ft. 7⁵/₈ in.) In the pathos of some of his statuettes he reflected the art of Roger van der Weyden and the great Brabantine sculptor, Jan Borman. Also in Brussels, the brass-beater Martin van Rhodes deserves to be mentioned for the manner in which, on top of the spire of the Brussels City Hall, he was able to install the elegant weather vane showing Saint Michael overcoming the devil (1454).

The metalworkers also participated in funerary art; there vandalism has taken a heavy toll because the material can be so easily re-used. The centers of Bruges and Ghent produced plaques for tombstones and monuments which, technically and esthetically, are closer to the art of engraving. Many of these plaques were exported to Germany, England, Scandinavia, and Spain. Funeral monuments with recumbent figures in bronze and sometimes with statuettes decorating the side walls, gave the founders a chance to raise their art to the level of great sculpture. The sculptors were sometimes able to create models for the founders. Unfortunately, the tombs of Louis de Male (1455) and Duchess Joan of Brabant (1458-1459) have been lost. They were ordered by Philip the Good from Jacques de Gérines, the first for the Church of Saint-Pierre in Lille and the second for the Church of the Carmelites in Brussels. What they were actually like can be seen from the statuettes preserved in the Rijksmuseum in Amsterdam (cat. nos. 101-102). The quality of this funeral art is still attested to by the tombs of Mary of Burgundy (1496-1502) and Charles the Bold (1558-1562) (Bruges, Notre-Dame).

The art of metal is also represented by *ironwork, arms,* and *armor.* Dated objects in the field of ironwork are very rare. Anonymous craftsmen manifested this art in door-hinges ("pentures") (Hal, Notre-Dame), chandeliers (Alost, Saint-Martin; Diest, City Museum), chests decorated in iron, locks (Hal, Notre-Dame, door of the baptistry), and in kitchen utensils (cat. nos. 121-122). According to documents in the archives it appears that the armorers of Tournai and Bruges were very prosperous and that those in Ghent were engaged in the production of luxury arms. In this field also, Brussels was the most active center. It is known that the Dukes of Burgundy ordered their arms, armor, and trappings there for numerous jousts which can be seen illustrated in many manuscripts. The pieces of armor which are preserved (cat. nos. 139-147) are difficult to attribute with certainty to a given center. However, thanks to the careful detail in Flemish painting, and sometimes in goldsmith's work (cat. no. 133), there is a basis from which certain deductions can be made.

Goldsmith's work is another artistic expression of the arts of metal which had a new period of splendor in the 15th century. The Meuse region had already been widely known in this field from the 11th to the 13th centuries. Texts of archives give a good idea of the extraordinary vogue experienced by goldsmith's work in the 14th and 15th centuries. This may be explained by various factors: the taste for luxury which people wanted to display, the table services in precious metal which provided a "war treasury" for the princes and an investment for rich bourgeois, and, finally, the piety of the faithful who made numerous donations to the churches. The value of metal is the basic cause for the disappearance of so many works. Thus, in the field of jewelry and precious table services the main source of information is, once again, the Flemish Primitives. The 15th century objects in this field are not as imposing as those done in the centuries which preceded. It was no longer the period of large, finely wrought reliquaries decorated with enamel, such as were produced in the 12th and 13th centuries. Altarpieces and altar-frontals in gold or silver were no longer being made. Chalices (cat. no. 134), ciboria, reliquaries (cat. no. 136), ostensories (cat. no. 132), and statuettes (cat. no. 135), constituted from then on the religious goldsmith's production whose decor and structure were derived from contemporary architectural forms. Around 1400, the goldsmiths of the Netherlands emerged from the French influence which they had been under since the 13th century. The statuettes of Tongres (cat. no. 127) demonstrate the renewal of sculpture which was seen in that period. From the middle of the 15th century the goldsmiths, in certain works, underwent the growing influence of the Flemish Primitives which manifested itself in all the plastic arts. The reliquary of Charles the Bold (cat. no. 133) which was made by the goldsmith Gérard Loyet (1466-1467) illustrates the free interpretation of a theme shown by Jan van Eyck in his painting The Madonna with Canon van der Paele (Bruges, Stedelijk Museum).

However, in other works from the end of the 15th century, such as the statuettes in the Church of Saint-Pierre in Louvain (cat. no. 135), an influence from Brabantine sculpture, then at its peak, is seen. Goldsmith's work of the various centers of production in the Netherlands has not yet been adequately studied. The Bruges, Ghent, and Brussels workshops were among the most active and the quality of their production was recognized: it was in Brussels, for example, that Louis XI, future king of France, ordered a monstrance to give to the Church of Notre-Dame in Hal.

The 15th century is also characterized by the beginning and development of the *arts of the print:* the arts of engraving in relief, practised mainly on wood (xylography) but also on metal (metal-cuts and white-line engraving for relief printing, "Metallschnitte" and "Schrottblätter") and the engraving in intaglio (line-engraving). From the start, Flanders and Brabant took a leading part in these new methods of expression and reproduction in Western Europe. Starting from written documents and style criticism, it is proved that these provinces were among the countries which produced (ca. 1400) the first and most beautiful wood-engravings. Throughout the development of this art, particularly in the 15th century, the Southern Netherlands continued to have a prominent place, also as regards the blockbook production.

The same may be said for line-engraving. One of the leaders in this field, the Master of the Death of Mary (ca. 1430), is unanimously held as a Fleming who is at least contemporaneous with the leading German line-engraver, the Master of the Playing Cards.

The origin and evolution of the print are particularly revealing of the needs of man in the 15th century. They mark an important date in the history of European civilization, by the birth of the printed image of which typography is a development. It is as well not to forget that this is one of the particularly significant events of the 15th century. The xylographic prints produced during the 15th century are innumerable. Wood-engraving was widely practised and diffused in towns, monasteries and places of pilgrimage. When more research will have been done in this field, our knowledge of the social, religious, economic and artistic life will be much more complete. More will be known also about the activity and spirit of the workshops where the stained-glass windows, the tapestries, the sculptures and the paintings of that time, were created. The comparisons and attributions which have already been established are very revealing on this subject. The line-engravings were equally integrated in the general artistic activity of the 15th century. They were however first used in the goldsmith's workshop before going to that of the painter. Thanks to engraving more so than to xylography, the worldly and the more intimate life of man in the 15th century has become better known. An achievement of the 15th century engravers, by no means the least, is that they began and practised an art whose formal purity is continued in the works of the artists up to the 20th century.

In the 15th century the art of *glass* was most beautifully manifested by stained-glass windows. Already in the 14th century there were numerous artists in stained-glass, but many of their works have disappeared. Some fragments are, however, left from that period: in the Beguine Convent of Louvain, the church in Sichem, and the Musées Royaux d'Art et d'Histoire in Brussels. The few stained-glas windows which remain from the 15th century give only a faint idea of what that art must then have been. They were often dominated by yellow and red tones. Examples can still be seen in churches in Lierre, Anderlecht, Hal, and Bruges (cat. nos. 165-168), and others, coming from the Chapel of the Holy Blood in Bruges are preserved in the Victoria and Albert Museum in London. These works confirm that the quality was equal to that in other techniques and show that the artists in stained-glass found their inspiration in contemporary painting.

From the 14th century, the glassmaking industry developed in the Netherlands, especially in the Principality of Liège where the Colinet family of glass-makers seems to have played an important role. The production of flasks, drinking glasses (cat. no. 169) and other liquid recipients in glass was very extensive in the 15th century. Although a true industry existed, only a small part of its production remains. Once again, the Flemish Primitives provide the means of filling the gaps. An hour-glass and a kind of bottle are seen in the study of Saint Jerome by van Eyck (cat. no. 5). In the central panel of the Last Supper by Dieric Bouts (Louvain, Church of Saint-Pierre) can be seen different types of decorated drinking glasses (see illustration p. 105).

A review of the art of the Southern Netherlands of the 15th century would be incomplete without a look at the *iconography* which determined the choice of subjects and their presentation and thus reflected the spiritual and intellectual atmosphere of the period. In this regard 15th century Flemish art was particularly eloquent and great quantities of works were intended to represent religious subjects. A breath of mysticism seems to have passed over the people of the end of the Middle Ages. This mysticism expressed itself time and again on the level of pathos and human tenderness. The former evoked a passionate and sorrowful art and the latter gave it a more tender expression. This art always tells a story, tries to show all, and attempts to move the spectator; for example, Christ's suffering had to be perceptible, His tears visible, and His wounds bloody. Each individual, corporation and confraternity wanted to have its own patron. This explains the subjects of numerous works and the growing number of paintings and statues representing saints whose patronage was invoked.

Secular iconography was no less revealing. The taste for antiquity explains, in part, the choice of ancient subjects (cat. no. 44). The nobility still dreamed of knightly prowess and, lacking actual combat, had to be satisfied with jousts and tournaments. If they lacked these, they fed their imagination on representations: Hercules became a 15th century lord and his twelve labors became so many jousts (cat. no. 152); Hector was no longer more than a prancing knight for whom the war of Troy was only a succession of tournaments (cat. no. 150). Court literature was always in fashion and it also inspired the artists. As she wove, Penelope (cat. no. 153) was a woman who languidly awaited the return of her knight. This was a theme sung by minstrels and troubadours. That which the nobility read or heard, they also saw illustrated in tapestries on the walls of their castles. The Duke of Burgundy wanted to see himself portrayed (cat. no. 13) as did the nobility in general (cat. no. 22). Rich merchants gave away their fortunes in order that they might be recorded in portrait as donors. Gradually man drew away from his status as a praying believer (cat. no. 19) and from the protection of his patron saint. He abandoned this kind of representation and posed as a man independent and sure of himself. This new type of portrait, thoroughly secularized, came increasingly into vogue from the beginning of the 16th century.

Around 1500, Flemish art began to lose its force. Artists became bound by set formulas which paralyzed creative spirit. The port of Bruges, more and more endangered by silt, was less and less frequented by merchants and foreign agents. They preferred to settle in Antwerp where economic liberalism was not smothered by cumbersome regulations. In spite of attempts to check this disaffection, the other large Flemish cities suffered from this crisis, and the decadence of the former County of Flanders only served to accentuate it. During the 16th century, new problems beset the Netherlands: religious troubles and iconoclasts, wars and foreign occupations. All these events not only undermined economic and cultural activity but did great damage to the artistic patrimony. The capture of Antwerp in 1585 had very important consequences for both politics and art. It was this event which marked the division of the Seventeen Provinces: the northern part of the Netherlands seceded and became independent while the southern part remained under Spanish domination. A religious split occurred also: the South remained faithful to Catholicism while the North became predominently Protestant, and numerous artists emigrated to the North. There was an artistic split too because, from then on, the arts which developed in the North and South no longer followed common roads.

When the Belgium of today, successor to the Flemish culture of the 15th century, considers the numerous collections which, all over the world, have gathered together the spiritual inheritance of Flanders, it experiences a great feeling of satisfaction. This tiny corner of Europe has spread almost everywhere the quintessence of its civilization and contributed to the artistic enrichment of younger cultures. In this respect, the United States has been particularly favored. Among its numerous museums, The Metropolitan Museum of Art of New York, the Philadelphia Museum of Art with the John G. Johnson Collection in Philadelphia, the National Gallery of Art in Washington, The Walters Art Gallery in Baltimore, and The Detroit Institute of Arts in Detroit, in particular, have gathered together a very large portion of the Flemish artistic heritage for the enjoyment of all mankind.

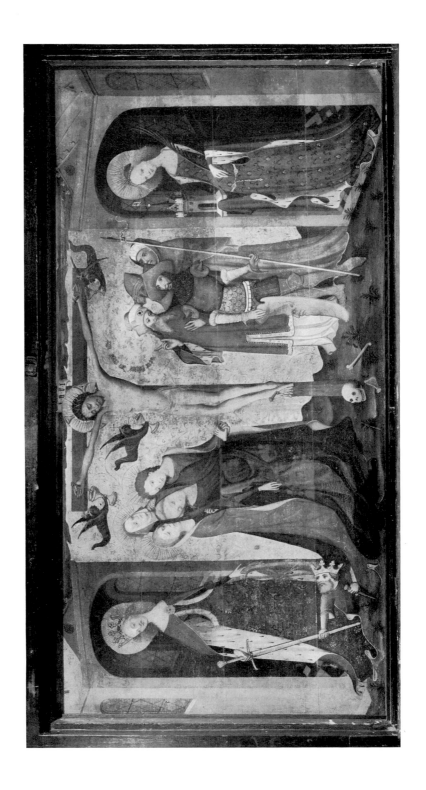

FLEMISH, ca. 1390-1400

1. ALTARPIECE OF THE CRUCIFIXION ("THE CALVARY OF THE TANNERS")

Bruges, Museum of the Cathedral of Saint-Sauveur

This painting is one of the very rare surviving Flemish paintings on panel, done before van Eyck. It has, therefore, an exceptional documentary value.

It is presumed to be of Bruges origin: first, because it was acquired by a collector of Damme (near Bruges) in a public sale at the beginning of the 19th century; second, because a local historian of the middle of that century reported a traditional story which said that the painting belonged to the Tanners Guild of Bruges; finally, because no better reason has been found up to now to classify it in any other regional school. Its execution is placed around 1390-1400; this is only an approximation, because the datable elements of comparison are insufficient.

The composition of this panel includes three different scenes. The one in the center is twice as wide as the other two, a practice which emerged later in triptychs. The iconography of the main scene, the Calvary with two clearly distinct groups of figures on either side of the cross, Christ's followers on the left and the soldiers and the Pharisees on the right, is of 13th century Italian origin and reached Northern Europe sometime in the 14th century. The gold background, here decorated in ornamental foliage with slight relief, was fashionable in the pre-Eyckian period. The presentation of the two compositions flanking the Calvary, St. Catherine and St. Barbara, isolated in small shelters, was probably inspired by the scenery of the mystery plays, theatrical pieces of the period. The unexpected gesture of the saint's persecutor, the emperor Maximian, the attribute of St. Catherine who is always shown groveling at her feet, seizing St. Catherine's sword, may also be derived from theatrical scenes. Emperor Maximian holds a dagger *"à rognons"* of Flemish type. An identical one is found in the Musée d'armes et d'armures in Brussels (Inv. 506). He is holding the dagger in his left hand which is exceptional for the period (four daggers of this type are exhibited here as nos. 139-142).

Physical data: Oak, 28 $^{13}/_{16}$ x 56 $^{1}/_{4}$ in. (73.2 x 143 cm.). The medium is aqueous, probably egg glair and not glue (analysis at the Institut Royal du Patrimoine Artistique, Brussels, 1948). Gilded and embossed background. Frame probably original, painted dark red. The frame is enclosed within a case with a hinged cover which opens downward, and which appears old; it is painted dark green with a scattering of gold stars on the inside. Inscription in Gothic letters in the gilded background to the right of Christ: *Vere Filius Dei erad iste.*

History: Acquired at a public sale at the beginning of the 19th century by the collector Vermeire of Damme; offered by him to the Cathedral of Saint-Sauveur; reputed to

57

Flemish, ca. 1390-1400

have belonged to the local Tanners Guild in Bruges (GAILLIARD, 1847, p. 169);
belonged in 1852 to the Cathedral of Saint-Sauveur (*Inventory*, 1852, no. 1).
Exhibitions: Bruges, 1867, no. 1; Bruges, 1902, no. 4; London, 1927, no. 2; Amsterdam
and Rotterdam, 1946, no. 43.

The most recent studies by specialists have scarcely modified the opinions
of the early commentators as to the date of this work: ca. 1400. WEALE (1899-1900,
p. XI), HULIN DE LOO (1902, no. 4), DUCLOS (1910, pp. 366-367), and DUVERGER
(1955, p. 91, note 36) place it around 1390-1400. No indication has appeared
either to confirm or to refute the tradition which recounts that the altarpiece
decorated the hall of the Tanners Guild. The latter, which had St. Bavon as its
patron saint, possessed a chapel in the Church of Notre-Dame.

STERLING (1942, p. 8, no. 26) finds the style of the altarpiece very close
to that of the Antwerp-Baltimore polyptych (part of which is shown in this
exhibition as no. 2), which he locates in the Hesdin-Valenciennes region. TOLNAY
(1949, pp. 49-54) sees in it a French influence. PANOFSKY (1953, pp. 96-97, 106,
note 3, and 204) discerns the local Bruges style and definitely Flemish characteristics. DUVERGER (1955, p. 91, note 36) also sees it as a Bruges work and
suggests as the possible painter Jan Coene, Willem van Meenen, or another
painter noted in documents of that period who worked on panel. TOLNAY
(1949, pp. 49-54) indicates the origin of the composition of the Calvary which
is found in this painting: it was created in Italy by Cimabue and Giotto, introduced in France around the beginning of the 14th century, went from there to
Germany about the middle of that century, and into Flanders a little later.

The Gospel text on the gold background near Christ says: "He, truly, was
the son of God". It is the text which appears in the Gospel according to St. Mark
(15. 39) who gives these words to the Centurion, and according to St. Matthew
(27.54) who said they were pronounced by the Centurion and the guards who
accompanied him. Here, as in many other paintings of the Crucifixion of that
period and even throughout the 15th century, the Centurion is looking at Christ,
but it is someone else who points to Christ and pronounces the words.

FLEMISH, ca. 1400

2.   THE ANNUNCIATION; on the reverse: THE BAPTISM OF CHRIST
      THE CALVARY
      Two wings of a quadriptych

Baltimore, Md., The Walters Art Gallery. Acc. no. 37.1683

These two panels are part of a quadriptych which is now dismembered and
divided between The Walters Art Gallery in Baltimore and the Museum Mayer
van den Bergh in Antwerp (cat. 374). This quadriptych was originally composed
of two panels forming a fixed central part and two wings painted on both sides.

58

59

Flemish, ca. 1400

The central section consists of a *Nativity* (Antwerp) and a *Calvary* (Baltimore). The left wing (Baltimore) contains the *Annunciation* with the *Baptism of Christ* on the reverse. The right wing (Antwerp) shows the *Resurrection* with *Saint Christopher* on the reverse.

The panels were long attributed to an artist close to Melchior Broederlam, and sometimes to the painter himself. They are now generally considered the work of a Flemish or Limburg artist of around 1400.

The *Annunciation* shows the Virgin seated on a Gothic throne, as was usual in manuscript miniatures of this subject. The *Crucifixion* takes the form of a Calvary with the Virgin and St. John on either side of Christ, whose blood is being caught by tiny angels while He speaks to His Father. The *Baptism of Christ* is a little different from the way in which this scene is usually presented. Here, instead of joining His hands, Christ is blessing with His right hand.

Physical data: Oak, each panel: 14 $^5/_{16}$ x 10 $^3/_{16}$ in. (36.3 x 25.9 cm.). The *Calvary* panel, which measured only 12 $^{13}/_{16}$ x 9 $^7/_8$ in. (35 x 20 cm.), has wood strips added which, by giving it the same dimensions as the other panels, undoubtedly restores its original dimensions. Gold background with engraved decoration, except the *Baptism of Christ,* where the sky is red.

Inscriptions: *Annunciation* panel: on the streamer held by the Archangel Gabriel: *Ave gracia plena dominus tecom;* on the book of God the Father: *alpha et* ω; on the Virgin's book: *ecce ancilla domini.* *Calvary* panel: streamer coming from Christ: *eloy eloy lama sabatani;* on the placard affixed to the cross: *I·N·R·I·;* on God the Father's book: *ego sum via ūitas.*

History: From the Carthusian Monastery of Champmol near Dijon, like the other panels of the same altarpiece which are preserved in Antwerp; given by Louis XV to Charles-Antoine de la Roche-Aymon, his chaplain, and preserved in the Chapel of Champigny-les-Vitraux; at the chaplain's death, became the property of Charles-Guillaume de la Roche-Aymon, who died in 1851 (information furnished to Henry Walters by Arnold Seligmann, Rey and Co. in 1919); Cuvillier Coll., Niort (BOUCHOT, 1904, pl. XX); Arnold Seligmann, Rey and Co., art dealers, New York, until April, 1919; Henry Walters Coll., New York, from April, 1919 until his death in November, 1931; Mrs. Henry Walters Coll.; acquired by The Walters Art Gallery in June, 1939.

Exhibitions: Paris, 1904, not in catalogue.

Exterior   Interior (left)

60

Flemish, ca. 1400

The fact that the Baltimore and Antwerp panels have traditionally been considered as coming from the Carthusian Monastery of Champmol near Dijon has long supported their comparison with the famous wings painted by Melchior Broederlam of Ypres in 1394-99 for the altarpiece of Jacques de Baerze, destined for the same Dijon Monastery. In addition, the Antwerp panels come from the Bertholomey Collection in Dijon (sold in Paris on January 23, 1843, no. 73; DE COO, 1958, p. 186, note 1). WEESE (1927, p. 93) goes so far as to attribute them to Broederlam himself, and believes they were part of the Champmol altarpiece, while several others see them as the work of a painter of Broederlam's workshop (FIERENS-GEVAERT, I, 1927, p. 32; BALDASS, 1934, p. 379; TOVELL, 1950, pl. 20-21). Others consider them more as a purely Burgundian work of around 1400 (MICHEL, 1924, p. 42; DEZARROIS, 1932, pp. 76 and 78; DUPONT, 1937, p. 18). LEMOISNE (1931, p. 52) also views them as the product of a Dijon workshop of around 1390-1400, but reflecting a strong Parisian influence. Still other authors attribute these panels to a French workshop, either of the Paris School of around 1380-90 (BOUCHOT, 1904, no paging), or from Northern France, with an influence from the Avignon School ([CORNETTE], 1932, pp. 18-19). STERLING (1938, figs. 26-31), who had first proposed attributing them to a Franco-Flemish workshop active in Paris about 1390-1400, later (1942, caption of pl. 26) inclined toward a Hainault workshop with a strong Parisian influence. Although accepting this kinship with the Paris School, RING (1949, p. 194, no. 20) detects a style which is more Flemish than Franco-Flemish. The tendency toward placing them in a Northern school is confirmed by more recent studies. PANOFSKY (1953, pp. 94 and 97) proposes placing them in the Lower Rhine region, perhaps in Guelders, about 1400-1410. Another specialist, DE COO (1958, pp. 186-198), who also dates the work around 1400, attempts to localize it through an iconographic peculiarity of the *Nativity* in the Museum Mayer van den Bergh, where St. Joseph is cutting his stocking to use it to cover the Child. Since this legend probably originated in Aix-la-Chapelle, where swaddling-clothes

Interior (right)   *Exterior*

61

Flemish, ca. 1400

of Jesus are venerated, DE COO places the polyptych within the area of the pilgrimage to Aix-la-Chapelle. Another interesting point is that in the *Baptism of Christ*, instead of letting the water run through his fingers as he is typically shown in Flemish painting, St. John the Baptist pours the water from a small jug. STRZYGOWSKI (1885, cited by RÉAU, II, 2, pp. 300 and 310) views this feature as characteristic of German painting. Interestingly enough, however, the very same detail is found in a *Baptism of Christ* in the *Petites Heures* of Jean de Berry, attributed to Jacquemart de Hesdin, in the Bibliothèque Nationale in Paris (ms. lat. 18014, fol. 209 v°; cf. PANOFSKY, II, 1953, fig. 31), the style of which, moreover, is similar to that of the Baltimore panel. Whatever its origins, this quadriptych appears to be most appropriately placed within the Northern European schools. HULIN DE LOO (1911) thinks that the Baltimore panels are by another hand than the ones in Antwerp.

The original order of the different panels of this quadriptych is not definitely known, nor is the purpose for which the complete work was done. STERLING (1938, p. 150, note 22 and figs. 26-31) suggested placing the *Annunciation* and the *Nativity* in the center, the *Crucifixion* and the *Resurrection* at either end, and the *Baptism of Christ* and *St. Christopher* on the outside. More recently, PANOFSKY (1953, p. 93, note 1) proposed the most logical arrangement from an iconographic point of view and the most satisfactory from the point of view of composition: with the quadriptych open and going from left to right: the *Annunciation,* the *Nativity,* the *Crucifixion,* the *Resurrection* and, on the reverse, the *Baptism of Christ* and *St. Christopher*. He adds that such winged quadriptychs, although rare, did exist in French and Franco-Flemish painting of around 1400. This arrangement advanced by PANOFSKY in a lecture before the war had already been adopted by LEMOISNE (1931, p. 52), DUPONT (1937, p. 18) and SPENCER (1940, p. 30). The hypothesis seems to be confirmed by the facts: first, that the *Annunciation* and the *Baptism of Christ* are painted back to back, as are the *Resurrection* and *St. Christopher*, and, second, that the two panels considered as the outside of the wings (the *Baptism of Christ* in Baltimore and the *St. Christopher* in Antwerp) have red skies, while the other four panels have gold backgrounds, a material which is both too rich and fragile to be used on the outside of such a winged altarpiece. As to the object for which the complete work was intended, several authors have proposed to identify it as being elements of a shrine or a winged tabernacle, without defining how it should be arranged (BOUCHOT, 1904, no paging; MICHEL, 1924, p. 42; STERLING, 1938, p. 150, note 21). It is probably more reasonable to consider them as a small portable altarpiece in the form of a quadriptych, as STERLING (1938, p. 150, note 21 and 1942, p. 8, no. 26) and PANOFSKY (1953, p. 93) suggest.

PANOFSKY (1953, pp. 93, 94 and 127) discovers new iconographic ideas in the Baltimore panels, as in those of Antwerp, for example, the Virgin of the *Annunciation* crossing her arms in front of her bosom, an extremely rare gesture in French and Franco-Flemish painting, which appeared a quarter of a century later in the *Annunciation* of van Eyck's *Ghent Altarpiece*. As for the *Calvary,* it differs from all others because Christ, usually resigned, here pathetically raises

62

Flemish, ca. 1400

His head to cry: "Eloy, Eloy, lama sabatani". PANOFSKY thinks this painter was inspired, not by the Gospels, but by the paraphrase which St. Bridget made in her *Revelationes* (4. 70): *Vocem ex ymo pectoris, erecto capite, oculis in celum directis et lacrymantibus, emisit dicens "Deus, Deus, lama sabachtani"* (Deeply from His breast, raising His head, His weeping eyes turned heavenward, He gave a cry, saying "My God, My God, why hast Thou forsaken me ? ").

FLEMISH, first half of the 15th Century

3.　PORTRAIT OF JOHN THE FEARLESS

Antwerp, Musée Royal des Beaux-Arts. Cat. 1959, no. 540

This is a portrait of John the Fearless (1371-1419), son of Philip the Bold and the second of the Dukes of Burgundy (1404-1419). The specialists agree in considering it a copy of a lost original.

The original was probably done during the lifetime of the prince, between 1410 and 1419, judging from the model's age. The copy was probably made in the second quarter of the 15th century, after the death of John the Fearless. The original was, perhaps, a bust portrait, not showing the hands; these may have been added by the copyist. The original may have been the work of the painter Jean Malouel and, in that case, would date from 1415 at the latest, this painter having died in March of that year. The copy in the Antwerp Museum has been attributed successively to Hubert van Eyck, the Master of Flémalle, and Roger van der Weyden or his workshop. The last hypothesis seems the most reasonable.

His contemporaries described John the Fearless as a small dark man with blue eyes, courageous, ambitious, crafty, and distrusting. He had been brought up in Flanders with a Flemish teacher, the Provost of Saint-Donatien in Bruges, Baudouin de la Nieppe. He chose as his motto *ic houd*, "I hold". The Duke is soberly clothed and his high cap in the style of the time is decorated with only one jewel.

63

Physical data: Oak, 8 $^1/_2$ x 5 $^3/_4$ in. (21.5 x 14.6 cm.) (total surface). The panel has been slightly enlarged; original dimensions: approximately 8 $^1/_4$ x 5 $^1/_8$ in. (21 x 13 cm.) (total surface). Repainted in several places. Coats of arms on the arm-rest.

History: Collection of the Chevalier Florent van Ertborn, Antwerp; bequest of van Ertborn to the City of Antwerp in 1841 ([DELEN], 1958, no. 540).

Exhibitions: London, 1927, no. 5; Dijon, 1951, no. 5; Brussels, 1951, no. 2; Amsterdam, 1951, no. 2; Bruges, 1953, no. 1; Brussels, 1953, no. 98.

The model has been identified as John the Fearless, whose features are well known through other portraits. The coats of arms on the covering of the arm-rest are those of Burgundy and Flanders ([DELEN], 1958, no. 540). The original portrait cannot be placed before 1410, judging from the Duke's age (he was born in 1371), and by the composition of the portrait which, rather than being a profile, is seen almost in a three-quarters half-length view, including the hands. It is true that the hands could have been added by the copyist, as is suggested by BALDASS (1952, p. 62). WINKLER (1913, pp. 147-148, and 1924 p. 70) attributed the original of this portrait to a Burgundian court painter. CONWAY (1927, no. 5) specifies that he must have been a Flemish artist. FIERENS-GEVAERT (1927, p. 31) puts forth the names of Jean Malouel, the Duke's painter until 1415, and his successor, the Brabantine Henri Bellechose. WINKLER (XXIII, 1929, p. 599) favors the attribution to Malouel and points out that this painter made a portrait of the Duke in 1412 which was intended for the King of Portugal. He refers to KLEINCLAUSZ (1906, p. 166) who, himself, had referred to MONGET (II, 1901, p. 22). The latter published an entry from the archives of Burgundy: "Order given in Paris on March 15, 1412: *A Jehan Malouel(...) pour parfaire et accomplir ung certain tableau qu'il avait piéça encommencié, pour ycellui envoier au Roy de Portugal*". This is similar to another record published by DE SALLES (II, 1729, p. 138): "Account of Jean de Noident for 1415; *Jean Maluel(...) d'une image par lui contrefaire à la semblance de mondit Seigneur le Duc, et par lui envoyée au Roi de Portugal, par mandement donné à Chastillon sur Seine le 14 novembre 1415*". This means that Jean Malouel was payed in 1415 for a portrait of the Duke which he had made and which was sent by the Duke to the King of Portugal. WESCHER (1941, p. 196), referring only to DE SALLES, dates the portrait painted by Malouel in 1415, the year of the painter's death. This is also the date given by DE MONT (1905, no. 540) and maintained by DELEN (1958, no. 540), who both refer to the *Revue universelle des arts*, VIII, but without indicating the page. WAUTERS (1894-95, p. 263) gives the date 1413 for this portrait in making reference, only in a general way, to the same sources. Whatever it is from an historical point of view, WINKLER (1913, pp. 147-148; 1924, p. 70; XXIII, 1929, p. 599) and WESCHER (1941, p. 196) believe that this lost portrait could be the original of the one in Antwerp. If the hands are shown in the original portrait, it would be the oldest known half-length portrait, showing the hands, of the Flemish School (BEENKEN, 1941, pp. 16 and 49). It seems to be the first example of a portrait as an easel painting which is not a profile, but is seen almost in three-quarter view (PANOFSKY, 1953, p. 171). BEENKEN (1937, pp. 116-117)

64

attributed the original portrait of John the Fearless to the painter of the *Three Marys at the Tomb* of the former Cook Collection in Richmond, now in the Museum Boymans-van Beuningen in Rotterdam, and says it is, for this reason, from the early period of Hubert van Eyck.

According to RENDERS (I, 1931, pp. 94-95), the copy in the Antwerp Museum is from the hand of the Master of Flémalle (or Roger van der Weyden), who could have copied an older portrait while giving it "Rogeresque" style hands. SCHEEWE (1934, p. 212) challenges some of the arguments presented by RENDERS. WESCHER (1941, p. 196) adds other arguments to RENDERS's thesis: he believes the Antwerp portrait can be attributed to Roger van der Weyden. PANOFSKY (1953, pp. 171 and 291) assigns it to the workshop of Roger van der Weyden. BALDASS (1952, p. 67) places its execution around 1440 and attributes it to one of Roger's pupils or followers.

Another high quality example of this portrait, but without the hands, is in the Comte de Limburg Stirum Collection in Rumbeke, Belgium.

JAN VAN EYCK

Active notably in The Hague, Lille(?) and, especially, Bruges
May have originally come from Maeseyck in Limburg. Died in Bruges in 1441

The career of Jan van Eyck can be followed through several documents from the archives. It is thus known that he worked in The Hague from 1422 to 1424 for John of Bavaria, Count of Holland. He was named painter and "valet de chambre" for Philip the Good, Duke of Burgundy, on May 19, 1425, and made several trips for him, notably from Bruges to Lille in 1425, and from the Netherlands to Portugal in 1428-1429. From that time until his death, several traces of him are found in Bruges.

Jan van Eyck signed and dated a dozen works between the years 1432 and 1439, including the famous *Ghent Altarpiece* in 1432 and the portrait of his wife (see this catalogue, no. 4), in 1439. Another dozen paintings have been recognized as his. The illustrations of the *Très Belles Heures* of Jean, Duc de Berry, have been

Presumed portrait

65

Jan van Eyck

partially attributed to him, as well as several drawings. Notwithstanding the considerable influence which he exercised on the painting of his time, it is not known that he had any pupils. The precise attribution of paintings of an Eyckian character is made more difficult by the fact that certain authorities attribute several of them to Hubert van Eyck, although others deny that the latter even existed. In fact, the existence of Hubert, especially his collaboration in the *Ghent Altarpiece*, is bound to the authenticity of an inscription which appears on that altarpiece. This authenticity has been put in doubt by several historians and art historians, and, recently, by the Laboratory of the Institut Royal du Patrimoine Artistique in Brussels. In any case, it was unquestionably Jan van Eyck who was the leader of the Flemish School in the 15th century, with his new and individual style as well as new technical methods of painting. Without having invented oil painting, Jan van Eyck perfected it to the point, in fact, where the former aqueous tempera technique was soon abandoned in easel painting, first in the North and then in the South.

There are five Eyckian paintings in the United States: in Detroit, New York, Philadelphia, and Washington.

4.   PORTRAIT OF MARGARET VAN EYCK

Bruges, Stedelijk Museum voor Schone Kunsten (Groeningemuseum)
Cat. 1938, no. 162

An original inscription on the frame says that Jan van Eyck painted, in 1439, the portrait of his wife Margaret, then thirty-three years old. It is one of the last works by this artist. It is also the first portrait of an artist's wife known in Flemish painting, and with the sixty years later work by the Master of Frankfort, dated 1496, it is the only certain example of a portrait of this kind in 15th century Flemish painting. It could have inspired the lovely portrait of a woman wearing a head-dress by Roger van der Weyden in the Berlin Museum; that she is the painter's wife is only an hypothesis.

Margaret van Eyck is clothed in a red woollen dress. This cloth, which brought great wealth to Flanders in the 14th and the first half of the 15th centuries, was made principally with English wools and was exported everywhere in Europe, because it surpassed all others by the excellence of its workmanship and its dyes. The dress is lined with squirrel fur. This was called "fin gris" in the accounts of the time and was found very often in use in the wardrobes of the Dukes until about 1430. Margaret van Eyck covers her hair with a head-dress or hair-netting, as was the mode from the 13th to the 16th century. This hair-netting, which gives the appearance of a checker-board, holds the hair in two

66

Jan van Eyck

67

Jan van Eyck

masses in the shape of horns above the ears. Over this was placed a linen head-dress with a finely goffered edge.

Physical data: Oak, 13 $^1/_8$ x 10 $^9/_{16}$ in. (33.4 x 26.8 cm.) (total surface). Overpainted background; repainted on the points of the head-dress, the shadows of the face, and the fur of the collar. In the radiograph, the structure of the left sleeve appears very blurred and the hands are not visible (examination made at the Institut Royal du Patrimoine Artistique in 1956; JANSSENS DE BISTHOVEN, 1959, p. 53). On the reverse, reddish speckled coat of paint. Original frame painted in grey ochre veined in dark brown bearing inscriptions which are apparently original: cōῑv̄x m̄s ioнēs ɔplevit āno · 1439° · 17° · ιvnιj · , and etas mea triginta triv̄ ānorv̄ · aac · ixн · xan ·

History: Noted in 1769 as being in the archives room of the Bruges Painters Guild by DESCAMPS (1769, pp. 306-307); sold by Coppyn, the last Dean of the Guild, to Pierre van Lede; gift of Pierre van Lede to the Bruges Academy, November 22, 1808 (VIAENE, 1953, pp. 17-20). As the result of an error, WEALE wrote, in 1902, that the portrait was rediscovered in the Bruges fish market in 1808 (JANSSENS DE BISTHOVEN, 1959, p. 55).

Exhibitions: Bruges, 1902, no. 12; Paris, 1923, no. 3; London, 1927, no. 8; Paris, 1935, no. 42; Amsterdam and Rotterdam, 1946, no. 32; 's-Hertogenbosch, 1948, no. 375; Amsterdam, 1951, no. 23; Brussels, 1951, no. 7; Paris, 1952-53, no. 18; Bruges, 1953, no. 5; Brussels, 1953, no. 2; London, 1953-54, no. 19; Schaffhausen, 1955, no. 34; Madrid, 1958, no. 1.

The inscriptions painted on the frame may be translated: "My husband, Jan, finished me on June 17, 1439. My age is thirty-three years. As I can". These final words, a motto, also appear on the frames of two other paintings, accompanied this time by the name Jan van Eyck: *The Virgin at the Fountain* in the Musée Royal des Beaux-Arts in Antwerp (cat. 411), which bears the same date as the portrait of Margaret (1439), and the *Portrait of the Man in a Turban* in the National Gallery of London (cat. 222), dated 1433. The latter was believed by several authorities to be a probable self-portrait: CONWAY (1921, p. 67) suggests it; VAN PUYVELDE (1941, p. 25) believes he can recognize it as the companion piece to the portrait of Margaret; MEISS (1952, p. 137) offers several arguments along these lines; but both these earlier authors have grounded their opinions on erroneous measurements (MEISS, 1953, p. 27). PANOFSKY (1953, p. 198) is inclined to see it as a self-portrait also. DAVIES (1954, p. 131) could accept it as being a self-portrait, but he does not recognize it as a companion piece to the portrait of Margaret, and raises the objection, among others, of the six year difference in date between the two portraits. The question arises whether such a companion piece ever even existed. DESCAMPS (1769, pp. 306-307) claims to have heard it referred to, but WEALE and BROCKWELL (1912, p. 134) and FRIEDLÄNDER (I, 1924, p. 64) believe it is an unfounded legend. A discovery has very recently been made in private Bruges archives (G. de P.) of a manuscript memorandum by the archaeologist Joseph van Huerne, dated 1812 (VIAENE, 1960, p. 123), in which it is said that a portrait of Jan van Eyck was formerly in the rooms of the Painters Guild, along with that of his spouse, and that the artist's wife's portrait passed to the hands of Coppyn and then to Pierre van Lede, who gave it to the Academy. The memorandum continues with the statement that the painter's portrait was at that time in Vienna in the emperor's collection.

68

Detroit, Mich., The Detroit Institute of Arts. Acc. no. 25.4., cat. no. 33

Since a recent cleaning which removed its overpaintings, this panel has been considered a work of Jan van Eyck. It is generally identified as the artist's small *Saint Jerome,* described in the Inventory of the collections of Lorenzo de'Medici in 1492.

The iconographic type of St. Jerome (347-420), Father of the Church, translating or studying the Scriptures in his study developed especially toward the end of the Middle Ages and the beginning of the Renaissance, when the translator of the Bible was seen as a forerunner of humanism. The crimson cloak and hat give the illusion that St. Jerome held the title of cardinal, but this is apocryphal. The title was attributed to him by early biographers, who were unable to conceive that the translator of the Bible could hold a position inferior to that of a cardinal (cf. cat. no. 9). In addition to the books and writing materials, there are to be seen an astrolabe, a coral rosary, an hour-glass, a glass flask, and a majolica jar.

Physical data: Oak, 8 $^{1}/_{16}$ x 5 $^{1}/_{4}$ in. (20.5 x 13.3 cm.) (total surface). Transferred to a new panel in 1956. The presence of various layers under the ground, including one of lead minium, gives strong indication of a previous transfer. The date 1442 is painted at the upper left between the back of the chair and the curtain. Text of the letter placed on the table, written in minuscule Gothic letters: *Reuerendissimo in Christo patri et domino, domino Ieronimo, tituli Sancte Crucis in Iherusalem presbytero cardinali* (PANOFSKY, 1953, p. 189). Pentimenti: the astrolabe, the fingers of the Saint's right hand, and the cushion on the chair.

History: Coll. of a north German noble family (FRIEDLÄNDER, 1925, p. 297), who traditionally considered it as found in Italy (RICHARDSON, 1956, p. 227); Paul Bottenwieser, art dealer, Berlin-New York; acquired in 1925 by The Detroit Institute of Arts with city funds. Cleaned in 1956 by William Suhr.

Exhibitions: London, 1927, no. 14; Chicago, 1933, no. 35; Toledo, 1935, no. 5; Cleveland, 1936, no. 186; Worcester-Philadelphia, 1939, no. 2; New York, 1939, no. 114; New York, 1942, no no.; Cambridge, Mass., 1948, no catalogue.

The origin of this painting has been the subject of hypotheses based on the iconography of the work and its comparison with ancient literary sources. The deciphering of the letter, placed prominently on the table, of which the translation of the address is: "To the most Reverend Father and Lord in Christ, Lord Jerome, Cardinal-Priest of the Holy Cross of Jerusalem", furnished grounds for PANOFSKY (1953, p. 189, and 1954, pp. 106-108) to advance the hypothesis that Nicolas Albergati (whose portrait Jan van Eyck had painted in 1431, and who was titular cardinal of the church of Santa Croce in Gerusalemme in Rome, the position attributed by legend to St. Jerome) might have commissioned Jan van Eyck to do the work. In this connection, it might also be pointed out that Nicolas Albergati had been prior of the Carthusian Monastery of Saint-Jerome, near Bologna, in 1406 (WEALE, 1908, p. 58). In addition, several authors ([HEIL], 1930, no. 33; [VALENTINER], 1939, no. 114; FRIEDLÄNDER, XIV, 1937, p. 79; PANOFSKY, 1953, p. 189; RICHARDSON, 1956, p. 228) believe

69

Jan van Eyck

the Detroit panel to be the small *Saint Jerome* of Jan van Eyck, described in 1492 in the Inventory of the collection of Lorenzo de'Medici as: *Una tavoletta di Fiandra suvi uno San Girolamo a studio chon uno amarietto di prospettiva e uno lione a piedi, opera di maestro Giovanni di Bruggia, cholorita a olio in una guaiana, f.30* (MÜNTZ, 1888, p. 78) ("A small panel of Flanders of a St. Jerome in his study, with a little cupboard of many books in perspective and a lion at his feet, the work of Master John of Bruges, colored in oil, in a case, 30 florins"; cf. RICHARDSON, 1956, p. 228). However, the idea of identifying the small Medici-Detroit painting with the *Saint Jerome* described by the Anonimo Morelli in 1529 as being in the house of Antonio Pasqualino in Venice (RICHARDSON, 1956, p. 228)cannot be sustained because the description of the work (MORELLI, 1800, p. 74, and 1884, p. 188; WAAGEN, II, 1838, pp. 253-254) does not correspond to the picture in Detroit but rather to the *Saint Jerome* by Antonello da Messina in the National Gallery of London (cat. 1418; cf. DAVIES, 1951, p. 31).

The combined presence of both excellent qualities and weaknesses displayed by the painting before its recent cleaning explains the diversity of theories as to its attribution. The critics had first considered it an original work by Petrus Christus (FRIEDLÄNDER, 1925, p. 297; BORENIUS, 1925, p. 290; VALENTINER, 1924-25, p. 58; FRY, 1927, p. 67; CONWAY, 1927, no. 14; SCHÖNE, 1937, p. 158, note 2 and 1938, p. 56, no. 7), and later as a copy by Christus of either the Medici *Saint Jerome* or still another lost work of Jan van Eyck (STRÜMPELL, 1925-26, pp. 198-199; WINKLER, 1927, pp. 95-96; LAVALLEYE, 1936, p. 16, note 4; FRIEDLÄNDER, XIV, 1937, p. 79; TOLNAY, 1939, p. 76; MUSPER, 1948, p. 107; BAZIN, 1952, p. 204). Then, in 1927, BALDASS (1927, p. 82) proposed that it was an early work of Jan van Eyck himself. Soon several authors joined him, at least partially, in that opinion. In 1932, the discovery of the date 1442 prompted VALENTINER (lecture before the College Art Association, New York, 1932, reported by RICHARDSON, 1956, p. 229) to view the Detroit painting as a work started by Jan van Eyck (the upper part), left unfinished at his death in 1441, and completed by Petrus Christus (the lower part, the Saint's cloak, and the chair). He was followed by RICHARDSON (1936, no paging) and then by PANOFSKY (1953, p. 189), who finds the wording of the letter to be one additional argument for attributing at least part of the work to Jan van Eyck, and believes the painting is the Medici *Saint Jerome* itself, finished by Christus after the death of van Eyck. Meanwhile, BALDASS (1952, pp. 25 and 98, note 6), who had already (1950, p. 194, note 13) reaffirmed his original attribution of the painting to van Eyck, proposed to explain the date as indicating that the work was either an exceptionally careful copy by Christus of a work of the young Jan van Eyck, or an unfinished work of van Eyck completed by Christus in van Eyck's style.

The 1956 cleaning removed the overpaintings which had suggested the intervention of a second artist, and revealed that the date is old, but not original (RICHARDSON, 1956, pp. 230-233). Its attribution to Jan van Eyck alone was thus strengthened. The cleaning disclosed that the Saint's cloak and hat had

70

been entirely overpainted, as had the coral rosary which had been made into a blue cord, and the lion. Several "pentimenti" also appeared (cf. *Physical data*), which seem to exclude the possibility of a copy. As for the date 1442 discovered on the wall to the left (RICHARDSON, 1936, no paging; FRIEDLÄNDER, XIV, 1937, p. 79; SCHÖNE, 1937, p. 158, note 2), the cleaning has established that it was not a part of the original paint-layer and, thus, must have been added subsequently. However, its resistance to solvents shows it to be a very old addition. This date cannot, then, provide an argument for saying that the painting was finished by Petrus Christus. Recently CHÂTELET (1957, pp. 162 and 168) attempted to attribute the Detroit panel to Master H of the *Turin-Milan Hours,* perhaps the master of Petrus Christus or an illuminator by the name of Jan Coene, in which case it would be his last known work.

This composition has directly inspired, down to many details, a *Saint Jerome* in a Book of Hours of around 1455 preserved in The Walters Art Gallery in

71

Jan van Eyck

Baltimore (ms. 721, fol. 277 v°) (PANOFSKY, 1954, p. 102) and a *Saint Thomas Aquinas* in the *Turin-Milan Hours,* fol. 73v°, of shortly after the middle of the 15th century (STRÜMPELL, 1925-26, pp. 196-199 and pl. XLII; cf. DURRIEU, 1902, pp. 18, 26, and pl. XL). It has also been the source of two other representations of saints meditating in their studies, the *Saint Jerome* by Ghirlandajo and the *Saint Augustine* by Botticelli in the Church of the Ognissanti in Florence (FRIEDLÄNDER, 1925, p. 298; WINKLER, 1927, p. 94; PANOFSKY, 1954, p. 102). This would confirm the presence of the small Eyckian panel in Italy in the 15th century, and would support the hypothesis of its commission by Cardinal Albergati and its presence in the collections of Lorenzo de' Medici at the end of the same century. An additional argument is that in a recent analysis of the different objects in St. Jerome's study, which are so many disguised symbols, BERGSTRÖM (1957, pp. 1-20) points out that the new iconography which they represent is reflected in the art of Northern Italy.

An astrolabe of the type suspended from the bookshelf is shown in this exhibition as no. 108.

MASTER OF FLEMALLE

Active ca. 1410-1440

The traditional name, Master of Flémalle, was given to the painter of the wings of a large altarpiece which was said at that time to have come from an abbey near Liège, and which is now in the Städelsches Kunstinstitut in Frankfort. The authorities also give to him the triptych of the Annunciation called *The Merode Altarpiece,* now in The Cloisters in New York. A certain number of paintings done in the same style and spirit have been grouped around these two important works which have been taken as a base. Their execution is placed approximately between 1410 and 1440, and the group includes a dated work, the *Werl Panels* of 1438 in the Prado in Madrid.

These works show style analogies with a group of paintings attributed to Roger van der Weyden's early period as well as to Jacques Daret. As there is documentary evidence that both were pupils of Robert Campin, a painter mentioned in the Tournai archives between 1406 and 1444, certain art historians have identified the Master of Flémalle as being Robert Campin. Another group of specialists consider the paintings by the Master of Flémalle as the early production of Roger van der Weyden. Whatever may be the solution, the interest in this problem goes beyond that of the individual career of the Master of Flémalle, Robert Campin, or Roger van der Weyden, for it is important to know whether the great era of Flemish Primitives began about 1406 with Robert Campin or the Master of Flémalle, or some fifteen years later with Jan van Eyck.

72

One of the basic works of the Master of Flémalle is in the United States: the Annunciation called *The Merode Altarpiece*, after one of its last owners. Without counting the numerous works which are only a reflection of this great painter's art, there are, in New York, Philadelphia, and Washington, five other works from the hand of this master or from his workshop.

6. VIRGIN AND CHILD IN AN APSE

New York, N.Y., and London, Julius H. Weitzner

This painting is often considered the best among numerous replicas of a lost original by the Master of Flémalle.

The subject, the Virgin nursing the Christ Child in an apse with two musician angels, brings to mind that of van Eyck's *Virgin in a Church*. In the latter work, however, she is shown as a queen wearing a crown, while here she is simply clothed and bare-headed, as a Virgin of Humility.

> *Physical data:* Oak, 18 $^1/_{16}$ x 13 $^3/_8$ in. (45.9 x 34 cm.) (total surface). At the time of a recent cleaning, x-ray and infra-red examination revealed elements of two other figures above and behind the two angels.
>
> *History:* Germanisches Museum, Nürnberg (cat. 65), until 1923; Böhler und Steinmeyer, art dealers, Lucerne, 1924; The Minneapolis Institute of Arts, 1924-1958; acquired from The Minneapolis Institute of Arts by Julius H. Weitzner, New York and London, in 1958.
>
> *Note:* This painting is inventoried by FRIEDLÄNDER (II, 1924, p. 115) under no. 74a. In a subsequent volume this author (XIV, 1937, p. 88) erroneously notes that another *Virgin and Child in an Apse*, which he classified as no. 74b, had been acquired by The Minneapolis Institute of Arts. In fact, The Minneapolis Institute acquired no. 74a, while 74b remained part of the Coray Stoop Collection in Zurich.
>
> *Exhibitions:* New York, 1929, no. 6 (erroneously noted as coming from the Coray Stoop Collection in Zurich in 1922: cf. note above).

The original composition, the *Virgin and Child in an Apse*, is clearly the work of the Master of Flémalle. It is known through numerous copies made in the 15th and early 16th centuries (BAZIN, 1931, pp. 495-500), none of which can be identified as the original (FRIEDLÄNDER, II, 1924, p. 114). Among the oldest, where the architecture is seen from a high point of view, that of the Weitzner Collection is considered by FRIEDLÄNDER (II, 1924, p. 114) to come closest to the original, along with that of the Metropolitan Museum in New York (WEHLE and SALINGER, 1947, p. 27). TOLNAY (1939, p. 59, no. 1) and PANOFSKY (1953, p. 175) feel the best existing replica is that of the Metropolitan Museum. FRIEDLÄNDER (II, 1924, p. 116) and PANOFSKY (1953, p. 175) are in agreement that the original is a work done by the Master of Flémalle in his youth. FRIEDLÄNDER places it more precisely around 1428, the same period as the *Nativity* of the Musée des Beaux-Arts in Dijon (cat. 150).

73

This composition experienced a renewed success during the archaizing movement at the beginning of the 16th century, sometimes rather freely interpreted and placed in another setting. Among these is that by Gerard David in the Epstein Collection in Chicago, the one by Bernard van Orley in the Prado (cat. 1920), and those of Quentin Metsys in the collection of Count Seilern in London, and in the Musée des Beaux-Arts in Lyon, France (Inv. A. 2908).

ROBINSON (1905, p. 387) thought he could recognize in this composition the apse of the Old Cathedral of Salamanca, and deduced that the artist must have spent some time in Spain. He found more support for this in the fact that he saw the Virgin as being clothed in a white robe and a blue cloak, according to a rule of the Spanish Church which was still often observed by Spanish painters of the 17th century; but, in fact, both the robe and cloak are bluish-

Master of Flémalle

white. WINKLER (1913, p. 8, note 3) believes, however, that the apse in which the work is set was not painted from a model or a particular recollection, and that its architectural style is not more Spanish than Flemish or French. The ROBINSON theory was also opposed by DAVIES (I, 1953, p. 61, no. 35), who suggests that the apse of this composition should more properly be compared to that in the *Communion of the Apostles* by Joos van Gent in the Galleria Nazionale delle Marche in Urbino.

The lute being played by the angel on the right of the Virgin is a model rarely found in Flanders in the 15th century, because it has four sound-holes instead of only one, two, or sometimes three, and nine strings instead of five, six or, more often, seven (DENIS, 1944, pp. 97-99).

ROGER VAN DER WEYDEN

Active mostly in Brussels
Born in Tournai ca. 1399. Died in Brussels in 1464

Several documents about Roger van der Weyden exist in the archives. According to them, it appears that he obtained his mastership in Tournai, his native city, in 1432, after an apprenticeship in the workshop of the painter Robert Campin, often identified as the Master of Flémalle. In 1435, Roger came to live in Brussels, where he was appointed official painter of the city and where he enjoyed great prestige. He seems to have spent the rest of his life there. In 1450, however, he may have made a trip to Italy, which is probably the time when he is known to have worked for the Este family. Philip the Good and Charles the Bold, Dukes of Burgundy, ordered various works from him and it is thought that he held the title of portrait painter of the court, in fact if not in name. Several authorities identify his early production, with varying success, as being that of the Master of Flémalle.

No painting bears the signature of Roger van der Weyden and none of the works noted in contemporary documents as being from his hand have been preserved. It is only on the faith of documents of more than a century later and in working from a whole

Presumed portrait

75

Roger van der Weyden

series of presumptions that it has been possible to attribute to him a few works which have served as the basis for establishing the catalogue of his production. The most important of these works is his famous *Descent from the Cross* of the Escorial, now in the Prado, Madrid. The catalogue of his presumed works is sizeable and some specialists attribute to him, in addition, all the works of the Master of Flémalle. It is often difficult to distinguish between Roger's own paintings and those of his workshop, which was much frequented by foreign artists, who wanted to be initiated in the Flemish technique. He had a preponderant influence on several generations of painters, and even sculptors. To him are attributed several works of decorative sculpture, drawings, and miniatures, including the title page of the *Chronique du Hainaut* (Brussels) (see illustration p. 40). He was celebrated all over the Europe of his time and was regarded by his contemporaries as the greatest northern master, after van Eyck.

The United States is rich in important works by Roger van der Weyden. It possesses, in particular, a wing of a triptych which is one of his basic works. The attribution of this painting is attested by documents which are of later date, but which can be believed. This triptych is now divided between the Capilla Real in Granada and the New York Metropolitan Museum of Art. The United States also possesses the original of the altarpiece which the artist is supposed to have painted for the Painters Guild of Brussels, in which he showed himself in the form of Saint Luke drawing the portrait of the Virgin. This work belongs to the Boston Museum and is being shown in this exhibition as no. 7. A total of eleven other works are preserved in the cities of Chicago, Detroit, Greenville (S.C.), Houston, New York, Philadelphia, San Diego, San Marino, and Washington, in addition to numerous works of his workshop and his school.

7.   SAINT LUKE DRAWING THE PORTRAIT OF THE VIRGIN*

Boston, Mass., Museum of Fine Arts. Acc. no. 93.153

This painting is one of four versions of a picture probably painted for the chapel of the Painters Guild in Brussels. Since a cleaning made before the last world war, it has been recognized by the majority of art historians as the original, the other examples being workshop or school copies. It is generally placed rather early in the artist's development because of its close kinship of composition, especially in the landscape, with the *Virgin with Chancellor Rolin* by Jan van Eyck in the Louvre. This same composition was again borrowed by another Brussels painter of the end of the century, the Master of the View of Sainte-Gudule,

---

* *This entry has been prepared on the basis of data collected by Colin Eisler for the Corpus of Flemish Primitives in New England museums (to be published soon).*

Roger van der Weyden

77

Roger van der Weyden

in a painting in the Musée Diocésain in Liège, being shown in this exhibition as no. 27.

The iconographic subject, widely known in the Middle Ages, is inspired by a legend started in the Golden Legend. The Virgin nursing the Child is seated in front of the bench, almost on the floor, and is thus shown as a Virgin of Humility. Saint Luke is drawing her portrait with a silver-point on a sheet of parchment. He may be identified by his symbol, the ox, sleeping in the adjoining room, and by the open book placed in the same room, which book probably represents his Gospel, communicated by the Virgin. Saint Luke is considered by several authors as a self-portrait of Roger van der Weyden.

Physical data: Oak, 54 1/4 x 43 7/8 in. (138 x 111.3 cm.) (total surface). Cradled panel. According to a recent examination at the Museum of Fine Arts in Boston: worn over the entire painted surface, various damaged areas, especially in the Virgin's garments and the tile flooring. The picture was restored in 1932-33 and in 1943. Modification of the position of the Virgin's head, which was more inclined in the initial drawing, and pentimenti in Saint Luke's head and cap, which were reduced in relation to their original position. FRIEDLÄNDER (IV, 1926, p. 127), who has erroneously noted the presence of the seal of Anthony, Bastard of Burgundy, on the reverse of the panel, subsequently retracted this observation (XIV, 1937, p. 88) in saying that this seal was on the reverse of a copy of St. Luke alone, in the National Gallery of Ireland in Dublin.

History: Said to have come from Toledo and to have entered the Museo Nacional de la Trinidad in Madrid after 1834, date of the museum's founding (PASSAVANT, 1853, p. 134); Coll. of the Infant don Sebastian-Gabriel Bórbon y Braganza confiscated after 1833 by Queen Isabella II; probably returned to the Infant in 1859, date at which he recognized Queen Isabella (TEIXEIRA, I, 1859, p. 16) and very probably before 1868, date at which WAAGEN (1868, pp. 32-55) made up a list of important Flemish works in the Museo Nacional in which the Saint Luke was not included; collection of heirs of the Infant don Sebastian in Pau (Cat. Pau, 1876, p. 72); noted in Pau in 1886 (JUSTI, 1886, p. 98); don Pedro, Duque de Dúrcal Coll., Spain, and sold in New York (American Art Association), April 5-6, 1889, no. 67 (Frick Art Reference Library, New York); Henry Lee Higginson Coll., Boston; gift of Mr. and Mrs. Henry Lee Higginson to the Museum of Fine Arts in Boston, May, 1893. Restored before 1893, in 1932-1933 in Berlin by Ruhemann (RUHEMANN, 1934, pp. 3-15), in 1943 by Lowe at the Museum of Fine Arts, and in 1948.

Exhibitions: Cambridge, Mass., 1909, no no.; Brussels, 1935, no. 7.

Four almost identical versions of this composition exist: the one being shown in this exhibition, lent by the Museum of Fine Arts in Boston, one in the Hermitage in Leningrad (cat. 445), one in the Munich Pinakothek (cat. 100), and one in the Wilzcek Collection in Burg Kreuzenstein (not known if it is still there). Until a few years before World War II, each of these in turn, had been considered as the original painted by Roger, probably for the Painters Guild in Brussels. During the last century it was first the Munich example which was thought to be the original (PASSAVANT, 1853, p. 134, and 1858, p. 13; WAUTERS, 1855, p. 94; CROWE and CAVALCASELLE, 1857, p. 185; HOTHO, 1867, p. 185; WAAGEN, 1870, p. 117). Later several authors came out in favor of the one in Leningrad (HULIN DE LOO, 1902, no. 116; DESTRÉE, 1930, pp. 113-115) or that of Boston (RANKIN, 1905, pp. 24-25; FRY and BROCKWELL, 1911, p. 87; CONWAY, 1921, p. 132; HENDY, 1931, p. 42), or even the Wilzcek painting (GLÜCK, 1930, p. 77). Numerous experts did not feel they could resolve the

78

Roger van der Weyden

question by recognizing one or the other as being from the hand of van der Weyden, but viewed them as copies, more or less good, of a lost original by Roger (VOLL, 1906, pp. 311-312; FRIEDLÄNDER, 1903, p. 9; 1906, p. 144; 1909, p. 551; II, 1924, p. 31; LAFOND, 1912, pp. 82-84; WINKLER, 1913, p. 111; RING, 1913, p. 105; SCHMARSOW, 1928, p. 83; BALDASS, 1930, p. 130). More recently PANOFSKY (1953, p. 252) also gave the opinion that all four were replicas, the best of which, he thinks, is the one in Boston. However, since its cleaning in 1932-1933, the Boston painting has been almost unanimously recognized as the original (FRIEDLÄNDER, 1933, p. 57; RENDERS, 1933, p. 74; NIEDERSTEIN, 1933, p. 336; Cat. Brussels Exhib., 1935, no. 7; HULIN DE LOO, 1938, cols. 234-235; BEENKEN, 1951, p. 191; FIERENS, 1953, p. 253; HELD, 1955, p. 226; TOVELL, 1955, pp. 29-30).

The great majority of writers agree in placing this composition in Roger van der Weyden's early period, because of the very clear dependence which it shows in relation to the *Virgin with Chancellor Rolin* by Jan van Eyck, in the Louvre (cat. 1986), generally dated between 1432 and 1436 (HULIN DE LOO, 1903, p. 28; FRIEDLÄNDER, II, 1924, p. 31, and 1933, p. 57; KLEIN, 1933, pp. 38 and 43; WINKLER, 1942, p. 472; MUSPER, 1948, p. 58; BEENKEN, 1951, p. 131). PANOFSKY (1953, p. 253) places it in the same period, between 1432, year of Roger's mastership, and 1436, date of his appointment as painter of Brussels. Others, who consider the style further evolved, believe it should rather be placed in the 1440's (RENDERS, 1933, p. 74; NIEDERSTEIN, 1933, p. 336; SCHEEWE, 1934, p. 212); HELD (1955, p. 226) also dates it in this period, but by comparing it to the *Rolin Virgin* which, according to him, should itself be referred to a later date. BURGER (1923, p. 35), on the other hand, thinks that Roger could not have seen the *Rolin Virgin*, presumed to have been then in Autun, until the time when he delivered the *Last Judgment* which he painted for the Hôtel-Dieu in Beaune around 1445-1450. Only VOLL (1906, pp. 311-312) dates the composition of *Saint Luke Drawing a Portrait of the Virgin* in the late period of the artist's career.

Throughout the history of painting, most works showing this subject represent Saint Luke doing a painted portrait of the Virgin. In the Boston picture, he is drawing it with a silver-point on a sheet of parchment (LEBEER, 1957, p. 76), according to a technique discussed by MEDER (1919, p. 84) and STOUT (1941, p. 4). The figure of St. Luke has been regarded by numerous authors as a self-portrait, more or less idealized, of Roger van der Weyden (HULIN DE LOO, 1903, p. 28; VOLL, 1906, pp. 79-80; LAFOND, 1912, p. 105; DESTRÉE, 1930, frontispiece; KLEIN, 1933, p. 39, note 197; GOLDSCHEIDER, 1936, p. 7; FIERENS, 1953, p. 67). RING (1913, p. 105) adds that it is the oldest known example of an artist's self-portrait in the role of head of his guild. PANOFSKY (1953, pp. 253-254) finds that the resemblance of St. Luke to the portrait of "Master Rogiel" in the *Recueil d'Arras* must be more than mere chance. KAUFMAN (1916, p. 25), on the other hand, believes that the early date which has been assigned to the work militates against the idea that it could be a self-portrait of Roger. HULIN DE LOO (1938, col. 235) believes the Boston

79

picture to be, in fact, the *Sanct Lucas Tafel* seen by Dürer in 1520 in the chapel of the Painters Guild in Brussels. But, since Dürer himself does not cite Roger's name along with this painting, even though he did place the four large pictures of Justice in the Brussels City Hall under that name, PANOFSKY (1953, p. 253) remains sceptical as to this identification.

A great many partial copies have been made after this composition, especially of the *Virgin Nursing the Child,* in half-length (FRIEDLÄNDER, II, 1924, no. 107; RICHARDSON, 1939, pp. 41-42), and sometimes of Saint Luke, as for example in the National Gallery of Ireland in Dublin and the convent of the Descalzas Reales in Madrid. The Boston composition, but reversed and with some variations, also appears in a Brussels tapestry of the first quarter of the 16th century in the Louvre Museum.

8.   VIRGIN AND CHILD

Houston, Texas, The Museum of Fine Arts of Houston
Acc. no. 44-535, cat.no. 27

This Virgin is considered by some as a work from the hand of Roger van der Weyden himself, and by others as a workshop replica. The painting, or its prototype, is generally placed among the later works of the artist.

The composition, particularly the motif of the Child turning toward His mother and bringing His head close to hers, can be traced to the famous Italo-Byzantine Virgin brought from Rome in 1440, preserved since 1450 in the Cathedral of Cambrai, and known as *Notre-Dame de Grâces de Cambrai*. The Middle Ages revered this picture in Cambrai as a portrait of the Virgin which, according to a very ancient legend, was painted by Saint Luke.

Physical data: Oak, 12 1/2 x 8 15/16 in. (31.7 x 22.7 cm.) (total surface).
History: Hungarian private collection (FRIEDLÄNDER, II, 1924, p. 102, no. 35); P. Cassirer, art dealer, Amsterdam, 1924 *(ib.);* Hess Coll., Berlin (FRIEDLÄNDER, XIV, 1937, p. 87, no. 35); Hess sale, Lucerne (Cassirer), September 1, 1931, no. 1 (SCHÖNE, 1938, p. 61, no. 28); Strölin, art dealer, Switzerland (WESCHER, 1931, p. 436); Edith A. and Percy S. Straus Collection, New York; bequest of Edith A. and Percy S. Straus to The Museum of Fine Arts of Houston, November, 1944.
Exhibitions: New York, 1939, no. 411.

FRIEDLÄNDER (II, 1924, pp. 36 and 102, no. 35), SCHÖNE (1938, p. 61, no. 29) and the catalogue of the Straus Collection in the Houston Museum (1945, no. 27) recognize the Houston Virgin as an original work by Roger van der Weyden. DESTRÉE (1930, pp. 119, 201 and pl. 43) is reluctant to accept this attribution. Further doubt has also been expressed by BEENKEN (1951, p. 99), who believes that even the conception could not have been that of van der Weyden, and by PANOFSKY (1953, p. 296, and 296, note 6), who judges the

Roger van der Weyden

defects in draftmanship to be incompatible with an execution by the hand of Roger himself. Nevertheless, all except SCHÖNE agree that this painting is a late work, or the replica of a late work, by van der Weyden. FRIEDLÄNDER (II, 1924, pp. 36 and 37) places it after the Virgin in the Huntington Art Gallery in San Marino (cat. 25), which he dates a little before 1459 (II, 1924, p. 104, nos. 39-40), and just before the Renders Virgin, now in the Musée des Beaux-Arts in Tournai, and the Mancel Virgin in the Musée des Beaux-Arts in Caen, which he places around 1460 (II, 1924, p. 102, no. 31). SCHÖNE (1938, p. 61, no. 29) classifies it immediately after the *Bladelin Altarpiece,* which he dates around 1454. PANOFSKY (1953, pp. 296, 317, and 317, note 2) believes

81

that it is the last in date among Roger's half-length compositions of the Virgin, since it derives from *Notre-Dame de Grâces de Cambrai*. The latter work did not become popular in Flanders until after 1454, when three copies were made by Petrus Christus and twelve copies by Jean Hayne of Brussels (one copy attributed to Hayne belongs to the Nelson Gallery in Kansas City). The Virgin of Cambrai might have been copied by Roger at the time he delivered his famous *Cambrai Altarpiece*, now lost, in 1459 (ROLLAND, 1948, p. 106, and PANOFSKY, 1953, p. 297). If this were the case, the Houston Virgin would be subsequent to that date. If not, Roger might have come to know it either by the exact copy which is preserved in Frasnes-lez-Buissenal, Belgium, but the history of which is unknown (cf. ROLLAND, 1948, pp. 97-106 and fig. 1), or through one of the numerous then-existing copies by Petrus Christus and Jean Hayne of Brussels.

This composition, in turn, has served as a source of inspiration for Flemish and northern French works of the *Virgin and Child*, notably for those of Dieric Bouts, in the New York Metropolitan Museum of Art (PANOFSKY, 1953, p. 317), of Memlinc, in the Lady Ludlow Collection in London (FRIEDLÄNDER, II, 1924, p. 103 and STRIEDER, 1959, p. 255), and especially for those of the Master of the Saint Giles Legend (HELD, 1955, p. 228), in the Carmelite Monastery in Bruges and the Musée des Beaux-Arts in Besançon. In these two latter works the pose of the Child is closely copied from that of the Houston composition. The Houston painting is also reflected in a poor copy in the Sigmaringen Museum (cat. 38; FRIEDLÄNDER, II, 1924, p. 102, no. 35a; photograph in the R.K.D., The Hague).

9. SAINT JEROME IN THE DESERT

Detroit, Mich., The Detroit Institute of Arts. Acc. no. 46.359, cat. no. 885

This small panel, only known since shortly before the last war, is almost unanimously attributed to Roger van der Weyden, who would have painted it near the end of his career.

Saint Jerome shown extracting the thorn from the lion's foot illustrates a legend which worked its way into the otherwise well-documented biography of the Father of the Church. This legend is combined here with the theme of St. Jerome as a hermit in the desert, shown in the background. The Cardinal's robe and hat are also derived from the legend (cf. cat. no. 5).

Physical data: Oak, 12 7/16 x 10 3/8 in. (31.6 x 26.3 cm.) (total surface).

History: Paris, private collection, before 1936 (FRIEDLÄNDER, XIV, 1937, p. 89); New York, Arnold Seligmann, Rey and Co., art dealer, from 1936 *(ib.)*, at least until 1941 (Cat. Detroit Exhib., 1941, no. 69); New York, private collection, 1945 (RING, 1945, caption fig. 1); gift of Mr. and Mrs. Edgar B. Whitcomb to The Detroit Institute of Arts, 1946.

Exhibitions: Milwaukee, 1938, no. 1; Worcester-Philadelphia, 1939, no. 9; San Francisco, 1940, no. 135; Detroit, 1941, no. 69.

82

83

Roger van der Weyden

This painting is generally considered a work of Roger van der Weyden (FRIEDLÄNDER, XIV, 1937, p. 89; RING, 1945, p. 190; RICHARDSON, 1947, p. 54 and 1954, p. 65). RICHARDSON *(ibidem)* places it in the latter period of his activity, after his probable trip to Rome in 1450. However, BEENKEN (1951, p. 99) considers it to be, at least in part, a product of his workshop in the 1450's. He believes that the Saint might have been painted by Roger or, if not, at least from his drawing, but that the lion and the background are incompatible with Roger's style. PANOFSKY (1953, p. 249, note 3) doubts that the painting is even partially the work of Roger, although he believes it to be of his invention. HELD (1955, p. 206) joins him in this opinion.

Grete RING (1945, p. 190) thinks it is a reduced version, from the hand of the artist himself, of a larger lost composition which influenced numerous paintings, sculptures, miniatures, and engravings until the beginning of the 16th century. The almost identical composition, but more complete and in grisaille, is found on the reverse of the wings of the *Sforza Triptych* done in Roger van der Weyden's workshop and now in the Brussels Musée des Beaux-Arts (FRIEDLÄNDER, XIV, 1937, p. 89). It appears again, with slight variations, in a panel by Memlinc (RING, 1945, p. 191) which was acquired by the A.S. Drey Gallery in London in 1950 (R.K.D., The Hague). It seems also to have served as the model for a sculpture of the same subject by Tilman Riemenschneider (ca. 1460-1531) in The Cleveland Museum of Art (BIER, 1951, p. 227).

The origin of the theme itself remains obscure, but its wide use by artists was instigated, in the middle of the 14th century, by the jurist Joannes Andreas of Bologna. He dedicated himself to bringing about the revival of the cult of Saint Jerome, honored as patron of the humanists (RING, 1945, pp. 188-190). The lion is presented here in a form popularized by bronze ewers (Cat. Detroit Exhib., 1941, no. 69) and by medieval books of models, such as the album of Villard de Honnecourt (RING, 1945, p. 191).

10.   THE MASS OF SAINT GREGORY

New York, N.Y., Nicholas M. Acquavella Galleries

Long considered a replica or a copy of a lost work of the Master of Flémalle, this *Mass of Saint Gregory* is now accepted by several authorities as an original work by Roger van der Weyden and placed early in his career.

The subject shown is the most popular among the miraculous masses of Saint Gregory, the one during which, in answer to the Pope's prayer, Christ appeared on the altar bearing the wounds and surrounded by the Instruments of the Passion, in order to reaffirm the faith of one of the congregation who doubted the real presence of Christ in the Host. This legend originated in the Church of Santa Croce in Gerusalemme in Rome, where the miracle is supposed to have

84

occured, and did not appear until rather late. It had not yet made its appearance by the time of the Golden Legend, which dates from the 13th century. The indulgences granted by the Church to the illustrations of this miracle conferred on it an enormous success in the 15th and 16th centuries, until the Counter-Reformation, after which this subject disappeared from the artistic repertory.

Physical data: Oak, 32 ⁷/₈ x 27 ¹⁵/₁₆ in. (83.5 x 71 cm.). Traces of gold background found on upper right, behind the altar (WOERMANN, 1912 sale cat., no. 6). Inscription at lower right: M.Vᶜ.X. (the last figure is rubbed-out) *(ibidem)*. Text as read by HYMANS (1902, p. 198) on the placard hanging on the wall under the windows: *Dees tafel was ghemaeckt int jaer Ons Heeren MVᶜXIV* ("This picture was painted in the Year of Our Lord 1514").

History: Art dealer, Hamburg, 1883 (WOERMANN, 1912 sale cat., no. 6); Eduard F. Weber Coll., Hamburg, at least after 1899 (FIRMENICH-RICHARTZ, 1899, p. 11); Eduard F. Weber sale, Berlin (Lepke), February 20, 1912, no. 6; O[sborn] Kling Coll., Stockholm, at least after 1937 (FRIEDLÄNDER, XIV, 1937, p. 88); O. Kling sale, Stockholm, December 6, 1922, no. 41 (R.K.D., The Hague); Dr. Ernst Schwarz Coll., New York; Schwarz Coll. sale, London (Christie's), June 26, 1959 *(Burl. Mag.,* June, 1959, p. ii); acquired at that sale by Nicholas M. Acquavella Galleries, New York.

Exhibitions: Bruges, 1902, no. 156; Bruges, 1907, no. 182.

85

Roger van der Weyden

First attributed to Dieric Bouts, and then to the school of van Eyck (cf. WOERMANN, 1912 sale cat., no. 6), this *Mass of Saint Gregory* was later considered by many art historians as a replica or a copy of a lost work by the Master of Flémalle (TSCHUDI, 1898, p. 11; KOCH, 1901, p. 291; HULIN DE LOO, 1902, no. 156; HYMANS, 1902, p. 198; FRIEDLÄNDER, 1903, p. 73 and II, 1924, no. 73; WOERMANN, 1912 sale cat., no. 6; WINKLER, 1924, p. 70; DESTRÉE, 1928, p. 147; MUSPER, 1948, p. 58). Several, moreover, consider it the best of the known copies of this composition (TOLNAY, 1939, p. 60, no. 5; PANOFSKY, 1953, p. 175). VALENTINER (1945, p. 241) recognizes the New York painting as an original work by Roger van der Weyden and as one of the most important by this artist in the United States. He judges it superior to the example in the Musées Royaux des Beaux-Arts in Brussels (cat. 1036). MUSPER (1952, pp. 89-94), on the other hand, considers the Brussels painting to be the original, basing his opinion on an analysis of style and an examination of recent radiographs, and places the New York painting in the group around Simon Marmion. Accepting the credibility of the date (151?) which appears at the lower right, HULIN DE LOO (1902, no. 56) dated the work between 1510 and 1520. FRIEDLÄNDER (cited by VALENTINER, 1945, p. 243), following a cleaning of the painting, changed his initial attribution and recognized it as a work by Roger van der Weyden. He dated the Acquavella picture ca. 1430, in the artist's early period. The same author had, in 1924 (II, 1924, no. 73 a), already commented that the style did not correspond to the date appearing on the painting (cf. *Physical data*).

According to VALENTINER (1945, p. 243), the New York painting could be the very *Mass of Saint Gregory* noted in the Inventory of the collections of Margaret of Austria. It appears, in fact, under the name of Roger van der Weyden in the Inventory of 1516 and in that of 1523. This *Mass of Saint Gregory* was the companion piece to a *Crucifixion*.

The pope is aided by a cardinal and a deacon holding a long twisted candle. Christ is surrounded by the symbols of the Passion; on the left: the column and the whips of the Flagellation, the head of a soldier, the veil of Veronica, and the lance; on the cross: the three robes of Christ, the crown of thorns, and the nails; on the right: the sponge, the reed sceptre, the head of a soldier mocking Christ, and a hand giving Him a blow. All the architectural and furnishing details of this romanesque style chapel show what could have been seen in a 15th century church. The front of the altar is decorated with a brocade piece serving as an antependium. On the altar is an altarpiece of relief in gold showing scenes from the Passion: from left to right, *Christ before Pilate, The Flagellation, The Crucifixion, The Entombment,* and *The Resurrection*. This altarpiece is placed on a wooden predella with the busts of the twelve Apostles in medallions standing out against a red background. In addition to the chalice, the altar-book, and the candlestick placed on the altar, a gold pax can be seen on the right against the predella. At the right of the altar, a niche holds the altar-cruets. At the extreme right can be observed a washstand with basin, ewer, and towel. On the capitals of the columns at the left are seen *The Adoration of the Magi*,

86

Roger van der Weyden

The Massacre of the Innocents(?) and *The Flight into Egypt*. Other scenes decorate the two stained-glass windows at the left: in the upper part of the left window, *Christ's Entry into Jerusalem*, and in the lower part *The Agony in the Garden;* in the upper part of the right window, *The Arrest of Christ*, and in the lower part, *Christ Bearing His Cross*. The entire decorative scheme of this chapel is thus centered on the Passion of Christ. Under the windows is hung a placard on which a text is inscribed, probably intended to recall the indulgences attached to the veneration of this representation.

Another version of the same composition is pointed out by FRIEDLÄNDER (1903, p. 73 and II, 1924, no. 74 b) as in the J. Moreira Collection in Lisbon. He published it as an exact replica of the New York painting. A *Mass of Saint Gregory* which was clearly inspired by the one in New York, a 15th century Westphalian painting, is in the Landesmuseum in Münster (DE BORCHGRAVE D'ALTENA, 1959, p. 12 and fig. 19).

11.   ECCE HOMO

Greenville, S.C., Bob Jones University Art Gallery. Acc. no. 78A-B

These two wings are thought to be the work either of Roger van der Weyden himself or a painter of his workshop, or even the result of a collaboration between Roger and one of his pupils, probably Vrancke van der Stockt.

They represent Christ being shown to the Jews or the *Ecce Homo*. Since they are painted in grisaille, it is probable that they were originally the reverses of the wings of a triptych, this being a very normal procedure in the 15th century.

Physical data: Oak, painted surface of left wing: 36 $^3/_4$ x 11 in. (93.4 x 28 cm.), and of right wing: 36 $^3/_4$ x 10 $^{13}/_{16}$ in. (93.4 x 27.5 cm.). Cradled panels. The two paintings were transferred onto a kind of mahogany wood with a new ground.

History: Stefano Bardini sale, London, May 30, 1902, no. 628; Bardini, art dealer, Florence, 1913 (FRIEDLÄNDER, II, 1924, p. 120, no. 87a); Stefano Bardini sale, New York (American Art Galleries), April 23-27, 1918, no. 446; E. and A. Silberman Galleries, New York; acquired by Bob Jones University in 1955.

Exhibitions: Buffalo, 1950, no. 1.

Several critics think that these two wings are the work of Roger van der Weyden himself, perhaps with the collaboration of his pupil Vrancke van der Stockt (1420-1495), who was his successor as official painter of the City of Brussels (written statements by MARLIER, SCHARF, and VALENTINER to the President of Bob Jones University; TOLNAY, pre-publication statement cited in the catalogue of the Buffalo Exhibition, 1950, no. 1). Several other authors,

87

88

Roger van der Weyden

however, attribute these panels to the workshop of Roger (FRIEDLÄNDER, II, 1924, p. 120, no. 87a; HELD, statement to Bob Jones University). FRIEDLÄNDER dates them about 1460 and notes the similarity which they bear to the reverse sides of the wings of the so-called *Cambrai Altarpiece,* or the *Redemption of the Prado,* commonly attributed to Vrancke van der Stockt (Madrid, Prado, cat. 1881-1892). The latter two are also in grisaille and represent *Christ and the Tribute Money.* PANOFSKY (1953, p. 302, note 2) concurs in this comparison. TOLNAY (cf. Cat. Buffalo Exhib., 1950, no. 1) suggests that the Greenville wings may actually be the reverse sides of the wings of the *Triptych of the Crucifixion* in the Abegg Collection (Buonas Castle, Zuger See) of which dimensions (40 $^1/_2$ x 12 $^5/_8$ in. or 103 x 32 cm. each) correspond approximately. PANOFSKY (1953, p. 302, note 2) does not agree with this hypothesis. He points out that the dimensions of the Greenville wings are perceptibly smaller than those of the Abegg wings and that, in addition, they show no signs of having been reduced in height. As a result of their transfer, these panels do not have the usual unpainted edges and, thus, it is not possible to say definitely that they were not diminished in their height or width.

Another version of this composition was formerly in the church of Sant' Ansano near Florence and is now in the Museo Opera Pia Bandini in Fiesole. This version was attributed by FRIEDLÄNDER (II, 1924, p. 120, no. 87) to the workshop of Roger van der Weyden, by HULIN DE LOO (1927, col. 72) to Vrancke van der Stockt, and by HOOGEWERFF (II, 1937, p. 231) to a Haarlem artist of the 1460's. It is further to be noted that the same arrangement with pointed niches, polygonal bases, and a circular bell-shaped canopy identical with that of Greenville is to be found in the representation of *Adam and Eve Banished from Paradise* on the back side of the wings of the Valencia *Last Judgment* by Vrancke van der Stockt (Madrid, private collection; cf. LAVALLEYE, 1953, pp. 35-37, no. 46 and pl. LIII).

12. THE LAMENTATION OVER CHRIST

San Diego, Calif., The Fine Arts Gallery of San Diego. Acc. no. 42:131

This *Lamentation* spent many years in the hands of art dealers, and it was acquired by The Fine Arts Gallery of San Diego only in 1942. This is probably the reason why it has until now escaped study by Roger van der Weyden specialists, although its style is closely akin to that of the artist.

The composition includes four figures: the dead Christ supported by Joseph of Arimathaea and the Virgin aided by Saint John. The absence of Mary-Magdalene is rare in the presentation of this subject, although more frequent than in paintings of the Crucifixion. The fact that the raised edge and

89

the unpainted border are present only at the upper edge seems to indicate that the panel was shortened, even if only a little, at the other three edges. The composition appears incomplete, especially at the left, where Christ's feet, as well as the clothes of the Virgin and Saint John, are cut off.

Physical data: Oak, 25 x 16 ⁷/₈ in. (63.5 x 42.9 cm.) (total surface). The usual raised edge and unpainted border are present only on the upper edge of the panel.

History: Paul Bottenwieser, art dealer, Berlin, 1929; Henry Schniewind Coll., New York, at least as from 1936 (Cat. Cleveland Exhib., 1936, no. 211), and until 1942; gift of Misses Anne R. and Amy Putnam to The Fine Arts Gallery of San Diego, 1942.

Exhibitions: Chicago, 1934, no. 130; Cleveland, 1936, no. 211; Brooklyn, 1936, no. 18; Kansas City, 1940-41, no. 62; Brooklyn, 1956, no. 13.

90

Roger van der Weyden

This work has appeared under the name of Roger van der Weyden in several exhibitions. It was also published under that attribution by DESTRÉE (I, 1930, p. 148), who thus seconded the opinion of HULIN DE LOO (cited by DESTRÉE, *ibidem*). The work was further assigned to van der Weyden in written statements to its owners by BALDASS, COHEN, GLÜCK, FRIEDLÄNDER, and WINKLER. The attribution to Roger was not, however, repeated by FRIEDLÄNDER in his additions to the catalogue of the artist (XIV, 1937, pp. 88-89). It was equally challenged by WINKLER (1942, p. 475), who wonders if it might not be the work of a follower. This *Lamentation* would not seem necessarily to have to be attributed to Roger van der Weyden because the facial characteristics are different from his usual types and the handling is in a more summary manner, particularly in the details of clothing. However, it seems clear that the work originated somewhere in the group around Roger. Although the facial features, very individualized, are different from those of Roger, they are inspired in a general way by his creations. In this respect the face of the Virgin in the San Diego *Lamentation* may be compared to that in the *Calvary with Ecclesiastical Donor* in The Cleveland Museum of Art (acc. no. 31.449), which is attributed to a follower of van der Weyden. The landscape is almost like a series of stage flats, bordered by rounded bushes, with a view of the city outlined in the background, and is very closely akin to the landscapes in works by Roger, especially to that in the *Lamentation* of the *Miraflores Altarpiece* in the Museum Dahlem in Berlin (cat. 534 A). The composition is not a copy of any known *Lamentation*, either by Roger or another Flemish painter of the 15th century. It does, however, draw very freely from other representations of the Lamentation by Roger van der Weyden in the Musées Royaux des Beaux-Arts in Brussels (cat. 516), in the Prado (cat. 2540), in the collection of Lord Powis in London, in the *Miraflores Altarpiece* in the Berlin Museum, and in a panel of the replica of the Berlin altarpiece in the Capilla Real in Granada. Another composition similar to that in San Diego, but reversed, is found in the *Lamentation* in the Mauritshuis in The Hague (cat. 264), also attributed to a follower of van der Weyden: the same four persons are shown there in the central group, in very similar poses. Like the *Calvary* in Cleveland and the *Lamentation* in The Hague, the San Diego painting must come from somewhere in the group around Roger van der Weyden, the work of either a pupil or a close follower. Judging from the costume of Joseph of Arimathaea, it would probably not date later than in the 1460's unless the painting is a faithful copy of an original dating from then.

Roger van der Weyden

13. PORTRAIT OF PHILIP THE GOOD

Bruges, Stedelijk Museum voor Schone Kunsten (Groeningemuseum)
Cat. 1938, no. 203

This portrait is one of the numerous still-existing copies of a portrait of the third Duke of Burgundy, Philip the Good, son of John the Fearless. The lost original of this portrait is considered by all specialists as a work by Roger van der Weyden.

Philip the Good, born in 1396, succeeded his father in 1419. His reign lasted almost half a century, from 1419 to 1467. This portrait is one of the numerous still-existing copies of a portrait of the Duke of which the lost original is unanimously considered as an original work by Roger van der Weyden. Among the many copies or replicas, must be mentioned especially, those of the museums of Dijon, Paris (Louvre), Lille (Musée des Beaux-Arts), Gotha (Gustav-Freytag Museum), Antwerp (Musée Royal des Beaux-Arts), also in the Palacio Real of Madrid, Windsor Castle, Ath (Hospice de la Madeleine), London (Society of Antiquaries).

Some of these portraits represent the Duke bare-headed; others, as the Bruges example, show him wearing a large hat with a piece of twisted cloth around the crown of which one end falls to his shoulder. In the Bruges example, both his headgear and garments are black, and he is wearing the collar of the Order of the Golden Fleece which he founded at the time of his marriage to Isabella of Portugal in January 1430 (a similar collar is exhibited here as no. 130). The existence of a companion piece is suggested by the fact that he is shown turned toward the right.

Physical data: Oak, 12 ³/₄ x 8 ¹³/₁₆ in. (32.5 x 22.4 cm.) (total surface). Complete overpainting of the green background, the blackish clothing, and the black hat (JANSSENS DE BISTHOVEN, 1959, p. 108). The frame, which is not original, bears inscriptions which identify the subject.

History: George Salting Coll., London, 1899 (Cat. London Exhib., 1899-1900, p. 14, no. 59); J.C. Agnew, art dealer, London, 1907 (Cat. Bruges Exhib., 1907, no. 8); acquired for the Bruges Museum with the assistance of the "Friends of the Bruges Museum", 1907.

Exhibitions: London, 1899-1900, no. 59; Bruges, 1907, no. 8; Paris, 1935, no. 32; Brussels, 1935, no. 20; Bruges, 1953, no. 7; Bruges, 1959, no. 1.

92

Roger van der Weyden

All authorities agree in considering this portrait as a copy of a lost original by Roger van der Weyden. HOSTEN and STRUBBE (1938, no. 203) judge it to date from the 15th century. Eleven portraits of Philip the Good were assembled in the Exhibition of the Order of the Golden Fleece at Bruges in 1907. Of that number FRIEDLÄNDER (II, 1924, nos. 125-125g) recognizes at least seven, including this one, as old copies of one or more originals by Roger van der Weyden. The copy in the Bruges Museum is most closely akin to the one in the Louvre in Paris (cat. 997b). PANOFSKY (1953, pp. 293-294) thinks the beautiful *Portrait of a Lady of Noble Rank* in the John D. Rockefeller Collection in New York, which is probably a portrait of Isabella of Portugal, could have been the pendant to the original from which the Bruges *Portrait of Philip the Good* was copied.

PETRUS CHRISTUS

Active in Bruges from 1444 to 1472-73
Born in Baerle. Died in Bruges in 1472 or 1473

Petrus Christus was born in Baerle, in Flanders or in Brabant (the identification of this town has not been established with certainty). It is not known where he spent his formative period. The first known fact in his development is that he became a citizen of Bruges on July 6, 1444, "to be a painter", according to the archives. He signed several paintings in an abridged form made up of Latin and Greek letters side by side (PETRUS XPͅ). His dated works number only five or six, running between 1446 and 1452 (or perhaps 1457).

Although at the time of the admission of Christus to Bruges citizenry, Jan van Eyck had already been dead for three years, Christus was long considered his pupil and successor. This supposition rests on the fact that he copied compositions by Jan van Eyck and that his style was deeply impregnated by that of his great predecessor. He also borrowed from Roger van der Weyden and Dieric Bouts. Notwithstanding this eclecticism, a very individual character emerges from his works, especially his portraits. He may have influenced the style of Antonello da Messina and taught him the Flemish technique during a trip which he is thought to have made to Italy. This supposition, however, is based on a document which might refer to another artist. Since his dated works are restricted to a period of only a few years, there is not yet a general agreement on his chronological development. The growing tendency is to believe that it was toward the end of his career that he was influenced by the works of Jan van Eyck.

The United States is the world's richest country in works by Petrus Christus. Fifteen paintings are found there which can be attributed to him, including two which are signed and dated: ten in New York, three in Washington, one in Kansas City, and one in Los Angeles.

93

*Kansas City, Mo., William Rockhill Nelson Gallery of Art
and Atkins Museum of Fine Arts.* Acc. no. 65.51

This painting was exhibited almost a century ago. It had completely disappeared since that time, only coming to light again in 1956. It is one of the most important early Flemish paintings discovered since the war. All those who have studied it since its recent reappearance have immediately recognized in it the hand of Petrus Christus. It is, moreover, one of the most personal and best preserved works of the artist. The effects of light and shade, as well as the linear perspective, attain a mastery rarely achieved in Flanders during the 15th century.

The subject of the Virgin and Child shown in a bedroom is very rare in 15th century Flemish painting. This very simple, almost bourgeois, representation deviates noticeably from the type of the Virgin by Jan van Eyck, richly clothed, seated on a throne, and crowned as a queen. The two statuettes adorning the upper part of the head of the bed can be identified, one as a prophet, the other as St. Catherine of Alexandria. The chandelier suspended from the ceiling beams is a beautiful example of the Gothic domestic lighting device which could be raised and lowered. A chandelier of the same type, but larger and intended for use in a church, is shown in this exhibition as no. 107.

Physical data: Oak, 27 $^3/_8$ x 20 in. (69.5 x 50.8 cm.).

History: Named in the collection of the Duchess of Berry, daughter-in-law of Charles X of France, in the Palazzo Vendramin in Venice in 1856 (ZANOTTO, 1856); sold in the second sale of that collection, Paris (Drouot), April 17-18, 1865, no. 434 (entry in the sale catalogue, glued to the back of the panel); Comte de la Ferronays Coll., 1866 (Cat. Paris Exhib., 1866, no. 24); Paul Demidoff Coll., sold in Paris, April 1-3, 1869, no. 3; art dealer, New York, 1955; acquired by the Nelson Gallery-Atkins Museum, Kansas City, 1956.
Cleaned by William Suhr in New York in 1955-56.

Exhibitions: Paris, 1866, no. 24.

Before being completely forgotten for almost a century, the work was briefly mentioned on four occasions soon after the middle of the 19th century: the first time in 1856, under the name of Lucas van Leiden (ZANOTTO, 1856), when it was in the collection of the Duchess of Berry; then, under the same attribution, at the sale of this collection (sale cat., 1865, no. 434); again, at the retrospective exhibition in Paris in 1866 (Cat. Paris Exhib., 1866, no. 24), already under the name of Petrus Christus; and, finally, by MICHIELS (III, 1866, p. 420), who judged this attribution to be incontestable. After its acquisition by the Nelson Gallery in Kansas City in 1956, it was once again recognized as one of the best works of Christus (KELLEHER, 1957, pp. 113-116; M[ARLIER], 1957, p. 5; KOCH, 1957, p. 271; FRIEDLÄNDER and PANOFSKY, cited by KELLEHER). It was, perhaps, signed like several works of Christus on the now lost original frame. Very soon after its rediscovery it was the object of a thorough study by KOCH (1957, pp. 271-276). This writer considers it an excellent example of

94

95

Petrus Christus

Christus's ability to borrow the motifs of compositions from both his predecessors, Jan van Eyck and the Master of Flémalle, and his contemporaries, Roger van der Weyden and Dieric Bouts, and to bring them together in a unified form which is his own. This work seems to KOCH especially personal in the rendering of spatial perspective, in which he surpasses the other Flemish painters of his time, and in the sensitivity he shows in the subtle variations of light and color values. This same author places the work in the second period of Christus' activity, probably after the *Altarpiece of Saint John the Baptist* by Roger van der Weyden, in the Museum Dahlem in Berlin (cat. 534 B), which dates from 1452-53. The Kansas City picture derives its spatial perspective, showing several rooms in succession, from the Berlin work, amplifying and perfecting it.

The theme of the Child standing on the Virgin's knees, turned toward the viewer and holding in His hand a globe topped by a cross, is also seen in another composition of the *Virgin and Child* by Petrus Christus of which three copies exist: one in the Prado in Madrid (cat. 1921), one in a private collection in Madrid (LAVALLEYE, 1, 1953, no. 34 and pl. XXXVIII), and one which was at Knoedler and Co. in New York in 1931. KOCH (1957, p. 276) believes that the latter composition, which is placed between 1460 and Christus' death in 1472-73, was probably inspired by the one in Kansas City. This author thinks the Kansas City picture dates from around 1460. FRIEDLÄNDER (statement to Nelson Gallery in 1956, reported by KELLEHER, 1957, p. 113) places it about 1450, and PANOFSKY *(ibidem)* around 1455. M[ARLIER] (1957, p. 5) also dates the painting in the middle period of Christus' career, around 1450. In any case, this painting is typical of Petrus Christus and his personality, formed through contact with his great predecessors and contemporaries. This work reflects the strong colors of Jan van Eyck (red, blue, green) as well as his realistic rendering of objects, and the space perspective of Roger van der Weyden. The picture is characterized, moreover, by the simplification of the major elements of the composition and an accomplished sense of perspective and light (KELLEHER, 1957, p. 115).

This work is personal in its iconography also. Except for the Annunciation scene, as KOCH (1957, p. 276) points out, Flemish painters almost never placed the Virgin in a bedroom. Aside from the Kansas City painting, the only other known example of this is the *Virgin and Child* in the Galleria Sabauda in Turin (cat. 188; ARU and GERADON, 1952, no. 16), which is attributed to Petrus Christus and which seems to have been inspired by another of this artist's works which is close to the one in Kansas City. Two statuettes are on the top of the head of the bed. KOCH (1957, p. 274) suggests that the one on the left shows a bearded prophet who is holding an unidentifiable object in his left hand and is raising his right hand in a teaching gesture, and that the one on the right is St. Catherine of Alexandria. The presence of St. Catherine is rather surprising because, normally, only figures from the Old Testament can be represented in the scenes of Christ's childhood. The carved lion on the arm of the seat next to the bed and the one on the chandelier are, perhaps, symbols of Christ. The lilies which decorate the head of the bed, as well as the enclosed garden seen through the window, are symbols of the Virgin's purity (KOCH, *ibidem*). The fruit

96

Petrus Christus

97

Petrus Christus

placed on the window-sill, and which often appears in paintings of the Annunciation, symbolizes by its freshness the joys of Paradise found again by Mary and Christ (PANOFSKY, 1953, pp. 144 and 203). The Christ Child holds a crystal globe topped by a cross, symbol of God's sovereignty over the world. This latter attribute, generally reserved for God the Father or Christ as an adult, is shown in the Child's hands in several works by Jan van Eyck and especially by Petrus Christus. St. Joseph leans on a cane and, in a very rare motif, holds a rosary between his fingers. Some have viewed this scene as being the preparation for the Flight into Egypt (Kansas City *Gall. News*, Dec. 1956 and KELLEHER, 1957, pp. 115-116). KOCH (1957, p. 274) retorts that this scene takes place during the day while the Flight took place at night, and that, in addition, the Child is not ready for a journey. He views it more as an intimate representation of the Virgin and Child, in contrast to Jan van Eyck's Virgin seated on a throne, wearing jewels and richly embroidered clothes.

15.   PORTRAIT OF A MAN

Los Angeles, Calif., Los Angeles County Museum
Acc. no. L.2100.44-1074, cat. no. 1

This portrait is almost unanimously attributed by specialists to Petrus Christus. Among his works, this is the most closely related to those of the Sicilian painter Antonello da Messina (d. 1479). Antonello was profoundly influenced by the style and technique of the Flemish Primitives and most especially by Petrus Christus. This was the result, perhaps, of a trip which the latter supposedly made to Milan in 1457.

The model's clothing (fur lined coat and high cap) was worn by the bourgeois of the provinces of Burgundy after the middle of the 15th century.

Physical data: Oak, 18 $^3/_8$ x 13 $^7/_8$ in. (46.7 x 35.3 cm.) (total surface).

History: Sir George Lindsay Holford Coll., London and Westonbirt, Gloucestershire (HOLMES, 1924, no. 15); testamentary executors of Sir George Holford, 1927 (Cat. London Exhib., 1927, no. 15); Holford Coll. sale, London (Christie's), May 17-18, 1928 no. 9 (*Die Kunstauktion*, April 29, 1928, p. 2); Colnaghi and Co., art dealers, London (*Zeitschr. f. bild. Kunst*, 1928, p. 50); Allan C. Balch Coll., Los Angeles; bequeathed to Los Angeles County Museum, 1944. Erroneously referred to by FRIEDLÄNDER (XIV, 1937, p. 80) and by SCHÖNE (1938, p. 56, no. 8), as being in the Mellon Collection.

Exhibitions: London, 1921-22, no. 4; London, 1927, no. 15; Chicago, 1934, no. 116; Los Angeles, 1944, no. 17; New York, 1946, no. 1.

This portrait was attributed for the first time to Petrus Christus by HOLMES (1924, no. 15). Most of those who have published the work since then have concurred (BALDASS, 1927, p. 82; CONWAY, 1927, p. 10, no. 15; FRY, 1927, p. 62; BAZIN, 1952, p. 199, note 14 and p. 200; FEINBLATT, n.d., p. 32;

98

Petrus Christus

SCHÖNE, 1938, p. 56, no. 8). SCHÖNE places the portrait just before the *Saint Eligius,* dated 1449, in the Robert Lehman Collection in New York. FRIEDLÄNDER (XIV, 1937, p. 80) classifies it among the works of Christus, but only with a certain reserve. PANOFSKY (1953, p. 311, note 8), on the other hand, suggests eliminating it from the catalogue of the artist, without giving a reason for his opinion or making a suggestion as to its attribution.

The purely Flemish technique of this work in addition to its undeniable affinity with the portraits of Antonello da Messina would seem to weigh heavily in favor of its being attributed to Petrus Christus. The close similarity to the portraits of Antonello has been pointed out by FEINBLATT (n.d., p. 32), FRY (1927, p. 62), and BAZIN (1952, p. 200). The latter considers it as a Flemish version of the self-portraits of Antonello and relates it especially to the *Self-Portrait* in the National Gallery in London (cat. 1141). For BAZIN, the Los Angeles painting shows that Christus had undergone an influence by Antonello just as the latter had been influenced by Christus. Was this reciprocal influence a result of the time which Petrus Christus may have spent at the Court of Milan in 1457? FRIEDLÄNDER (I, 1924, p. 144) is opposed to the drawing of a too hastily formed conclusion based on the appearance of the name *Piero di Burges* in the Milan archives of that date and believes that this might refer to another artist.

WEALE (1903, p. 51) thought that he could recognize the model as being the same person whose portrait Christus had done in 1462 (National Gallery in London, cat. 2593), but at a later age.

16.   SAINT CATHERINE OF ALEXANDRIA

Brussels, Private Collection

This painting is known to only a few specialists. It appeared for the first time around 1932 in a sale in Paris. Some writers mention it, but very few have had the opportunity to see it, and only a few scholars knew where it was preserved. The owner has, for the first time, consented to show it, in order to allow art historians to compare it directly with other works assembled in this specialized exhibition. The painting clearly belongs within the orbit of Petrus Christus. It is particularly appropriate that it should be exhibited in the United States, which possesses many works of this master.

The picture shows St. Catherine of Alexandria, who is easily identifiable by her attributes, the wheel and the sword.

Physical data: Oak, 23 $^5/_{16}$ x 13 $^1/_8$ in. (59.3 x 33.4 cm.) (total surface). Reverse painted with blue protective paint layer on a grey-beige ground.
Numerous overpaintings; the face is the best preserved part. Heavily restored.

99

Petrus Christus

History: Sale, Paris (Drouot), around 1932; Collection of the Belgian writer Maurice d'Alta (DEZARROIS, 1932, pp. 172-176 and HEILMAIER, 1933, pp. 36-40).
Restored around 1932.
Exhibitions: None known.

DEZARROIS (1932, pp. 172-176) was the first to mention this painting. He attributed it to Jan van Eyck, mostly because of the face, the only part of the painting which is still almost intact, and said that the rest could have been the result of a collaboration with Petrus Christus. HEILMAIER (1933, pp. 36-40) noted the appearance of the painting in the sale and said that WINKLER and HULIN DE LOO considered it a work of Jan van Eyck, but that it had been considerably restored. SCHÖNE (1938, p. 57, no. 25), without having seen the painting, thought it should be attributed to Petrus Christus. According to the information generously furnished by the owner, HULIN DE LOO examined the painting before its restoration, May 10, 1932, and was inclined to view it as a work from the hand of Jan van

Eyck, but heavily restored. He based this attribution on the face, which had been very little damaged. FRIEDLÄNDER was hesitant to make a definite attribution, but he felt that, to the extent it is possible to judge a work which has greatly suffered, it comes closest to the style of Petrus Christus.

The head-dress of the Saint, with its crown joined to the peaked hair arrangement, seems to indicate an advanced period of the 15th century, somewhat later than Jan van Eyck. A crown in the same form and placed in the same fashion is seen in the panel of Margaret of Denmark by Hugo van der Goes, in Holyrood Palace near Edinburgh. It is found again in the *Virgin among the Saints* by the Master of the Saint Lucy Legend in the Musées Royaux des Beaux-Arts in Brussels (cat. 545).

100

Petrus Christus

DIERIC BOUTS

Active in Louvain from 1462(?) to 1475
Born in Haarlem (?). Died in Louvain in 1475

Nothing is known of the first part of the life of Dieric Bouts except that he was probably born in Haarlem in Holland. The first certain mention of the artist is in 1457; he was then established in Louvain where he would continue to be active until his death. For the last years of his life, archival documents and literary sources are not lacking.

Presumed portrait

The two basic and well-documented works for knowledge of the art of Dieric Bouts are the celebrated triptych of *The Last Supper* in the Church of Saint-Pierre in Louvain, of which the wings are shown in this exhibition (cat. no. 17), and the pair of panels comprising *The Justice of Emperor Otto*, of which Dieric Bouts had finished only one panel when death came to interrupt his work. Since its restoration in 1957-58 at the Institut Royal du Patrimoine Artistique in Brussels, this panel painting of *The Proof by Fire* has shown itself to be the best work of the artist and one of the masterpieces of Flemish painting. Even without the paintings attributed to the Master of the Pearl of Brabant or to the Master of the Munich Arrest of Christ, which are by some considered very close to Bouts, from 1462 on, it is reasonably possible to attribute a number of other works to Bouts, master of a very personal talent, marked with a certain stiffness which does not exclude nobility of expression. It is above all the influence of Roger van der Weyden which is felt in the style of Bouts. A collaboration with Hugo van der Goes is, however, not to be excluded in a consideration of the style of Dieric Bouts (cf. cat. no. 19).

Dieric Bouts is one example among others of a painter born outside of the Southern Netherlands but forming his style and centering his activity there. Like all the others, Bouts takes his place among the Flemish Primitives with whom he shares the same pictorial expression as much in style as in technique.

The United States has at Cambridge (Mass.), Cleveland, New York, Philadelphia, Richmond (Va.), and Washington six paintings catalogued under the name of Dieric Bouts of which several are certainly from the master's hand.

101

Dieric Bouts

102

Dieric Bouts

103

Dieric Bouts

17. ABRAHAM AND MELCHIZEDEK, THE JEWISH PASSOVER MEAL,
THE GATHERING OF THE MANNA, ELIJAH AND THE ANGEL
Wings of THE ALTARPIECE OF THE BLESSED SACRAMENT

Louvain, Collegiate Church of Saint-Pierre

These four scenes form the two wings of the famous triptych of the
Last Supper painted by Dieric Bouts from 1464 to 1468 for the Brotherhood of
the Blessed Sacrament in Louvain. The contract for this work specified that two
theologians would guide the artist in the interpretation of the iconographic
scheme established by the Brotherhood as to the subject of the painting. Thus, it
was with the assistance of two theology professors that Dieric Bouts achieved this
work, whose central panel shows the establishment of the Sacrament of the
Eucharist. The wings show scenes from the Old Testament which have been
considered since the Middle Ages as foreshadowings of the Eucharist: the
meeting of Abraham with Melchizedek, who offers him wine and bread *(Genesis,*
14); the Passover meal of a Jewish family eating the paschal lamb according to
the Biblical prescriptions, before leaving Egypt *(Exodus,* 12), the gathering of the
manna by the Jews at dawn in the desert during the Exodus *(Exodus,* 16),
and the Prophet Elijah being awakened in the desert by an angel who brings him
food and drink (I *Kings* 19).

An absolutely extraordinary occurrence in the history of Flemish painting
is the fact that both contract and receipt, duly signed by the artist, had been
preserved. Unfortunately, these documents perished during the last two world
wars. This painting is doubly important: first, because it is a basic work in
the study of Dieric Bouts and second, because it is, after the *Ghent Altarpiece*

104

Dieric Bouts

by van Eyck, one of the principal altarpieces with great historic, artistic, and iconographic meaning which are still left to us.

The United States is responsible for the restitution of these two precious wings to Louvain after the last world war; they were found in the American Zone of Germany.

Physical data: Oak, *Abraham and Melchizedek:* 34 1/2 x 27 3/16 in. (87.6 x 70.2 cm.); *Jewish Passover Meal:* 34 1/4 x 28 1/16 in. (87.8 x 71.3 cm.); *Gathering of the Manna:* 34 1/2 x 27 3/4 in. (87.6 x 70.6 cm.); *Elijah and the Angel:* 34 5/8 x 28 in. (88 x 71.2 cm.) (total surface). Cradled panels; modern frames.

History: The contract for this triptych, an agreement dated March 15, 1464, was discovered in the church archives in 1898 and published by VAN EVEN (1898, pp. 469-478). This document no longer exists: the archive room was burned during World War I in 1914, and that which remained was placed in the library of Louvain University, which was, in turn, burned during the second world war in 1940. The contract stipulated the price of the work: 200 Rhenish florins, the subjects, the assistance of the two theology professors, and the agreement by the artist not to undertake any further work until he had entirely finished this one. Another document, the receipt, handwritten by Dieric Bouts in the register of the Brotherhood of the Blessed Sacrament and signed by the painter, was also destroyed in one of the same fires, in either 1914 or 1940. It bore the words: *ic, Dieric Bouts kenne mi vernucht en vol betaelt als van der werc dat ic ghemaect hebben den Heilichen Sacrament (s) Dieric Bouts.*
The latter document was discovered and published in 1867 by VAN EVEN (1867, p. 272, note 1) and reproduced by him (1870, pp. 166-167). The wings, probably sold sometime in the 18th century, entered the Bettendorf Collection, which was taken from Brussels to Aix-la-Chapelle in 1814. The Boisserée brothers acquired *The Meeting of Abraham with Melchizedek* and *The Gathering of the Manna.* These two panels were sold in the Boisserée sale (1827, nos. 42 and 43) to Ludwig I of Bavaria and subsequently entered the Munich Pinakothek (nos. 110 and 111). The *Jewish Passover Meal* and *Elijah* remained in the Bettendorf Collection and were acquired in 1834 by the Berlin Museum

105

(cat. 539 and 533) (SCHÖNE, 1938, p. 90). The four scenes were each restored and cradled when they belonged to the Munich and Berlin museums. In 1919, the Treaty of Versailles stipulated that the four scenes owned by the Berlin and Munich museums be returned to Belgium. They were exhibited in Brussels in 1920 (Cat. Brussels Exhib., 1920, no no.) before being replaced in the Church of Saint-Pierre in Louvain. They were removed from the church during the last world war and taken by the Germans in 1942 (FRANCOTTE, 1951-52, pp. 135-136). After they were returned in 1945, the four scenes were restored by Jozef van der Veken (FRANCOTTE, 1951-52, p. 137). These wings were examined and studied at the Institut Royal du Patrimoine Artistique in Brussels (COREMANS, GETTENS, and THISSEN, 1952, pp. 1-29).

Exhibitions: Brussels, 1920, no no.; Paris, 1923, no. 17; Amsterdam and Rotterdam, 1946, no. 9; Paris, 1947, no. 14; Brussels, 1948, no. 6; Brussels-Delft, 1957-58, nos. 12-16.

In the 18th century, the central panel, then exhibited in the church without the wings, was attributed to Quentin Metsys (DESCAMPS, 1769, p. 102). Later, it was attributed to Memlinc (SCHOPENHAUER, I, 1822, pp. 169-171). It was in 1847 that the four scenes in Berlin and Munich, which had been attributed either to Roger van der Weyden or Memlinc or even Joos van Gent, were connected with the central panel remaining in Louvain (KUGLER and BURCKHARDT, II, 1847, pp. 121 and 131-132, and WAAGEN, 1847, p. 179). Once VAN EVEN had discovered the receipt (1867, p. 272) and the contract (1898, pp. 469-478), there was no longer any doubt as to who had painted the triptych. The text of the receipt signed by Dieric Bouts is: "I, Dieric Bouts, declare myself to be satisfied and fully paid for the work I have done of the Blessed Sacrament".

The contract, which specified the subjects of the central panel and the wings, also included what was to appear on the outside: there had to be a single scene for each wing. It was specified that the twelve shew-breads should be shown on one side; because of a gap in the document, the statement about the other scene has disappeared (LEFÈVE and VAN MOLLE, 1960, p. 12). It is quite possible, in fact, that the outside wings were never painted.

The original order of the four scenes of the wings has prompted much comment. For historical, biblical, and esthetic reasons, FRIEDLÄNDER (1925, pp. 21-22), SCHÖNE (1938, p. 90), and FRANCOTTE (1951-52, pp. 137-143) have each supported different arrangements, and still another solution was presented when the work was exhibited in 1957-58, after its restoration (Cat. Brussels Exhib., 1958, p. 44). Based on the wording of the contract which indicates that each wing was originally composed of a single panel, the question of the original order was again examined. The Institut Royal du Patrimoine Artistique made a study of the structure of the wood of the panels and from this it was possible to determine the original placement; it is one of those which had been suggested by FRIEDLÄNDER (LEFÈVE and VAN MOLLE, 1960, pp. 5-19). This is the one which has now been re-established.

The iconographic parallel found in the *Speculum Humanae Salvationis* and the *Biblia Pauperum* generally places three scenes from the Old Testament in relationship with one scene from the New Testament. Compositional requirements made it necessary to show four scenes; to the three traditional scenes was added the representation of the Prophet Elijah. This appears to be the first

106

Dieric Bouts

example of its introduction into such a grouping (SCHÖNE, 1938, p. 93). This is probably one of the reasons why the Brotherhood of the Blessed Sacrament

employed two doctors of theology. It has been proposed that the two figures shown near the left edge of the scene of *Abraham and Melchizedek* are portraits of the two theologians (PEETERS, 1926, p. 15, no. 1). The one on the left (see ill. this page) is clearly a portrait and the other is probably one also. Both these figures are dressed in ecclesiastical or bourgeois clothing of the time. VAN GELDER (1951, pp. 51-52), followed by DENIS (1957, pp. 12-13), suggests that they should be viewed as two of the witnesses who were present at the signing of the contract with the artist. This is, of course, hypothetical. The scene of the *Jewish Passover Meal* shows an example of furniture, notably a kind of table which is very characteristic of the 15th century. This table, instead of resting on four legs, stood on a single leg formed by a vertical panel, plain or ornamented, attached to two long bases. The top of the table was usually movable. One single example of this kind of table still exists in Belgium; it belongs to Saint Elizabeth's Hospital in Alost. On the table in the *Jewish Passover Meal* can be seen the type of glasses made in the Meuse and Brabant regions, a lovely example of which is being shown in this exhibition as no. 169.

18.   VIRGIN AND CHILD

Antwerp, Musée Royal des Beaux-Arts. Cat. 1959, no. 28

Paintings showing the Virgin and Child were extraordinarily numerous in the 15th century. It may be said that they were copied at will by secondary masters who often introduced variations. Thus, certain characteristics of one or the other of the best artists are often present, but without sufficient clarity to enable one to attribute the work to them. This is, in fact, the case with the Antwerp *Virgin and Child*, of which the attribution to Dieric Bouts has many times been both defended and contested.

Physical data: Oak, 11 1/4 x 7 7/8 in. (28.6 x 20 cm.).
History: Acquired in 1823 in Holland by the Chevalier Florent van Ertborn; bequest of that collector to the City of Antwerp in 1841.
Cleaned before 1957-58 (BAUDOUIN, 1957-58, no. 68).
Exhibitions: Amsterdam and Rotterdam, 1946, no. 6; Duisburg, 1953, no no.; Brussels-Delft, 1958, no. 68.

107

Dieric Bouts

This painting has long been attributed to Dieric Bouts, without hesitation by HYMANS (I, 1894, p. 97) and with reserve by LAFENESTRE (1895, p. 182), DE MONT (1905, no. 28), and GOFFIN (1907, p. 107). Its definite attribution to Dieric Bouts was taken up again by WINKLER (1913, p. 74), CONWAY (1921, p. 166), and VOLL (1928, p. 113), while FRIEDLÄNDER (III, 1924, p. 48 and no. 92) and BALDASS (1932, p. 111) consider it only the work of a follower. SCHÖNE (1938, p. 203) agrees with the latter theory but attributes it to a painter close to Dieric Bouts. He considers it to be close to Albert Bouts' style and dates it between 1485 and 1490. BAUDOUIN (1957-58, no. 68), who first believed that the recent cleaning gave more support to its being attributed to Dieric Bouts, soon afterwards withdrew his first impression (1958, p. 140) and thought that it definitely cannot be assigned to this great master.

There are numerous works which show the Virgin with almost the same face as in the Antwerp painting and these probably derive from the same prototype. The head of the Antwerp *Virgin* is often compared to that of the *Virgin* in the Jesse Strauss Collection in New York.

Certain affinities may also be discovered between this painting in the Antwerp Museum and the features of the Virgin in the works by the Master of the Tiburtine Sibyl.

DIERIC BOUTS and HUGO VAN DER GOES

For the biography of Dieric Bouts, see page 101
For the biography of Hugo van der Goes, see page 116

19. TRIPTYCH OF THE MARTYRDOM OF SAINT HIPPOLYTUS

Bruges, Museum of the Cathedral of Saint-Sauveur

This triptych is one of the extremely rare examples of a probable collaboration between two eminent painters, one of whom is Dieric Bouts, or perhaps one of his best disciples whose work is often confused with that of Bouts, and the other, Hugo van der Goes. The work once adorned the altar of the Chapel of the Guild

108

of Lime Porters and Measurers in the Cathedral of Saint-Sauveur in Bruges. This chapel was dedicated to Saint Sylvester. The donors of the triptych appear on the left wing, while the central panel represents the martyrdom of Saint Hippolytus, patron saint of the donor, Hippolytus de Berthoz. The Saint is shown being torn asunder by four horses. The right wing is an unidentified episode in the legend of St. Hippolytus. The reverse sides of the wings show, in grisaille, Saint Hippolytus and Saint Elizabeth of Hungary, patrons of the donors. Two supplementary panels were subsequently added to the triptych. They represent, also in grisaille, Saint Charlemagne and Saint Margaret, patrons of the son of the donor and of the son's wife.

For reasons of style, authorities attribute the central panel and the right wing to Dieric Bouts or one of his close disciples, the Master of the Pearl of Brabant or the Master of the Arrest of Munich, and they place them in date around 1470-1472. Again for reasons of style, there is agreement in attributing the portraits of the donors on the left wing to Hugo van der Goes. Some date these latter around 1470-1472, while others place them around 1479-1480, a date which matches the one, 1479, said to have been on the original frame, now lost.

It is exceptional to see, as here, donors who are not accompanied by their patron saints, although the Master of Flémalle thus represented the donors in the *Merode Annunciation* in The Cloisters in New York. Van der Goes often innovated, for example, as regards composition, which he enriched by previously unknown creations. The clothing and the head-dress of the donatrix are typical of the style of around 1470 to 1475: two other examples may be seen in this exhibition (nos. 27 and 29), the second of which is dated precisely in 1473. The castle appearing in the landscape of the right wing is probably an interpretation of the ducal castle which dominated the city of Louvain, near its ramparts.

Physical data: Oak, central panel: 35 $^{13}/_{16}$ x 35 $^{13}/_{16}$ in. (91 x 91 cm.), wings: 35 $^{13}/_{16}$ x 15 $^3/_4$ in. (91 x 40 cm).

History: The date 1479 is said to have appeared on the former frame, now lost (SCHOPENHAUER, I, 1822, p. 153); decorated the Chapel of Saint-Sylvester in the Cathedral of Saint-Sauveur in 1694 (described in a manuscript of 1694: VERSCHELDE, 1863, p. 69); described as in the church in 1769 by DESCAMPS (1769, pp. 276-277). Restored in 1905 *(Bull. Comm. Roy. Art et Archéol.,* 1905, p. 89). Cleaned at the Institut Royal du Patrimoine Artistique in Brussels in 1948.

Exhibitions: Bruges, 1902, no. 37; Paris, 1947, no. 19; Bruges, 1953, no. 12 (left wing only); London, 1953-54, no. 36 (left wing only); Brussels-Delft, 1957-58, nos. 26-28.

This triptych reputedly belonged to the Guild Lime Porters and Measurers of Bruges, who had been granted the Chapel of Saint-Adrien by the Council of the Church of Saint-Sauveur, September 1, 1460, and who also honored Saint Sylvester (DOCHY, 1959, p. 20). It was, moreover, in a chapel called after Saint-Sylvester in 1694. The donors have been identified by their coats of arms on the grisaille exteriors of the wings. They were Hippolytus de Berthoz and his wife, Elizabeth van Keverwijck. Supplementary wings, clearly added at the beginning of the 16th century, judging by their style, show in grisaille Saints Charlemagne

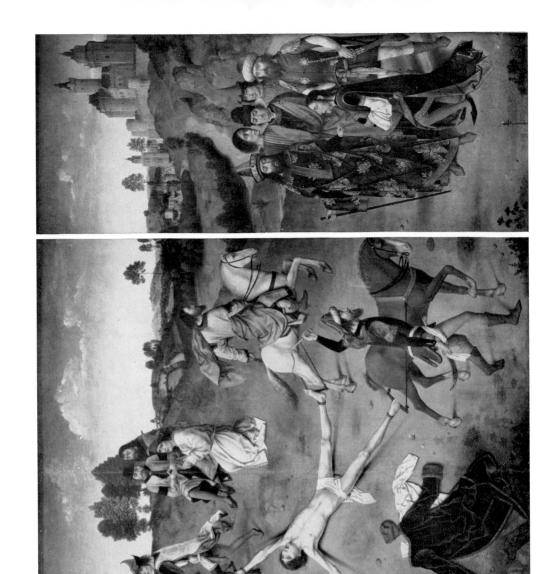

and Margaret, patrons of Charles, son of Hippolytus de Berthoz, and his wife. The coats of arms of the latter two persons appear on the lower part of these added wings (DOCHY, 1959, p. 24). It is known that Hippolytus de Berthoz was adviser to Philip the Good, that he was first married to Elizabeth van Keverwijck (the date of their marriage is unknown), that he was subsequently married in 1494 to Elizabeth Hugheins, and that he died in 1502. There were definite relationships between the Berthoz family and the Church of Saint-Sauveur: the name of Hippolytus de Berthoz's widow is mentioned, for example, in the account books of the church in 1504 (VERSCHELDE, 1863, p. 69). It is, thus, entirely conceivable that the triptych was given to the church, and probably to the Guild of Lime Porters and Measurers, by one of the Berthoz family, either the father or the son. The right wing may represent St. Sylvester and Emperor Constantine: this might be suggested by the fact that the chapel was dedicated to St. Sylvester.

WAAGEN (1847, no. 47, p. 185) was the first to reject the former attribution to Memlinc and suggested it was the work of Joos van Gent. WEALE (1862, p. 67) was the first to recognize it as a work by Dieric Bouts. HULIN DE LOO (1902, no. 37) views it as a work of the end of the painter's career, except for the donors' wing, which he attributes to Hugo van der Goes. He says that this collaboration may have come about from the fact that Bouts could not go to Bruges to paint these portraits or that, the work having been left unfinished, its completion was assigned to Hugo van der Goes after the death of Dieric Bouts. FRIEDLÄNDER (III, 1925, p. 29) joins in this double attribution. He places the part by Dieric Bouts around 1470, between the execution of the *Blessed Sacrament* in the Church of Saint-Pierre in Louvain (the wings of which are shown in this exhibition as no. 17) and *The Justice of Otto*, done for the Louvain Town Hall and presently in the Musées Royaux des Beaux-Arts in Brussels (cat. 65-66). It is worth recalling here that the contract which Dieric Bouts signed to do the *Blessed Sacrament* stipulated that he could not undertake any new work before its completion (thus, in fact, from 1464 to 1470), and that he began *The Justice of Otto* after November 1, 1470 (VAN MOLLE, 1958, p. 9).

BALDASS (1932, p. 104), VAN PUYVELDE (1953, p. 205), WINKLER (1958, pp. 3-4), BOON (1958, p. 11) and BAUDOUIN (1958, p. 130) agree in attributing the center and the right wing of the triptych to Dieric Bouts and the other wing to Hugo van der Goes. HEILAND (1902, p. 154) does not accept the attribution to Dieric Bouts, but sees in it the hand of the Master of the Pearl of Brabant, while SCHÖNE (1938, p. 168, no. 51 and pp. 39-40) attributes the work to the Master of the Arrest of Munich, around 1470 (some scholars do not distinguish these last two masters from Dieric Bouts). SCHÖNE believes, further, that in doing the central panel the painter was inspired by an already existing composition which also was the source for a miniature of the same subject dating from before 1467 (*Histoire du bon roi Alexandre*, Paris, Petit Palais, Dutuit Collection). He thinks the right panel was an original creation by the Master of the Arrest of Munich as does PANOFSKY (1953, pp. 300, 336, and 336,

111

note 2). SCHÖNE attributes the central panel and the right wing of the triptych to a painter of Dieric Bouts' workshop, but he does not name this artist.

PFISTER (1923, p. 26) thinks the left wing was painted by van der Goes. SCHÖNE (1938, p. 168, no. 51) dates it from the same period as the other wing and the central panel. Moreover, he believes that van der Goes also painted the grisailles of St. Hippolytus and St. Elizabeth, as FRIEDLÄNDER (XIV, 1937, p. 90) had already affirmed. OETTINGER (1938, p. 57) does not agree and contends that the part attributable to van der Goes should be limited to the two portraits, and that he painted them on an already existing landscape which Dieric Bouts had done. He believes, in addition, that these portraits were painted later and should be dated at the end of the career of van der Goes, in the period of *The Death of the Virgin* in the Bruges City Museum (cat. 204) and the Bonkil wings in Holyrood Palace in Edinburgh, thus, ca. 1480. This last hypothesis would be confirmed if the observation made by SCHOPENHAUER (1822, p. 153) that he had read the date 1479 on the original frame lent itself to confirmation.

The painter of the grisailles of Saint Charlemagne and Saint Margaret, which date from the beginning of the 16th century, is unknown. An unusual occurrence is the presence of a small furred animal at Charlemagne's feet. In this regard, it may be recalled that Charlemagne had the reputation of being a great hunter and was sometimes chosen as its patron saint by the Furriers Guild.

112

Dieric Bouts and Hugo van der Goes

JOOS VAN GENT (JOOS VAN WASSENHOVE ?)

Active in Antwerp, Ghent, and Urbino, from 1460 until at least 1475

It is generally accepted that Joos van Wassenhove and Joos van Gent were one and the same person. There is no painting known which can be authenticated as having been done by the former. It is known only that he was active in Antwerp (1460), later in Ghent (1464-69), and that he subsequently left for Italy (before 1470). As to the latter, known in Italy as "Giusto da Guanto", it is certain that he painted the *Communion of the Apostles* (record of payments made between 1470 and 1475) for the Duke Federigo de Montefeltre in Urbino, Italy. His participation in other paintings ordered in Urbino by the same prince is less certain: twenty-eight portraits of *Illustrious Men* (Urbino and the Louvre), *Federigo and his Son* (Urbino), and *Federigo and Others at a Lecture* (Windsor Castle). Winkler was the first who, on a stylistic basis, established the analogy between the *Communion* of Joos van Gent and a triptych in the Cathedral of Ghent, a *Crucifixion,* the principal work attributed to Joos van Wassenhove. Other attributions are derived from this comparison, notably that of the *Adoration of the Magi* in New York (cat. no. 20). Jacques Lavalleye, a specialist on Joos van Gent, is at this moment finishing a revision of this artist's activity, after a new study of his principal paintings in Urbino and Paris.

The employment of a Flemish master by an Italian prince is one example, among others, of the great esteem enjoyed by Flemish painting in foreign countries. It also explains the great influence then exercised by this art in numerous countries throughout Europe.

The *Adoration of the Magi* in The Metropolitan Museum of Art is the only work in the United States which can be attributed with sufficient certainty to Joos van Gent.

20. THE ADORATION OF THE MAGI

New York, N.Y., The Metropolitan Museum of Art. Acc. no. 41.190.21

This *Adoration of the Magi,* unanimously attributed to Joos van Gent, is especially important because, along with the *Triptych of the Crucifixion* in Saint-Bavon in Ghent, it is probably the only evidence of Joos' activity in Flanders before his departure for Italy. It is the only work of this artist in America.

In addition, it is one of the rare well-preserved examples of water tempera painting on linen from 15th century Flanders. According to the records, this technique must have been common at that time, although only a few works of this type still exist, usually in bad condition. Another tempera painting on linen is included in this exhibition as no. 23.

113

114

Joos van Gent

Physical data: Linen, $42^1/_8$ x 62 $^1/_2$ in. (107 x 158.8 cm.) (sight measurement).

History: Dukes of Frias Coll., Convento de Santa Clara, Medina de Pomar (Province of Burgos); Jacques Seligmann, art dealer, Paris, 1922; George and Florence Blumenthal Coll., New York; bequest of George Blumenthal to The Metropolitan Museum of Art, 1941.

Exhibitions: New York, 1929, no. 17.

By comparing its style with the *Communion of the Apostles* in the Galleria Nazionale delle Marche in Urbino, a work authenticated by documents, and with the *Triptych of the Crucifixion* in the Cathedral of Saint-Bavon in Ghent, this *Adoration of the Magi* has been recognized as the work of Joos van Gent since its discovery in Spain.

With the exception of PÄCHT (1927-28, pp. 49-50), who places the work after the *Communion of the Apostles,* painted in Urbino for the Duke of Montefeltre in 1472-74, all others agree in dating the New York painting within the artist's Flemish period, i.e. before 1468-69. Several among them consider the work to be later than his Saint-Bavon triptych, which is generally placed around 1464-65, thus, either a little after the latter work (FRIEDLÄNDER, III, 1925, p. 129, no. 101; WEHLE, 1943-44, p. 136; WEHLE and SALINGER, 1947, p. 54), or just before Joos' departure for Italy in 1468-69 (DEMONTS, 1925, p. 66). Only LAVALLEYE (1936, p. 81), and more recently PANOFSKY (1953, p. 341 and 341, note 2) consider the *Adoration of the Magi* to be the first known work of Joos van Gent, done between his mastership in Ghent (1460) and the *Triptych of the Crucifixion* (1464-65). In any event, this work bears some striking similarities to the triptych in Saint-Bavon, as well as to the *Communion* in Urbino. Its affinity with the latter painting has been emphasized by DEMONTS (1925, p. 65), WEHLE (1943, p. 136), and particularly LAVALLEYE (1936, p. 80). The features and poses of certain figures are very analogous to those in the Ghent *Crucifixion*: the Asiatic facial types, the unstable posture of St. Joseph which calls to mind very strongly that of Moses and Aaron in the Ghent wings, and the tightly-drawn group of shepherds which resembles the Jews looking at the Brazen Serpent.

Although the style and composition of this work bear the strong personal imprint of the artist, various influences can be detected as coming from Roger van der Weyden (PANOFSKY, 1953, p. 341), Dieric Bouts, particularly in the group of the Virgin and Child (WINKLER, 1924, p. 114 and PANOFSKY, 1953, p. 34), and, especially, Hugo van der Goes (WINKLER, 1924, p. 114; DEMONTS, 1925, pp. 57 and 66).

The motif of the Virgin seated on a bed holding the Christ Child as He receives the homage of the Magi is rarely found in Flemish paintings of the 15th century. DEMONTS (1925, pp. 58-60 and 72) points out two other later examples, one in a miniature of the *Hortulus Animae Christianae* (1510-1524) in the Vienna National Bibliothek (cod. 2706) and the other in a painting by a follower of Joos van Gent in the Trevi Museum. This motif is also found in the central panel of the *Pearl of Brabant* by Dieric Bouts in the Munich Pinakothek (cat. 107-109). DEMONTS (1925, p. 68) suggests seeing a portrait of Hugo van der Goes (whose admission to the Painters Guild of Ghent in 1467 was sponsored by Joos) in the man in green, wearing a red cap, who is behind the column at the left, as well as a self-portrait of the artist in the bearded, bare-headed figure in blue at the extreme left of the painting.

An *Adoration of the Magi,* in which certain elements are almost identical with those of the New York painting while others are totally different, was formerly part of the Odiot Collection in Paris (Odiot sale, April 26, 1889, no. 1, and then Kleinberger Galleries). It is considered either a work done by Joos in his very early period (FRIEDLÄNDER, III, 1925, pp. 86-87 and pl. LXXXIV), or a later free copy (LAVALLEYE, 1936, p. 80, note 1).

The time at which this work was first brought to Spain is not known, but the fact that it belonged to the Dukes of Frias permits the hypothesis that it may have been brought there by Juan Fernandez de Velasco, the sixth Duke of Frias, who was ambassador to England and travelled in Flanders around 1600 (WEHLE, 1943, p. 136).

HUGO VAN DER GOES

Active especially in Ghent beginning in 1467
Born in Ghent(?). Died in 1482 at Rouge-Cloître, near Brussels

From public records and old literary sources it is known that Hugo van der Goes was probably born in Ghent, that he was enrolled in 1467 as a free master in the Painters Guild of that city, and that he was active there until 1477-78. He withdrew to the Convent of the Rouge-Cloître, near Brussels, as a lay brother. He continued to work there as a painter in spite of the fact that his reason began to leave him. He worked also in Bruges (1468) and in Louvain (1479), after the death of Dieric Bouts in 1475.

The key work of Hugo van der Goes is the triptych of the *Nativity* (ca. 1476-77), which was ordered from him by Tommaso Portinari, agent of the Medici in Bruges, for the Portinari's chapel in Florence. This work is now in the museum of the Uffizi in Florence. It was starting especially from this triptych that other works have been attributed to him. The specialists assign to him some fifteen paintings, none of which bears a signature or a date.

Jan van Eyck, Roger van der Weyden, Hugo van der Goes and Hieronymus Bosch are the four great masters of 15th century Flanders. Together with Bosch,

116

Hugo van der Goes

van der Goes is also considered as the main artist of the second half of that century. He was, at the same time, the leader of the Ghent School. His influence was great in the field of painting and manuscript illuminations.

Five works by Hugo van der Goes are in the United States: three in New York, one in Baltimore (being shown in this exhibition as no. 22), and one in Philadelphia.

21.   SAINT ANNE, THE VIRGIN AND CHILD, AND A DONOR

Brussels, Musées Royaux des Beaux-Arts. Cat. 1957, no. 544

This painting is probably an original work by Hugo van der Goes, although some specialists consider it a work of his early period, when the artist had not yet fully developed his genius. This painting is characterized by the usual light

Hugo van der Goes

118

Hugo van der Goes

colors of this master (particularly, the light blue of the book) and the always striking originality which he displayed. Nevertheless, not all authorities agree in attributing it to van der Goes.

The subject is the glorious descendants of Saint Anne, the iconography of which was extremely varied in the 15th century, both in painting and in sculpture. Sometimes St. Anne, seated or standing, carries the Virgin who, in turn, carries the Child; often the composition follows, more or less, that of the Trinity. Here the artist managed to place the Child in the center of the composition. Finding his inspiration in the iconography of the Virgin known as the Virgin of Humility, created by the Master of Flémalle, van der Goes shows the Virgin seated on the ground, in front of the low grass-topped stone wall on which St. Anne is sitting. The donor, a monk, perhaps a Franciscan, is a remarkable portrait which has not been identified.

> *Physical data:* Oak, 12 ³/₄ x 15 ³/₈ in. (32.5 x 39 cm.) (total surface).
>
> *History:* Comtesse de Thiennes Coll., Ghent; acquired by Mr. Slaes, who sold it to the Brussels Museum in 1877.
>
> *Exhibitions:* Bruges, 1867, no. 23 bis; London, 1927, no. 52; Paris, 1935, no. 43; Worcester-Philadelphia, 1939, no. 13; Paris, 1947, no. 44; Ghent, 1957, no. 57.

In 1887 SCHEIBLER (1887, pp. 279-280) attributed this painting to Hugo van der Goes in comparing it to *The Lamentation over Christ* by that master in the Kunsthistorisches Museum in Vienna (cat. 630). PFISTER (1923, p. 25) and DESTRÉE (1917, p. 130) attributed it to the same master. FRIEDLÄNDER (IV, 1926, pp. 30-34) believes it is an early work by van der Goes and judges the composition to be an original creation. He considers the portrait of the donor as being excellent, and done from life. It seems to him that the composition is a little stiff, but that this fault may be imputed to the youth of the painter. He compares the head of the Virgin to that of the *Virgin and Child* of the John G. Johnson Collection in Philadelphia (cat. 336), which he also considers an early work. BALDASS (1930, p. 132), who had previously thought of it as a product of the workshop, later came over to FRIEDLÄNDER's opinion. VAN PUYVELDE (1953, pp. 225-226) feels it is definitely a work by the master, whether in his youth or his mature period. HELD (1955, p. 231) considers it was done by van der Goes in his early period. OETTINGER (1938, p. 61) views it as being very close to the work of the master, but, nevertheless, from his workshop, perhaps by the master who painted the Liechtenstein Altarpiece. TOLNAY (1944, p. 189, note 2) believes it came from the workshop, while PANOFSKY (1953, p. 347, note 1) thinks it was done by an imitator.

HIPPOLYTUS DE BERTHOZ AND ELIZABETH VAN KEVERWIJCK
Left wing of the TRIPTYCH OF THE MARTYRDOM OF SAINT HIPPOLYTUS

See entry of the entire triptych under Dieric Bouts, pp. 108-112, and illustration p. 118.

119

Baltimore, Md., The Walters Art Gallery. Acc. no. 37.296, cat. no. 296

This painting is generally considered as a work done by Hugo van der Goes at the end of his career.

It is one of the rare examples of a portrait executed by the artist which is not part of a larger composition. The joined hands of the donor and the gesture of St. John permit the supposition that this panel was originally the right wing of a diptych whose left wing, now lost, must have represented a Virgin and Child. St. John the Baptist can be identified by his hermit-brown tunic over which is thrown the crimson cloak evoking his martyrdom, and by his raised finger, recalling his mission as Precursor of Christ.

> *Physical data:* Oak, 12 $^{11}/_{16}$ x 8 $^{7}/_{8}$ in. (32.2 x 22.5 cm.). A cleaning, in 1939, revealed the hands of the donor and traces of a collar of an order around his neck.
>
> *History:* P.A. Borger Coll., Arnhem (FRIEDLÄNDER, IV, 1926, p. 128), sold in Amsterdam (Fr. Muller), November 13, 1882, no. 16; acquired at that sale by Mr. Leembruggen (DESTRÉE, 1914, p. 122) and loaned by him to the Rijksmuseum, where it was exhibited from 1903 to 1920 (cat. no. 984 A); Leembruggen sale, Amsterdam (Fr. Muller), April 13, 1920, no. 66 (FRIEDLÄNDER, IV, 1926, p. 128); New York, private coll. (FRIEDLÄNDER, in THIEME-BECKER, XIV, 1921, p. 312); acquired from J. Seligmann by Henry Walters on December 7, 1920; bequest to the City of Baltimore as part of the Walters Coll. in 1932 and exhibited since then at The Walters Art Gallery.
>
> *Exhibitions:* New York, 1929, no. 18; Worcester-Philadelphia, 1939, no. 14.

Unanimously attributed to Hugo van der Goes, this work is generally placed in the last period of his activity. OETTINGER (1938, p. 57) judges it to be a work contemporary with the panels in Holyrood Palace in Edinburgh, thus, after 1473. DESTRÉE (1914, p. 122) and CONWAY (1921, p. 184) believe it dates from the same period as the wing with donors executed by van der Goes after 1475 in order to complete the unfinished triptych of the *Martyrdom of St. Hippolytus* by Dieric Bouts, in the Museum of the Cathedral of Saint-Sauveur in Bruges. The reasons for this late dating are based on considerations of style: the *sfumato* and the silver light which bathes the figures (TOLNAY, 1944, p. 184), and the composition which seems to burst the narrow limits of the frame (FRIEDLÄNDER, IV, 1926, p. 49). In the latter's opinion (*ibidem*, p. 128) van der Goes never attained a more advanced style than here. PANOFSKY (1953, p. 332, note 1) sees this as one of the only authentic portraits painted by the artist, along with the *Donor* of the Havemeyer Collection in the New York Metropolitan Museum.

According to PANOFSKY (1953, pp. 332, note 1, and 336, note 2), this panel may be a fragment of a larger composition. The presence of an unpainted edge along each of the two sides and the absence of this edge at the upper and lower ends of the panel (communication from The Walters Art Gallery) allow the hypothesis that the painting must have been cut in length, but not in width. It could then be a triptych wing which was shortened, as was suggested by the Amsterdam Catalogue (1911, no. 984 A) and DESTRÉE (1914, p. 122). But

120

Hugo van der Goes

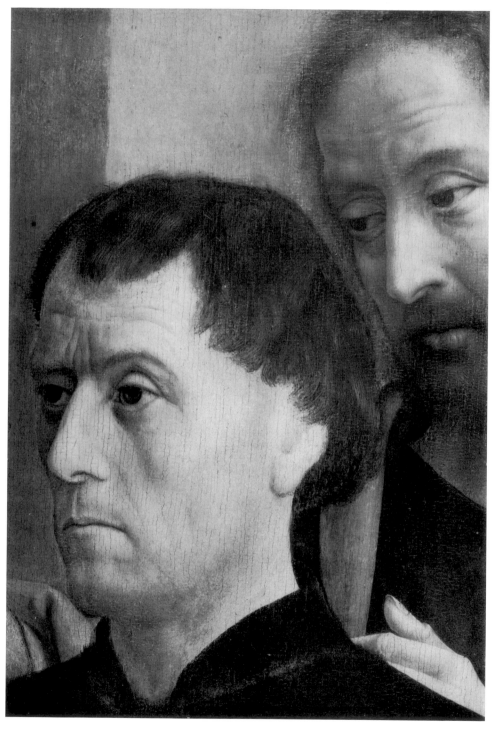

121

Hugo van der Goes

since that shortening might not have been more than some fractions of an inch, it remains possible that this panel is the wing of a diptych, as FRIEDLÄNDER believes (IV, 1926, p. 49). The traces of a collar around the neck of the donor, which were rediscovered at the time of the cleaning, could very well be those of a collar of the Order of the Golden Fleece (Cat. Worcester-Philadelphia Exhib., 1939, no. 14).

23.   THE DESCENT FROM THE CROSS

New York and Paris, Wildenstein and Company, Inc.

This canvas, which shows three figures, Joseph of Arimathaea, Nicodemus and another man, around Christ lowered from the cross, is the companion piece to another canvas of the same dimensions in the Berlin Museum. The latter shows a group of mourners formed by the Virgin, Saint John, and the three Marys. It completes the composition of the *Descent from the Cross*. Both paintings are almost unanimously attributed to Hugo van der Goes.

This is one of the rare water tempera paintings on linen in 15th century Flanders which has managed to survive in a reasonably good condition. Another painting being shown in this exhibition (cat. no. 20) is painted in the same technique.

> *Physical data:* Linen, 21 x 15 in. (53.3 x 38.2 cm.) (total surface).
> *History:* Private collection, Paris, 1950.
> *Exhibitions:* None known.

In 1913, on the basis of the existence of two works of the *Descent from the Cross* in the style of Hugo van der Goes, one on linen in the Lindenau-Museum in Altenburg (cat. 182), the other on panel in the Bargello in Florence (Carrand Coll., no. 24), RING (1913, pp. 85-87) concluded that there must exist an original *Descent from the Cross* by Hugo which would complete the composition in the Berlin Museum (cat. 1622; cf. FRIEDLÄNDER, IV, 1926, pp. 39-40, no. 7 and pl. VIII) and which would be, at the same time, the prototype of the Altenburg and Florence paintings. It was only in 1950 that the New York *Deposition*, considered since as the lost original, appeared in a Paris private collection and was published by FRIEDLÄNDER (1950, pp. 167-171). More recently WINKLER (1955, pp. 2-8) placed it in the first period of the artist, at the same time as the *Monforte Altarpiece* in the Berlin Museum (cat. 1718), the *Virgin and Child* in the Städelsches Kunstinstitut in Frankfort (cat. 802), and the *Diptych of the Redemption* in the Kunsthistorisches Museum in Vienna (nos. 629-631); that is to say, in any case before the *Portinari Altarpiece* in the Uffizi in Florence. The Berlin companion piece had, however, been placed by

122

Hugo van der Goes

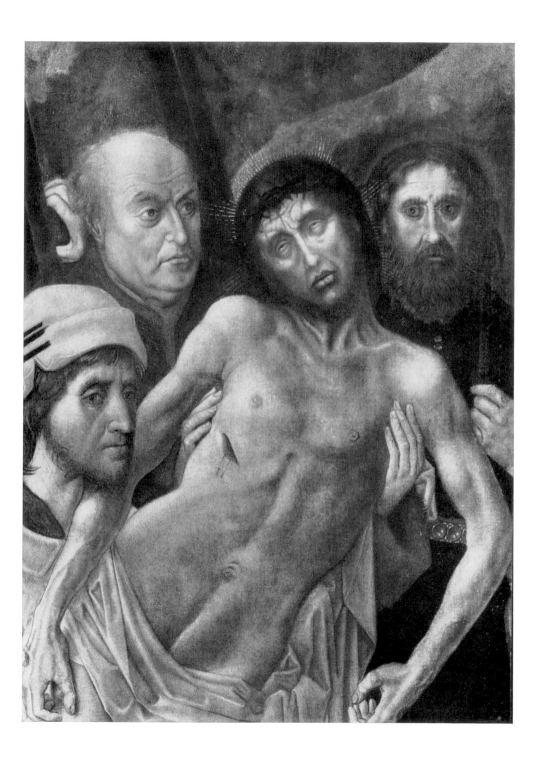

123

Hugo van der Goes

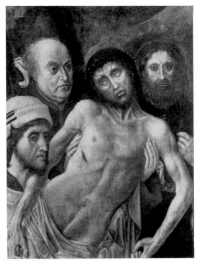

The picture on exhibition with its companion piece in Berlin

PFISTER (1923, p. 26) in the final period of van der Goes' activity. PANOFSKY (1953, p. 338 and 338, note 2) does not mention the New York painting, but sees in the one in Berlin the reflection of a lost original by Hugo which he dates, like the Vienna diptych, after the *Monforte Altarpiece*, the *Portinari Altarpiece*, and the Bonkil wings in Holyrood Palace in Edinburgh.

Since both the New York and Berlin compositions were painted on linen, it is reasonable to believe that they did not originally constitute a diptych in the true sense, where one half closes on the other, but two paintings to be shown side by side (FRIEDLÄNDER, IV, 1926, p. 40).

The iconographic subject, the *Descent from the Cross*, is shown here in a form little used in the North. It is more like an *Exposition of Christ's Body*, akin to that painted by Roger van der Weyden in 1450, now in the Uffizi in Florence (cat. 795). Nevertheless, the ladder at the upper left shows that it is indeed a *Descent from the Cross*.

Memlinc freely borrowed the subject of these two pictures for a diptych preserved in the Capilla Real in Granada (FRIEDLÄNDER, IV, 1926, p. 40; IDEM, VI, 1928, p. 18, no. 13 and pl. XV-XVI; IDEM, 1950, pp. 167 and 170). However, it is really no more than a free interpretation of this composition, because the figures are not faithfully copied from Hugo and their expressions are modified. The particular value of this diptych is in casting some light on the relationship between these two artists and to emphasize the contrasts in their personalities, Memlinc manifesting the emotions which van der Goes expresses only in a restrained fashion (FRIEDLÄNDER, 1950, p. 170).

124

Hugo van der Goes

MASTER OF THE TIBURTINE SIBYL

Active in Haarlem and/or Louvain, end of the 15th century

Friedländer gave this conventional name to the painter of a picture now in the Städelsches Kunstinstitut in Frankfort, *The Tiburtine Sibyl Announcing the Birth of Christ to Emperor Augustus*. He dates this work between 1480 and 1495 in consideration of its style and the mode of the costumes. The same author also attributes to this master a *Resurrection of Lazarus* in the San Carlo Museum in Mexico City, a *Marriage of the Virgin* in the John G. Johnson Collection in Philadelphia, and a *Crucifixion* in The Detroit Institute of Arts (being shown in this exhibition as no. 24).

The exact origin of this artist is unknown. Some authorities believe he was an unidentified Dutch painter of the Haarlem School, while others, like Valentiner, have identified this master as Aelbrecht van Ouwater. Still others view him as an anonymous painter of Ouwater's school who may have worked in Louvain with Dieric Bouts. In any event, the influence of Bouts is preponderant in the composition, the facial characteristics of the figures, and the landscapes of the works grouped under the name of the Master of the Tiburtine Sibyl.

24. THE CRUCIFIXION

Detroit, Mich., The Detroit Institute of Arts. Acc. no. 41.126, cat. no. 666

This panel is unanimously attributed by the authorities to the Master of the Tiburtine Sibyl, regardless of which opinion they hold as to the actual identity of the painter himself. As a result of certain peculiarities in the dress of the figures, the work can be dated around 1485.

This composition is representative of a certain type of Crucifixion where the group of Christ's Mother and friends is on His right and that of the Jews on His left.

Physical data: Oak, 56 9/16 x 40 3/8 in. (143.8 x 102.7 cm.) (total surface). Cradled panel.
History: Crombez Coll., Paris (FRIEDLÄNDER, III, 1925, p. 122, no. 77); A. Seligmann, art dealer, Paris (FRIEDLÄNDER, XIV, 1937, p. 91, no. 77); Harriman Coll., New York; Mrs. Mary Harriman Rumsey Coll., New York; Duveen Brothers, New York; gift of Mr. and Mrs. Edgar B. Whitcomb to The Detroit Institute of Arts in 1941. Cleaned by William Suhr about 1945.
Exhibitions: Brussels and Delft, 1957-58, no. 50; Amsterdam, 1958, no. 12.

There is general agreement among authorities in attributing this panel to the Master of the Tiburtine Sibyl. Several writers consider it the work of an

125

Master of the Tiburtine Sibyl

126

Master of the Tiburtine Sibyl

anonymous painter who may have been a pupil of Dieric Bouts in Louvain, but who was also influenced by Aelbrecht Ouwater, perhaps during a trip the artist might have made to Haarlem (FRIEDLÄNDER, III, 1925, pp. 70-71 and 122, no. 77; HOOGEWERFF, II, 1937, p. 76; GERSON, 1950, p. 15 and fig. 18; SNYDER, 1960, p. 50). However, not all are of the opinion that it may be considered the work of an anonymous artist. VALENTINER (1943, pp. 78 and 81) has no hesitation in attributing it to Aelbrecht Ouwater. He identifies Ouwater as having been, in fact, both the Master of the Tiburtine Sibyl and the wood engraver of Haarlem, Master Bellaert, who illustrated several books between 1483 and 1485. In VALENTINER's opinion, the landscape in the background of the Detroit *Crucifixion* exemplifies Ouwater's well known landscapes. RICHARDSON 1954, p. 27) followed Valentiner's attribution of the Detroit panel to Ouwater, identified as the Master of the Tiburtine Sibyl. The details of dress allow the work to be dated rather exactly; wide-tipped shoes did not make their appearance until around 1483, and the complicated head-dress of the type worn by the Magdalene appeared around 1485 (VALENTINER, 1943, p. 78; SNYDER, 1960, p. 52).

Some of the figures around the cross are borrowed from other paintings: the man seen in a three-quarter back view at the right, looking at Christ, who appears in other works of the same period, is taken from Ouwater (BOON, 1947, p. 35); several figures among the left-hand group were borrowed from at least two works by Bouts, a lost *Crucifixion* known through a Rhenish copy owned by a Berlin art dealer (SCHÖNE, 1938, pl. 75c), and the *Descent from the Cross* of the Capilla Real in Granada; the group of Jews was doubtless borrowed from a lost work of Geertgen tot Sint Jans (SNYDER, 1960, p. 52).

MASTER OF THE SAINT BARBARA LEGEND

Active in Brussels, last third of the 15th century

The Master of the Saint Barbara Legend owes his name to a triptych of which the central panel belongs to the Musées Royaux des Beaux-Arts in Brussels; the left wing is in the Museum of the Brotherhood of the Holy Blood in Bruges, and the right wing is lost. Some other works have been grouped around this triptych. These are paintings dominated by characteristics generally considered as coming from Brussels, and reflecting the influence of Roger van der Weyden.

Two of the works included in this group are found in the United States, both in New York.

127

25. THE LEGEND OF SAINT BARBARA
   Left wing of a triptych

Bruges, Noble Brotherhood of the Holy Blood

This panel is the left wing of a triptych of the Saint Barbara Legend; the central panel belongs to the Musées Royaux des Beaux-Arts in Brussels and the right wing is lost. Two drawings also exist which are considered preparatory drawings for this triptych. One of these is being shown in this exhibition as no. 65.

The anonymous painter of this work was a follower of Roger van der Weyden in Brussels, in the last third of the 15th century.

Recently, Reverend de Gaiffier discovered the literary source of the iconography of this triptych, a version of the legend of Saint Barbara written by an Augustine monk, Jan de Wackerzeel. He compared this text with the iconography of the triptych and the two drawings and found that he could explain every detail of the composition, which faithfully interprets the text.

128

Master of the Saint Barbara Legend

The wing on exhibition with its central panel (Brussels)

Physical data: Oak, 29 ¹/₈ x 24 ¹³/₁₆ in. (74 x 63 cm.).

History: Collection of the widow Kerchove, Ghent; Vermandele Coll., Ghent; Vermandele sale, Ghent, April 7, 1859, no. 82; acquired at this sale by the Noble Brotherhood of the Holy Blood in Bruges (DUCLOS, 1910, p. 456).

Cleaned in 1957 by Leegenhoek, Bruges. This cleaning brought about the reappearance of the small figures in the right background and the masons working on top of the central tower.

Exhibitions: Bruges, 1867, no. 12; Bruges, 1902, no. 45; Paris, 1947, no. 55; Ghent, 1957, no. 68.

In 1902, this panel had been considered by HULIN DE LOO (1902, no. 45) as probably coming from the Ghent School of around 1480. FRIEDLÄNDER (1924-25, pp. 20-25) was the first to associate it with the central panel, which has since entered the Musées Royaux des Beaux-Arts in Brussels (cat. 1037). It was FRIEDLÄNDER who created the name of the Master of the Saint Barbara Legend.

Two drawings exist which are considered as coming from the same hand (FRIEDLÄNDER, IV, 1926, no. 57). It is believed that they were preliminary drawings for this triptych. One belongs to the Louvre in Paris and should correspond to the right part of the central panel and the lost right wing; the other, in The Pierpont Morgan Library in New York (being shown in this exhibition as no. 65), corresponds to the left part of the central panel.

Thanks to the discovery of DE GAIFFIER (1959, pp. 3-23), even the smallest details of the complicated iconography of the triptych and the two preparatory drawings take on exact meaning and it can be seen that the painter undertook to represent faithfully every detail of the narrative. The left wing of the triptych, shown here, illustrates the beginning of the story. Dioscorus has a residence in the form of a square tower constructed for his daughter, Barbara, and he has it filled with treasures worthy of a king. On the left Barbara is saying goodbye to her father before entering the tower, and a follower carries a small precious trunk. Meanwhile, on the right, messengers are bringing a letter to Dioscorus asking for his daughter's hand in marriage. In the tower Dioscorus informs his

129

Master of the Saint Barbara Legend

daughter of the message. Summoned by the emperor, Dioscorus leaves on horseback. Before entering the gates of the city, in the right background, he orders the architect to install a bath for his daughter in the tower. It is in this room that the water miraculously gushes forth for the baptism of the Saint.

26. HEROD LEARNING OF THE BIRTH OF CHRIST (?)
    THE QUEEN OF SHEBA BRINGING GIFTS TO SOLOMON
    Two wings of A TRIPTYCH OF THE NATIVITY

New York, N.Y., The Metropolitan Museum of Art. Acc. no. 32.100.56 A-B

These panels are the work of an anonymous Brabantine master, probably from Brussels. They are classified by art historians in the series of paintings which center around the Saint Barbara Legend.

Now framed together they are two wings of a triptych, the central panel of which, recently identified, is an *Adoration of the Magi*. The reverse sides, separated from their faces to permit simultaneous exhibition, show an *Annunciation* in grisaille on a red background, as was common in the Brussels School at the end of the 15th century.

Although the right wing is clearly recognizable as *The Queen of Sheba Bringing Gifts to Solomon*, there is no complete agreement as to the identification of the subject matter of the left wing, where a messenger is seen bringing a letter to a king. However, it probably represents Herod Learning of the Birth of Christ.

> *Physical data:* Oak, left wing: 36 $^5/_8$ x 17 $^5/_8$ in. (93 x 44.8 cm.); right wing: 36 $^5/_8$ x 17 $^{11}/_{16}$ in. (93 x 45 cm.) (total surface). Cradled panels.
>
> *History:* G. Aelbrechts Coll., Brussels, 1886; Charles-Léon Cardon Coll., Brussels, 1902; F. Kleinberger, art dealer, New York, 1920 (was thus not included in the Ch.-L. Cardon sales, Brussels, June 27 and July 13, 1921); Michael Friedsam Coll., New York, from 1920 to 1931; bequest of Michael Friedsam to The Metropolitan Museum of Art, New York, 1931.
>
> *Exhibitions:* Brussels, 1886, nos. 103-104; Bruges, 1902, no. 110.

The reconstruction of the triptych of which these wings were originally part was recently published by ZERI (1960, pp. 41-45), who identified the lost central panel in an *Adoration of the Magi* in the Galleria Colonna in Rome.

With the exception of MAETERLINCK (1913, captions of pl. 44-47), who places these panels in the early Ghent School of the second half of the 15th century, all authors, beginning with HULIN DE LOO (1902, p. 26, no. 110), have published it as the work of a Brabantine painter of the end of the century. FRIEDLÄNDER (1903, p. 75) first considered it closer to Dieric Bouts than to Roger van der Weyden. Later (1924-25, p. 23), however, by including

130

this work among those which center around the Saint Barbara Legend (IV, 1926, pp. 109-112 and 141, no. 68), he placed the artist in the Brussels School, just as DUMONT-WILDEN (1909, p. 16) had already done. CONWAY (1921, pp. 259-260) also views this as the work of a Brabantine painter, who combined the traditions of both van der Weyden and Bouts and was probably even a pupil of the latter. He calls this artist the "Master of the Solomons" on account of another panel by him in the Rijksmuseum in Amsterdam (cat. 342), sometimes identified as *The Idolatry of Solomon*. Subsequently, the works have always been attributed to the Master of the Saint Barbara Legend (BURROUGHS and WEHLE, 1932, p. 22; HOOGEWERFF, I, 1936, p. 497; WEHLE and SALINGER, 1947, p. 78).

131

Master of the Saint Barbara Legend

The relationship in composition existing between *The Queen of Sheba Bringing Gifts to Solomon* and *The Ordeal by Fire* of *The Justice of Emperor Otto* by Dieric Bouts (Brussels, Musées Royaux des Beaux-Arts, cat. 65-66), completed in 1473, furnishes a date *post quem* which is in accord with the style of the work as well as the dress of the figures.

The subject matter of the right wing, *The Queen of Sheba Bringing Gifts to Solomon* (I Kings 10. 1-13), is a foreshadowing in the Old Testament of the offerings brought to Christ by the Magi in the New and it usually accompanies an *Adoration of the Magi* (FRIEDLÄNDER, 1924-25, p. 23; WEHLE and SALINGER, 1947, pp. 79-80). Usually, however, the second wing of such triptychs represents the mighty men bringing water from Bethlehem to David; but this is not the case here. Authorities do not agree in their interpretation of the second wing. BURROUGHS and WEHLE (1913, p. 22) view it as David learning of the death of his rival, Uriah, the husband of Bathsheba (II Samuel 11. 18-25). WEHLE and SALINGER (1947, p. 80), recently followed by ZERI (1960, pp. 41-45), believe it represents David giving Uriah the letter which sent him to battle (II Samuel 11. 14-18); but, as HELD (1949, p. 140) points out, it is the messenger who is presenting the letter, and not the king. FRIEDLÄNDER (1924, p. 23 and IV, 1926, pp. 111-112) suggests that it shows Hezekiah receiving letters and a gift from Merodak-Baladan, son of the King of Babylon (II Kings 20. 12-13). HOOGEWERFF (I, 1936, p. 497) believes it is King Hezekiah receiving Sennacherib's messenger (Isaiah 37. 9-14). In any case, however, the panel does show a king receiving some news which disturbs him or makes him sad. Since the central panel is an *Adoration of the Magi,* it would perhaps be more logical to view the subject here as Herod learning of Christ's birth (Matthew 2. 1-3), rather than a scene from the Old Testament having no apparent connection with the principal subject.

Judging from their somber and austere clothes, the four donors appear to be members of a lay order (WEHLE and SALINGER, 1947, p. 80). The crosses which they hold in their hands indicate they had died. These crosses may have been added later, as the same authors believe (*ibidem*); but more probably the painting was a memorial in honor of its donors (CONWAY, 1921, p. 260; BURROUGHS and WEHLE, 1932, p. 22).

MASTER OF THE VIEW OF SAINTE-GUDULE

Active, probably in Brussels, around 1470-1490

The name Master of the View of Sainte-Gudule was provisionally given to the artist of a painting now in the Louvre in Paris, which shows, in the background, a view of the front of the Church of Sainte-Gudule in Brussels (see illustration p. 38). None of his works are dated, but, according to the style and

132

hundred and fitfty paintings belonging to the Memlinc group, which also includes the products of his workshop.

Among the 15th century Flemish masters, Memlinc is probably the one whose art is the most easily appreciated by non-specialists. His work is more pleasing than it is moving or passionate.

Some twenty works by him and his workshop are in the United States. More than half of these are in New York and the others are divided among the cities of Chicago, Cincinnati, Houston, Kansas City, Philadelphia, and San Diego.

30. TRIPTYCH OF THE ADORATION OF THE MAGI
called THE ALTARPIECE OF JAN FLOREINS

Bruges, Saint John's Hospital, Memlinc Museum

141

Hans Memlinc

142

Hans Memlinc

Only two paintings, this triptych and the *Mystic Marriage of Saint Catherine*, both in Saint John's Hospital in Bruges, bear old inscriptions authenticating them as works by Memlinc. Thus, this *Adoration of the Magi*, which bears the date 1479, is a basic work in the study of this painter. It was ordered by Friar Jan Floreins to adorn the hospital chapel. It has always remained there, and its state of preservation is excellent. It is still in its complete original frame, including the old lock. The inside wings show the *Nativity* and the *Presentation in the Temple*. The outside wings depict *St. John the Baptist*, patron saint of the donor and the hospital, and *St. Veronica*. The donor is portrayed in prayer at the left in the central panel; behind him can be seen his younger brother Jacques.

It is known that Jan Floreins later became Master of the Hospital and that, in 1489, he was the sole survivor of an epidemy or plague which decimated the hospital personnel.

Physical data: Oak, central panel: 18 $^5/_{16}$ x 22 $^1/_2$ in. (46.5 x 57.2 cm.), wings: 18 $^7/_8$ x 9$^3/_4$ in. (48 x 24.7 cm.) (both sight measurements). Total height with molded cornices, which appear original: 30 $^1/_2$ in. (77.5 cm.). Original frames painted in greyish color with brown and reddish graining; gilded inner molding; probably retouched. Inscription, perhaps renovated or partially retouched, painted on the lower slopes of the inner moldings: DIT · WERCK · DEDE · MAKEN · BROEDER · JAN · FLOREINS · / ALIAS · VANDER · RIIST · BROEDER · PROFFES · VANDEN · HOSPITALE · VAN · SINT · IANS · IN BRVGGHE · ANNO · M CCCC LXXIX / OPVS · IOHANNIS · HEMLING· On the outside frame the initials I F appear three times joined by a knotted cord, and two coats of arms are also shown. The lock is old.

History: Ordered by Jan Floreins, friar of the hospital; installed in 1479 (inscriptions on the frame); present in the hospital in the 17th century: engraving of St. John's head by Jacques van Oost, with a caption indicating that it was done from a painting in St. John's Hospital (Vienna, Albertina, no. 2100; WEALE, 1872-73. p. 45, ill.), and also noted as being there in the 18th century (DESCAMPS, 1769, p. 300).

Exhibitions: Bruges, 1902, no. 60; Bruges, 1939, no. 5; Amsterdam and Rotterdam, 1946, no. 50; Paris, 1947, no. 67.

The inscription on the frame says: "He who had this work done is Jan Floreins, alias van der Rijst, professed friar of the Saint John's Hospital in Bruges, in the year 1479; work of Jan Hemling". WAAGEN (1847, no. 47, p. 186) says this is the work which can be attributed to Memlinc with the greatest degree of certainty. HULIN DE LOO (1902, no. 60) considers this inscription as original; but only a laboratory examination can be conclusive. The fact that the first letter of the artist's name is written as an H instead of an M may be the result of a poor restoration, as is the case for the *Mystic Marriage of Saint Catherine* (COREMANS, SNEYERS and THISSEN, 1959, p. 91). In literature of the 17th century and later the name is sometimes spelt with an H. Nevertheless, the purport of the inscription has never been questioned. The initials I F and the coats of arms on the outside wings confirm the donor's identity (WEALE, 1901, pp. 20-21). He was in fact thirty-six years old in 1479, since he was born in 1443: the figure 36 painted as if engraved in stone near the donor's head is evidence supporting the authenticity of the inscription.

143

Hans Memlinc

Memlinc did not create an original composition for Jan Floreins; he slightly simplified and modified a composition by Roger van der Weyden, the *Saint-Colomban Altarpiece*. The latter dates from about 1460 and Memlinc may have seen it painted if, as is believed, he perfected his training in van der Weyden's workshop (FRIEDLÄNDER, VI, 1928, pp. 19-20). OETTINGER (1938, p. 69) thinks the St. John of Memlinc in the Munich Pinakothek was painted before the St. John of the Bruges triptych. BALDASS (1942, p. 42, no. 56) suggests that, in doing the outside wings of this triptych, Memlinc was inspired by a diptych he had previously painted, which work is now divided between the Munich Pinakothek *(Saint John the Baptist,* cat. no. 652) and the National Gallery of Art, Washington *(Saint Veronica,* Kress Coll.). Memlinc also painted a larger version of the *Adoration of the Magi,* known as the *Altarpiece of Charles V,* in the Prado in Madrid (cat. 1557), which FRIEDLÄNDER (VI, 1928, no. 2, pp. 31-32) thinks was done just a little before the *Altarpiece of Jan Floreins.* WINKLER (1940, p. 68), on the other hand, believes the latter work is a subsequent version of the Bruges altarpiece, and that it suffers from its rather excessive dimensions: central panel: $37\,^3/_8$ x $57\,^1/_{16}$ in. (95 x 145 cm.), and each wing: $37\,^3/_8$ x $24\,^3/_4$ in. (95 x 63 cm.).

144

Hans Memlinc

Rubbrecht (1910, p. 37) sees the features of Charles the Bold in the king kneeling at the left, and Wescher (1941, p. 198) reports this without either confirming or opposing it. It is probable that St. John the Baptist is not a portrait of the painter as is asserted in the caption of the engraving done in the 17th century by Jacques van Oost (see *History* above). Steppe (1953, pp. 187-200) recognizes the inside of the former Church of Saint-Donatien in Bruges in the wing of the triptych showing *The Presentation in the Temple.*

31. DIPTYCH OF MARTIN VAN NIEUWENHOVE

Bruges, Saint John's Hospital, Memlinc Museum

This diptych shows the Virgin and a donor according to a formula which had been established long before by Roger van der Weyden. An inscription on the frame indicates the name of the donor, Martin van Nieuwenhove, his age, twenty-three years, and the date, 1487; but the painter's name is not mentioned. The work has always been attributed to Memlinc and this has never been doubted because its form, color, and spirit are typically his, and Memlinc was, in fact, the recognized painter of the Bruges bourgeoisie of that time. In contrast to Roger van der Weyden, who preferred neutral backgrounds which focus all the attention on the figures, Memlinc gave great attention to she setting in which he placed his subjects. In the storied windows are seen Saints George and Christopher on the panel of the Virgin, and Saint Martin, patron of the donor, on the other.

Martin van Nieuwenhove was a guardian of St. Julian's Hospital in Bruges and later became Burgomaster of the city. He died while still young in 1500. His canting arms and motto are on the stained-glass window in the panel of the Virgin. His arms seem to appear also on the clasp of his Book of Hours.

Physical data: Oak, 17 5/16 x 13 in (44 x 33 cm.) each (sight measurements). Frames are probably original. Changes in the preliminary design and construction lines are visible under the paint layer, especially in the masonry of the window and in the hands of the donor. Painted inscription, perhaps altered, on the edge of the frame of each wing: HOC · OPVS · FIERI · FECIT · MARTINVS · DE · NEWENHOVEN · ANNO · DM̄ · 148Λ / ĀNⁿ · VERO · ETATIS · SVE · 23 ·. Each of these inscriptions is followed by a drawing of a small dragon. The clasp of the book has a coat of arms between two standing lions. In the stained-glass window behind the Virgin are the canting arms of the donor and the motto: IL · YA · CAVSE.

History: Originally in Saint Julian's Hospital, Bruges (Duclos, 1910, pp. 487-488).

Exhibitions: Bruges, 1902, no. 67; Paris, 1923, no. 18; London, 1927, no. 61; Copenhagen, 1931, no. 53; Paris, 1935, no. 70; Bruges, 1939, no. 11; Amsterdam and Rotterdam, 1946, no. 51; Brussels, 1953, no 11; Bruges, 1953, no. 15.

145

Hans Memlinc

HOC · OPVS · FIERI · FECIT · MARTINVS·D · NEWENHOVEN · ANNO · DM · 148Λ

The inscription on the frame says: "This work Martin de Nieuwenhoven had done in the year 1487 / in that year he was 23 years old". It is, perhaps, not original, but could then have been copied from the original inscription. The age which it attributes to the donor is exact, and the coat of arms and motto are those of the donor and his family (WEALE, 1901, p. 25). Thus, the exactness of the date 1487 may be believed.

The work reflects the general characteristics of Memlinc's style, and has always been attributed to him. It was already inventoried under his name in 1852 (*Inventaire...*, 1852, p. 356, no. 4). SCHÖNE (1939, pp. 294-296) considers the diptych one of Memlinc's masterpieces and views it as a link between the art of Hugo van der Goes and that of Quentin Metsys. The mirror in which the Virgin's back and the donor's profile are reflected is,

146

Hans Memlinc

according to SCHWARTZ (1959, pp. 99-100), the *Speculum sine macula,* symbol of the Virgin's purity.

The presentation of the Virgin in full-face and the donor in three-quarter view is traditional, but what is exceptional is the contrast between the frontal perspective of the setting in the panel of the Virgin and the receding perspective in that of the donor. RACKHAM(1936, pp. 107-108) points out that the stained-glass of the windows in this diptych shows an excellent example of the domestic type meant to be seen from a shorter distance than the stained-glass windows of a church which were ruled by other principles and were, therefore, different. In this painting, the small stained-glass roundels on a background of clear lattice-glass are more reminiscent of miniatures.

147

Hans Memlinc

32. SAINT STEPHEN and SAINT CHRISTOPHER
Two wings of a polyptych

Cincinnati, Ohio, The Cincinnati Art Museum
Acc. nos. 1956-11 and 1955-793

These two panels might originally have been part of a polyptych of the Nativity which is now dismembered. Two other wings of the same polyptych, *Saint John the Baptist* and *Mary-Magdalene,* are preserved in the Louvre. The central panel, said to have been a *Nativity* whose composition is unknown, has been lost for more than a century.

In the backgrounds are shown episodes in the martyrdom of these two Saints. On the panel of Saint Stephen is shown the scene of his stoning by the false witnesses whom he had confounded, and whose clothing is guarded by the young Saul, the future Saint Paul. In a building in the city may be identified, perhaps, his discussion with the Sanhedrin. Saint Stephen is carrying the three stones which evoke his martyrdom. In the background of the wing of Saint Christopher are shown the two episodes of his martyrdom: he is crowned with a red-hot iron helmet and later is decapitated. In the middle distance is seen the hermit of the legend, carrying a lantern.

Physical data: Oak, *Saint Stephen:* 18 $^7/_8$ x 6 $^5/_8$ in. (48 x 17 cm.); *Saint Christopher:* 19 x 6 $^5/_8$ in. (48.2 x 17 cm.). Cradled panels.

History: The polyptych to which these panels belonged is believed to have been in the Church of Saint-Gereon in Cologne, where it is supposed to have been shown from 1540 to 1657; it would then have become the property of the archbishop-electors of Trier, from 1657 until ca. 1790, and then passed to the royal court of Dresden about 1790; it then came into the possession of Napoléon Bonaparte (Cat. Cleveland Exhib., 1936, nos. 206-207); Lucien Bonaparte, Prince of Canino, Coll., sold in London, February 6, 1815, nos. 99-102 and May 16, 1815, nos. 127-129 (this last reference appears to be erroneous); William II of Holland Coll. (Nieuwenhuys, 1837, nos. 6 and 7 and 1843, nos. 10 and 11); sold at first sale of King William II Coll., The Hague, August 12, 1850, nos. 10 and 11 (Mireur, V, 1911, p. 157) (the two wings now in the Louvre were included in the sale as nos. 8 and 9); bought by the family of Orange (Cat. Cleveland Exhib., 1936, nos. 206-207); sold again at the second sale of the King William II Coll., The Hague, September 9, 1851, nos. 3 and 4 (Conway, 1927, p. 25, no. 51); acquired by Grand Duchess Sophia, wife of Grand Duke Karl-Alexander Weimar (S.z.S., 1923, pp. 547-548); collection of the Grand Dukes of Saxe-Weimar in the Weimar Castle (Michel, 1953, p. 197), until 1923 (S.z.S., 1923, pp. 547-548); Paul Cassirer, art dealer, Berlin, around 1925; Mr. and Mrs. Edward W. Edwards Coll., Cincinnati, from 1928 (Cat. New York Exhib., 1928); gift of Mr. and Mrs. Edward W. Edwards to The Cincinnati Art Museum in 1955-56.

Exhibitions: London, 1927, nos. 51 and 54; New York, 1928, nos. 1 and 2; New York, 1929, no. 26; Toledo, 1935, nos. 28-29; Cleveland, 1936, nos. 206-207.

The central panel of this dismembered polyptych, apparently a *Nativity,* is said to have been still present at the time of the sale of the Lucien Bonaparte Collection in 1815 (erroneous reference given by Conway, 1927, no. 54 and Friedländer, VI, 1928, no. 18) but was already no longer included in the catalogue of the King William II Collection by Nieuwenhuys (1837, nos. 4-7 and 1843, nos. 8-11). Crowe and Cavalcaselle (1857, p. 264) say that each of the wings was sawn, separating front from back; that was

148

Hans Memlinc

probably the case, in view of the fact that the panels were cradled. However, it does not appear that the pair in Cincinnati were the reverse of the pair in the Louvre, showing Saint John the Baptist and the Magdalene, because none of these four wings are painted in grisaille. In any case, at the time of the William II Collection sale, the wings were sold separately, two by two, two of them being acquired by the Louvre in 1851 (cat. 2024 and 2025; WEALE, 1901, p. 62). The Cincinnati wings having been preserved in their original form, it is possible to know the original dimensions of the panels in the Louvre, which were diminished in width and modified on the upper part (MICHEL, 1953, p. 196).

The wings in the Louvre

These panels were already catalogued under Memlinc's name in the catalogue by NIEUWENHUYS (1837, nos. 6 and 7 and 1843, nos. 10 and 11). This attribution has since been adopted by the specialists (WEALE, 1901, p. 62; WINKLER, 1924, p. 132; FRIEDLÄNDER, VI, 1928, no. 18). The stiffness of the figures and the high horizon of the panels in the Louvre prompted MICHEL (1953, p. 197) to place them early in the artist's production, around 1470, thus, at about the same period as the wings of the *Crucifixion* of Vicenza, preserved in the Morgan Library in New York (cat. 97-98). WINKLER (1924, p. 132) also places them in the early period of the artist.

33. THE ANNUNCIATION
Reverse of the wings of a TRIPTYCH OF THE CRUCIFIXION

Bruges, Stedelijk Museum voor Schone Kunsten (Groeningemuseum)
Condensed cat., 1954, nos. 95-1 and 95-2

These paintings in semi-grisaille belonged to a triptych of which the parts are now widely scattered: the central panel, a *Crucifixion* with a Cistercian donor, is in the Museum of Vicenza in Italy, and the wings, a donor and a donatrix, each accompanied by a patron saint, Saint William and Saint Anne respectively, are in The Pierpont Morgan Library in New York. The Bruges panels, the *Angel*

150

Hans Memlinc

and the *Virgin* of the *Annunciation,* were formerly on the outside of those wings; paintings rendered as sculptures with simulated niches were frequently so placed. The triptych is considered a work of Memlinc's early period.

Physical data: Oak, 32 ³/₄ x 10 ⁷/₁₆ in. (83.2 x 26.5 cm.) each (total surface). Cradled panels, very thin: ¹/₁₆ in. (0.2 cm.). Grisailles, except for the flesh parts, the hair of the figures, the flower vase, and the book cover, which are in natural colors. Restorations made to the base of the Angel and lower part of the Virgin's cloak.

History: English private collection, 1939 (Cat. Bruges Exhib., 1939, no. 22); acquired by Emile Renders, Bruges, and purchased along with his entire collection by Hermann Goering during the last war; found by the American Army in its occupation zone, brought to the Munich Collecting Point and returned to Belgium; placed in the Bruges City Museum by the Belgian Government in 1953 (JANSSENS DE BISTHOVEN, 1959, p. 106). Restored in 1955 by Albert Philippot in the Institut Royal du Patrimoine Artistique, Brussels (JANSSENS DE BISTHOVEN, 1959, pp. 104-106).

Exhibitions: London, 1906; Bruges, 1939, no. 22; Brussels, 1948, no. 33.

The extreme thinness of the panels reveals that they must have been sawn, separating the two painted surfaces. WINKLER (1940, p. VI and p. 249) suggested that they had belonged to the panels in The Pierpont Morgan Library, New York. This hypothesis was corroborated: a comparison of radiographs of the four panels at the Institut Royal du Patrimoine Artistique, Brussels, showed their interdependence and, also, which were the reverse of which (JANSSENS DE BISTHOVEN, 1959, p. 105). It has also been established that the New York wings belonged to the Vicenza *Crucifixion* because there is an ancient copy on canvas in the Galleria dell'Accademia in Venice (cat. 189) which reproduces in one single composition both the *Crucifixion* of the central panel and the donors of the wings. KÄMMERER (1899, pp. 73-74) thought he could recognize in this triptych the altarpiece which the miniaturist William Vrelant had ordered from Memlinc in 1478-1480 for the Chapel of Saint John of the Brotherhood in the Eeckhoute Abbey; but the work ordered by William Vrelant included four wings. Also, the donatrix of the New York painting appears too old to have been the wife of the donor, and she is on the left wing instead of the right, the position traditionally occupied by the donor's wife. In

Faces of the wings (New York)

152

Hans Memlinc

addition, for reasons of style, the triptych must be placed in a period earlier than 1478 (BALDASS, 1942, p. 37). FRIEDLÄNDER (VI, 1928, pp. 21, 115 and 1949, p. 33) considers it an early work by Memlinc and dates it around 1470 or earlier.

Memlinc did at least one other *Annunciation* in grisaille in the same style, where the figures are shown as statues on bases. It is also part of an altarpiece of the *Crucifixion,* that in the Marienkirche in Lübeck.

34. CHRIST BLESSING

New York, N.Y., M. Knoedler and Company, Inc. Acc. no. A-6680

All specialists who have published this painting agree in considering it as an original by Memlinc.

The iconographic type of Christ Blessing was probably introduced into Flemish painting by the Master of Flémalle, but remained relatively rare in the 15th century. Starting with Dieric Bouts, painters preferred religious pictures of a suffering Christ crowned with thorns and showing His wounds. However, there are several examples by Memlinc of a serene Christ, a type more consistent with the painter's own temperament. The type of Christ shown here corresponds to that described in the so-called Lentulus Letter, an apocryphal document of the Middle Ages which inspired innumerable works of art.

Physical data: Oak, 15 x 11 $^1/_8$ in. (38.1 x 28.2 cm.).
History: Coll. of Don Manoel, King of Portugal, Palacio das Necessidades, Lisbon; Lord Duveen of Millbank Coll., New York; Dr. and Mrs. Hamilton Rice Coll., New York.
Exhibitions: London, 1927, no. 62; New York, 1929, no. 23; New York, 1939, no. 252; New York, 1942, no. 13.

This *Christ Blessing* is unhesitatingly attributed by the specialists to Memlinc (KRONIG, 1910, p. 28; CONWAY, 1927, no. 62; FRIEDLÄNDER, 1927, pp. 211-212; IDEM, VI, 1928, no. 39). According to FRIEDLÄNDER, the painting bore the date 1478 on a part of the missing original frame. He considers that date plausible and important in Memlinc's chronology.

There is another version by Memlinc of the same subject, but more like the Christ of Dieric Bouts, in the William A. Coolidge Collection in Topsfield, Mass. (formerly at M. Knoedler and Co., New York). In addition, KRONIG (1910, p. 28) relates this panel to another *Christ Blessing* by Memlinc, in tondo form, which was in the former Kaufmann Collection (New York, The Metro-

153

politan Museum of Art, Acc. no. 32.100.54); but he considers the latter roughly painted in comparison with that of Knoedler. This type of Christ may derive, just as HELD (1949, p. 140) said of the painting in The Metropolitan Museum, from that of Roger van der Weyden in the central panel of the *Braque Triptych* in the Louvre (cat. 2195).

This Christ may have been the companion piece to a *Virgin at Prayer*, as in the painting by the Master of Flémalle in the John G. Johnson Collection in Philadelphia (cat. 332).

154

Hans Memlinc

San Diego, Calif., The Fine Arts Gallery of San Diego. Acc. no. 47:1

This portrait is little known even among specialists in the field of early Flemish painting. It is generally attributed to Memlinc by those who have published it.

The young man is shown here with his hands clasped; thus, he is a donor at prayer in front of a holy image, probably a *Virgin and Child*, with which the portrait must have formed a diptych. His long Florentine hair style and his cap give the impression that the donor was Italian (cf. also the portrait being shown in this exhibition as no. 36).

Physical data: Oak, 15 ³/₈ x 11 ³/₄ in. (39 x 30 cm.) (sight measurement). Partially old frame bearing the remains of an inscription on the lower edge.

History: Private collection, France, then Wildenstein and Co., New York, 1927 (Frick Art Ref. Library, New York); Duke of Anhalt Coll., Dessau; Vieweg Coll., Brunswick, before 1930 (FRIEDLÄNDER, XIV, 1937, p. 103); not included in the catalogue of the Vieweg sale on March 18, 1930; Duveen, art dealer, New York; William Goldman Coll., New York, from 1930 (Cat. Antwerp Exhib., 1930, no. 195) still there in 1939 (Cat. Bruges Exhib., 1939, no. 30); gift of the Misses Anne R. and Amy Putnam to The Fine Arts Gallery of San Diego, 1947.

Exhibitions: Antwerp, 1930, no. 195; Bruges, 1939, no. 39; New York, 1939, no. 251.

The few authors who have published this painting seem to agree that it is the work of Memlinc (LAMBOTTE, 1930, p. 17; FRANKFURTER, 1932, p. 21; FRIEDLÄNDER, XIV, 1937, p. 102; MILLIER, 1948, p. 9; GORIS, 1949, p. 7). FRIEDLÄNDER thinks it is a product of his early period (XIV, 1937, p. 102). This idea finds support in the fact that the subject is set against a red background, which is not usual for Memlinc, but is characteristic of the Brussels School. This red background may be, in fact, a carry-over from the time Memlinc spent in Roger van der Weyden's workshop in Brussels.

The hair style and cap seem to indicate the model was Italian; but, as in another of Memlinc's portraits being shown in this exhibition (no. 36), he may have been an Italian living in Flanders, since his clothing is of a northern style.

155

Hans Memlinc

Montreal, Quebec, Canada, The Montreal Museum of Fine Arts
Acc. no. 1129

This portrait is accepted unhesitatingly by specialists as a work by Hans Memlinc. The setting is characteristic of this artist, who usually silhouetted his models against a landscape background in the fashion of Italian painters of the same period. The young model of this portrait may, in fact, be an Italian, judging from his hair style and cap. He is holding a rolled piece of parchment between his fingers which may allude to his profession or could indicate that the portrait was made on the occasion of a particular event in his life.

Physical data: Oak, 13¹/₂ x 9 in. (33.4 x 22.8 cm.) (total surface). Cradled panel. Paint layer surface rubbed.

History: John Edward Taylor Coll., London; John Edward Taylor sale, London (Christie's), July, 1912, no. 39; Julius Böhler, art dealer, Munich; John N. Willys Coll., Toledo, Ohio, 1929 (Cat. New York Exhib., 1929, no. 20) and 1933 (Cat. Chicago Exhib., 1933, no. 51); Mrs. Van Wie Willys Coll., New York, from before 1939, sold in New York (Parke-Bernet), October 21, 1945 and acquired there by A. and R. Ball; acquired by The Montreal Museum of Fine Arts, 1956.

Exhibitions: Bruges, 1912, no. 70; Toledo, 1926; New York (Kleinberger Galleries), 1929, no. 20; Chicago, 1933, no. 51; New York, 1939, no. 255.

This portrait has been published several times as a Memlinc original by FRIEDLÄNDER (1920, p. 108 and VI, 1928, no. 80) and other authors (CONWAY, 1921, p. 239; FLINT, 1925, pp. 363, 366, and 367; [VALENTINER], 1939, p. 124, no. 255). Although FRIEDLÄNDER (1920, p. 108) considers the composition, the design, and the colors characteristic of the artist's mature period, CONWAY (1921, p. 239) classifies this portrait in the painter's early period. The same author believes the subject is Italian, undoubtedly because of his long hair in the Florentine style and the type of cap he is wearing. Since his clothing is of a northern style, he could have been one of the numerous Italians living in Bruges at that time. The same might be said of the other *Portrait of a Young Man* shown in this exhibition under no. 35.

156

Hans Memlinc

37. PORTRAIT OF AN OLD WOMAN

Houston, Texas, The Museum of Fine Arts of Houston. Acc. no. 44-530

This portrait is generally recognized as a Memlinc original. It is apparently the portrait of a widow, to judge from the type of head-dress.

Physical data: Oak, 10 $^1/_8$ x 7 in. (25.6 x 17.8 cm.) (total surface). The fur collar was brought out at the time of a cleaning, after 1934. The highlights on the wimple are modern overpaintings (the condition of the painting before its restoration may be seen in a photograph preserved in the R.K.D., The Hague, no. L. 9115).

History: Paris, art dealer, 1910 (BODE and FRIEDLÄNDER, 1912, no. 14); Carl von Hollitscher Coll., Berlin, from 1910 and still in 1914 (Cat. Berlin Exhib., 1914, no. 99); Stefan von Auspitz Coll., Vienna, until 1931; acquired as part of the von Auspitz Coll., by the Bachstitz Galleries, The Hague, in 1931 (Frick Art Reference Library, New York);

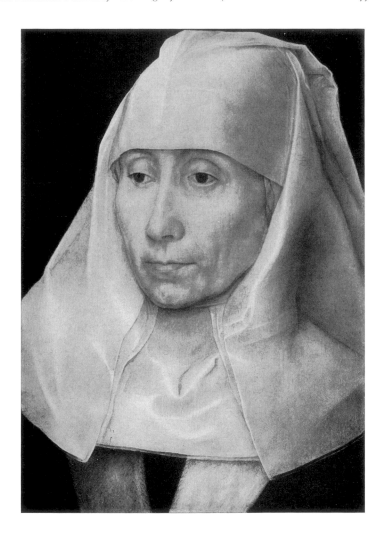

157

Hans Memlinc

Bachstitz Galleries, The Hague, 1931-1934; acquired by Edith A. and Percy S. Straus in 1934; bequest of Edith A. and Percy S. Straus to The Museum of Fine Arts of Houston, 1944. Restored after 1934.

Exhibitions: Berlin, 1914, no. 99; London (Agnew), 1932.

The art historians who have published this portrait agree in viewing it as a work by Memlinc (BODE and FRIEDLÄNDER, 1912, no. 14; WALDMANN, 1920, p. 532; FRIEDLÄNDER, VI, 1928, no. 93; BALDASS, von Auspitz Coll. cat., no date; GLÜCK and HULIN DE LOO, cited by WALDMANN).

The wimple worn by this old woman is that worn by widows of that period (cf. BEAULIEU and BAYLÉ, 1956, pp. 123-124). This head-dress is generally accompanied by a sober dress without a collar, and rarely a fur-bordered neckline as here. A widow's costume, however, did not necessarily exclude the wearing of certain furs (BEAULIEU and BAYLÉ, 1956, p. 123). The wimple and fur collar both appear to be original, because the radiograph shows no trace of extensive overpainting in these areas. Moreover, this same combination of a widow's head-dress and a fur collar is seen in the *Saint Anne Presenting the Female Donor* in a wing by Memlinc in The Pierpont Morgan Library in New York (cf. illustration p. 152 of this catalogue).

38. PORTRAIT OF A MONK

Antwerp, Musée Royal des Beaux-Arts. Cat. 1959, no. 253

This portrait of a monk in a white frock poses various problems. It is probably a fragment of a larger panel which showed him kneeling, perhaps accompanied by his patron saint. The donor and the order to which he belonged have not been identified, as the same white habit was worn by several orders.

There is also some hesitation as to its attribution. It was formerly ascribed to van Eyck and Memlinc, and the latter attribution is still retained by the Antwerp Museum. Nevertheless, almost all authorities classify the painting in the circle of Dieric Bouts. In any case its execution should probably be placed in the last quarter of the 15th century.

Physical data: Oak, 15 $^3/_8$ x 9 $^1/_{16}$ in. (39 x 23 cm.) (total surface, including a modern enlargement of the panel on the left; SCHÖNE, 1938, p. 185, no. 74). Overpainting of the green background.

History: Bequest of the Chevalier Florent van Ertborn to the City of Antwerp in 1841.

Exhibitions: Paris, 1952-53, no. 54; Bruges, 1953, no. 16; London, 1953-54, no. 13; Brussels-Delft, 1957-58, no. 67.

Attributed to Jan van Eyck as early as 1842 ([DELEN], 1958, no. 253), then generally assigned to Memlinc (WAAGEN, 1863, p. 150), the work was later

158

Hans Memlinc

attributed to the Master of the Pearl of Brabant by HEILAND (1902, p. 154), followed by VOLL (1923, p. 268) and then by SCHÖNE (1938, p. 185, no. 74), who places it in the descriptive catalogue of this master, whom he believes to be Dieric Bouts the Younger. BAUDOUIN (1957-58, no. 67) places it in the entourage of Dieric Bouts, and BOON (1958, p. 11) suggests attributing it to the pupil of Bouts who may have collaborated with him in the triptych of the *Martyrdom of Saint Hippolytus* in the Cathedral of Saint-Sauveur in Bruges, being shown in this exhibition as no. 19. It can be seen that these attributions scarcely deviate from those of FRIEDLÄNDER (III, 1925, no. 27) and BALDASS (1932, p. 4), who consider it a work by Dieric Bouts.

MASTER OF THE SAINT URSULA LEGEND

Active in Bruges, last quarter of the 15th century

This conventional name was given by Friedländer to the painter of the wings of an altarpiece which illustrate the legend of Saint Ursula and which belong to the Convent of the Black Sisters in Bruges (this catalogue, no. 39). Friedländer grouped twenty-four paintings which he believes can be attributed to this artist or his workshop. Winkler considers him the most important secondary Bruges master of the end of the 15th century. Two of the works attributed to this master bear the dates 1486 and 1488. A perceptible influence from Roger van der Weyden and from Memlinc can be detected in his paintings, especially in the composition.

There are now some fifteen works in the United States which may be included in this same group. They are in the Museums in Cambridge, Chicago, Denver, Detroit, Los Angeles, Minneapolis, New York, Philadelphia, Rochester, and Worcester, as well as in private collections in New York.

159

160

Master of the Saint Ursula Legend

161

Bruges, Convent of the Black Sisters. Since 1959, on loan to the
Stedelijk Museum voor Schone Kunsten (Groeningemuseum)

These two panels provide the origin for a conventional name given to an anonymous artist. They each represent four episodes in the legend of Saint Ursula, the princess of Brittany who attained martyrdom on her return from a pilgrimage made to Rome with eleven thousand companions. The reverses of the wings show, in grisaille, within arched niches, the figures of the four Evangelists and the four Doctors of the Roman Church.

These two paintings are probably the wings of an altarpiece, painted or carved, devoted to Saint Ursula. This Saint was honored most particularly in Cologne, the place of her martyrdom, but also in Bruges, where certain of her relics are possessed by the Chapel of Saint John's Hospital. In order to hold them, a new shrine was painted by Memlinc and dedicated in 1489. The wings from the Convent of the Black Sisters must be earlier than Memlinc's work, whose execution the specialists place between 1460 and 1489, and most probably between 1475 and 1485.

Physical data: Oak, each wing: 18 $^{11}/_{16}$-18$^1/_8$ x 11 $^{13}/_{16}$-11 $^{15}/_{16}$ in. (47.5-47.9 x 30-30.4 cm.) (sight measurements). Frames probably old but not original.

History: The first to note the presence of the panels in the Chapel of the Convent of the Black Sisters was WAAGEN (1847, p. 185); loaned to the Bruges City Museum in 1959 at the request of the "Amis des Musées Communaux".

Exhibitions: Bruges, 1867, no. 11; Bruges, 1902, no. 47; Bruges, 1930 (not included in catalogue); Bruges, 1939 (not included in catalogue); Bruges, 1953, no. 22; London, 1953-54, nos. 38 and 40.

These wings were first considered as an early work by Joos van Gent by WAAGEN (1847, no. 47, p. 185), who subsequently viewed them as an early work by Dieric Bouts wrongly attributed to Memlinc (WAAGEN, 1861, French translation: 1863, p. 122). WEALE (1862, p. 156) considers them the work of a Bruges master of about 1475. HULIN DE LOO (1902, no. 47) dates them between 1460 and 1475. He compares the reverse sides, in grisaille, to the two principal wings of a series of grisaille portraits of the Counts of Flanders, dating from about 1480, which are owned by the Seminary in Bruges. In his opinion, two other panels showing the Church and the Synagogue which also belong to the Convent of the Black Sisters were part of the same altarpiece. FRIEDLÄNDER (1903, p. 85) is in accord with these conclusions and, starting from these wings, gives the artist the conventional name of the Master of the Saint Ursula Legend. Later FRIED-LÄNDER (VI, 1928, p. 60 and no. 113) says that this work must be just a little earlier than Memlinc's shrine of St. Ursula (1489). WINKLER (1924, p. 373) places the execution of the wings around 1486 and detects a late influence by van der Weyden. The belfry of Bruges appears in the third scene without its octagonal third stage, which dates from between 1483 and 1487 (VERHAEGEN,

162

Master of the Saint Ursula Legend

1959, pp. 80-81), thus supplying an approximate date *ante quem*. CONWAY (1921, p. 247), who believes that the Church and the Synagogue are from the same hand as the eight panels of St. Ursula, considers the reverse sides as a workshop product. He dates the altarpiece between 1470 and 1495 and proposes that the painter was Pieter Casenbroot, who became a master in 1459. FIERENS-GEVAERT (1922, p. 22) proposes that the painter was Simon Marmion. VAN PUYVELDE (1941, p. 33) considers that he is a Bruges miniaturist.

The iconography of these wings follows the Golden Legend less faithfully than Memlinc did subsequently, and seems to have been drawn from another source (FIERENS-GEVAERT, 1922, p. 24). The eight scenes show: the King of England sending a messenger to the King of Brittany to request the hand in marriage for his son of the latter's daughter, Ursula; the embarkation of eleven thousand virgins for Brittany watched by the King and Queen of England; Ursula leaving her parents in order to lead her eleven thousand companions to Rome; the debarkation of Ursula at Cologne where an angel predicts her coming martyrdom; Ursula and her companions leaving Basel to go to Rome on foot; Ursula leaving Rome accompanied by the Pope; the martyrdom of the pilgrims

163

164

Master of the Saint Ursula Legend

by the Huns as they disembark at Cologne; the veneration in a church of the relics of the eleven thousand virgins. This final panel shows the faithful kneeling on the floor: chairs and pews were not yet in use in that period. A woman clothed in black and wearing a white head-dress may be seen in the left background of this scene; she is, perhaps, the donatrix.

40.   TRIPTYCH OF THE NATIVITY

Detroit, Mich., The Detroit Institute of Arts. Acc. no. 59.122, cat. no. 1330

This work is characteristic of the Bruges Master of the Saint Ursula Legend, both in its style and its composition. It has always been attributed to him.

The Nativity cycle, to which this triptych is devoted, originally began on the reverse of the wings with an *Annunciation*, now lost. It continues on the interior of the triptych with the *Visitation* on the left wing and the *Nativity* on the central panel. On the right panel, the donor is presented by his patron, the Archangel St. Raphael, identifiable by his traveller's staff and the background where he is seen with the young Tobias. In the background of the central panel one recognizes the towers of the belfry and of Notre-Dame of Bruges, the Annunciation to the Shepherds, and the Meeting of the three Magi at the cross-roads. In the middle distance, St. Joseph leads the midwife from the Apocryphal Gospels. The carved column which is seen in the foreground represents the one against which the Virgin is said to have leaned at the time of the Nativity.

Reverse of right wing (lost)

Physical data: Oak, central panel: 25 $^5/_8$ x 20 $^3/_4$ in. (65 x 52.8 cm.); left wing: 25 $^7/_8$ x 9 $^5/_8$ in. (65.7 x 24.5 cm.); right wing: 25 $^5/_8$ x 9 $^1/_2$ in. (65.1 x 24.2 cm.) (total surface).

History: Acquired by William B. Clarke before 1865; William B. Clarke Coll. and Mrs. Pauline C. Clarke Coll., Freiburg im-Breisgau; bequest of Mrs. Pauline C. Clarke to the Augustiner Museum, Freiburg im-Br., 1896; Augustiner Museum, Freiburg im-Br., from 1896 to 1957; sold in 1957 to the New York art dealer Dr. Hanns Schaeffer (statement of Dr. H. Gombert, Director of the Freiburg Museum); Dr. Rudolf J. Heinemann and M. Knoedler and Co., art dealers, New York; gift of the Metropolitan Opera Benefit Committee to The Detroit Institute of Arts, 1959.

Exhibitions: None known.

FRIEDLÄNDER (1906, p. 577, *sub* no. 38 and VI, 1928, no. 114) was the first to recognize this triptych as a work of the Master of the Saint Ursula Legend. As in several other of his religious paintings, the artist has been inspired

165

by compositions of Roger van der Weyden. WINKLER (1913, p. 72, note 4) relates the *Visitation* group to the wing by Roger now at the Galleria Sabauda in Turin (cat. 190). It can be compared as well to the older panel of the same subject, also by Roger, which was formerly preserved in Lützschena and is today in the Museum der bildenden Künste in Leipzig. FRIEDLÄNDER (VI, 1928, p. 64) recognizes in the Virgin adoring the Child the same group, yet reversed, as in the *Bladelin Triptych* by the same painter at the Museum Dahlem in Berlin (cat. 535). Memlinc also borrowed this motif several times in compositions which were all painted earlier than the Detroit triptych.

Thanks to a very precise representation of the city of Bruges in the background of the central panel, the Detroit altarpiece may be dated with some certainty, as, in fact, may be several works of the Master of the Saint Lucy Legend (FRIEDLÄNDER, VI, 1928, p. 70; VERHAEGEN, 1959, pp. 79-81). The octagonal upper section of the belfry is shown as it was after it burned in 1493 and before its reconstruction between 1499 and 1501 (RICHARDSON, 1959-60, p. 5), just as it is in the central panel of the *Triptych of the Lamentation over Christ* by the Master of the Saint Lucy Legend in The Minneapolis Institute of Arts, included in this exhibition as no. 42.

While the triptych was in the Clarke Collection and in the Augustiner Museum in Freiburg, it included a *Virgin* from an *Annunciation* (photograph G. Röbke, Freiburg im-Br., no. 427) on the reverse of the right wing (see ill. p. 165). However, the Archangel Gabriel which must have been on the reverse of the left wing had already disappeared by that time (statement of Dr. Gombert).

MASTER OF THE SAINT LUCY LEGEND

Active in Bruges, end of the 15th century

The Master of the Saint Lucy Legend derives his name from a painting of this subject in the Church of Saint-Jacques in Bruges, which bears the date 1480. Around this picture have been grouped numerous other paintings, certain of which, datable around 1520-1530, are certainly not from his hand. A view of the city of Bruges is often seen in the background of his paintings. A marked evolution toward Hispano-Flemish characteristics can be noticed in his works, and the possibility that the Master of the Saint Lucy Legend spent some time in Spain is not to be excluded.

More than a dozen of the works of this painter or from his workshop are found in the United States, certain of which are among his best. They are in Detroit, Minneapolis, New York, Philadelphia, San Francisco, Washington, and Williamstown, Mass.

166

167

Master of the Saint Lucy Legend

41. THE VIRGIN OF THE ROSE GARDEN

Detroit, Mich., The Detroit Institute of Arts. Acc. no. 26.387, cat. no. 140

This painting is a typical example of the charming works of the Bruges School as derived from Memlinc at the end of the 15th century.

The subject is a *Sacra Conversazione*, more exactly, a *Virgo inter Virgines*, shown here in an enclosed garden bordered by rose bushes, with Saints Ursula, Catherine, Barbara, and Cecilia. In the background may be seen the city of Bruges within its walls. Although the mountainous setting is pure fantasy, the representation of the city itself is one of the most precise we have from the end of the 15th century: the Church of Notre-Dame can be recognized at the left, with its characteristic tower, as well as the belfry and other buildings, among which is the turret of the Gruuthuse, behind the choir of Notre-Dame, but drawn here out of proportion with the neighboring buildings.

Physical data: Oak, 31 1/8 x 23 5/8 in. (79.1 x 60 cm.).

History: Weber Coll., Brussels (FRIEDLÄNDER, VI, 1928, p. 142, no. 154), sold in Brussels, May 15-17 and June 2-4, 1919, no. 22 (communication from Mr. J. Demeter, Brussels); de Wit van der Hoop, art dealer, Brussels, 1923, no no.); sold in Amsterdam (Fr. Muller) on July 13, 1926, no. 709 as part of "Collection de Bruxelles" (but not the Weber Coll. as was published by FRIEDLÄNDER, VI, 1928, p. 142, no. 154); D.A. Hoogendijk, art dealer, Amsterdam, 1926; gift of The Detroit Museum of Art Founders Society to The Detroit Institute of Arts, 1926. Cleaned in 1943.

Exhibitions: Brussels, 1923, cat. ms. (noted in catalogue of the 1926 sale in Amsterdam); London, 1927, no. 75; New York, 1942, no no.

FRIEDLÄNDER (1926-27, p. 29) is responsible for the attribution of this painting to the Master of the Saint Lucy Legend. He sees in the Virgin and Child a motif created by Roger van der Weyden around 1450 in a drawing preserved at the Boymans-van Beuningen Museum in Rotterdam (Koenigs Coll.). The same motif, which became widely used in the Bruges School, was borrowed a second time by the Master of the Saint Lucy Legend for a large similar composition called *The Virgin with Mary-Magdalene and the Virgins,* in the Musées Royaux des Beaux-Arts in Brussels (cat. 545).

The detailed manner in which the artist drew the monuments of Bruges in many of his paintings has enabled the formation of a basic chronology of his works (FRIEDLÄNDER, VI, 1928, p. 70), which has recently been enlarged and made more precise (VERHAEGEN, 1959, pp. 79-81). The Detroit painting shows the belfry as it was before the addition of an octagonal stage in 1483, and must thus have been done prior to that date. It would then have been almost contemporaneous with the fundamental work of the artist, *The Legend of Saint Lucy* (Bruges, Church of Saint-Jacques), dated 1480, and would have been a few years earlier than the Brussels *Sacra Conversazione,* given to Notre-Dame of Bruges in 1489 (Cat. Bruges Exhib., 1902, no. 114). Therefore, it is also at least ten years earlier than the *Lamentation Triptych* painted by the same master between 1493 and 1499-1501 and now in The Minneapolis Institute of Arts, being shown in this exhibition as no. 42.

168

Master of the Saint Lucy Legend

42.   TRIPTYCH OF THE LAMENTATION OVER CHRIST

Minneapolis, Minn., The Minneapolis Institute of Arts. Acc. no. 35.7.87

This triptych is one of the most characteristic and important works of the Master of the Saint Lucy Legend. On the wings are St. John the Baptist and St. Catherine of Alexandria. The center panel shows the body of Christ lying across the knees of the Virgin surrounded by St. John, Mary-Magdalene, another Mary, Joseph of Arimathaea, and Nicodemus. The city of Bruges, which serves as the setting for this *Lamentation,* as in most works by this painter, is supposed to represent Jerusalem. This painting, along with the *Virgin of the Rose Garden* by the same painter in The Detroit Institute of Arts (being shown in this exhibition as no. 41), displays one of the most complete and exact representations of Bruges at the end of the 15th century.

Physical data: Oak, central panel: 35 x 26 $^1/_4$ in. (89 x 66.5 cm.); each wing: 35 x 11 in. (88 x 28 cm.).

History: Spanish private collection; Spanish Art Gallery, London, 1913 (FRIEDLÄNDER, VI, 1928, no. 141); Satinover Galleries, New York, 1920 (R.K.D., The Hague); John R. Van Derlip Coll., Minneapolis; bequest of John R. Van Derlip to The Minneapolis Institute of Arts, 1935.

Exhibitions: Minneapolis, 1955.

The obvious kinship of style between this triptych and the artist's key work, *The Saint Lucy Legend* in the Church of Saint-Jacques in Bruges, leaves no doubt as to the creator's hand. While the latter work bears the date 1480, the Minneapolis *Lamentation* can be dated with reasonable certainty thanks to the careful way in which the artist represented the city of Bruges (FRIEDLÄNDER, VI, 1928, pp. 69-70; VERHAEGEN, 1959, pp. 79-81). The belfry appears here as it was between 1493 and 1499-1501, after the octagonal stage was burned, but before it was restored. This triptych is thus contemporary with both the *Virgin and Child with Two Angels* by the same Master, in the Arthur Sachs Collection in New York (FRIEDLÄNDER, VI, 1928, pl. LXIII), and the *Nativity Triptych* by another anonymous Bruges painter of the end of the 15th century, the Master of the Saint Ursula Legend, in The Detroit Institute of Arts (being shown in this exhibition as no. 40), where the belfry has not yet its octagonal stage.

The rather unpolished technique of this triptych, the facial types (especially Christ, the Virgin, and the Mary in three-quarter profile at the extreme left), and the Spanish source of the work could support the hypothesis advanced by VERHAEGEN (1959, pp. 80-82) that the Master of the St. Lucy Legend might have been either a Spaniard who had worked in Bruges or, more probably, a Bruges painter who finished his career in Spain.

Two wings of another triptych by the same Master, which belong to the National Trust in Upton House, Banbury, also show St. John the Baptist and St. Catherine, but the subject of the lost central panel is unknown. There are other very similar representations of St. Catherine by the same painter.

169

Master of the Saint Lucy Legend

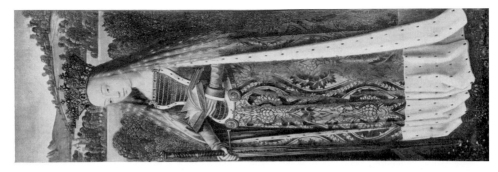

170

Master of the Saint Lucy Legend

One is in the Museo Nazionale di San Matteo in Pisa, where the same model was apparently used *(Bull. Minn.,* 1936, p. 50), and another, where the pose is almost identical, but reversed, on an isolated wing in the John G. Johnson Collection in Philadelphia (cat. 326).

MASTER OF 1499

Active in Ghent(?) and Bruges

The name Master of 1499, or Bruges Master of 1499, was given to the painter of the small diptych of Chrétien de Hondt, abbot of the former Abbey of the Dunes, near Furnes (this cat. no. 43); it bears the date 1499. One of the wings is a copy of a work by Jan van Eyck done some three-quarters of a century earlier. The precise and meticulous technique of this anonymous painter enables the recognition of his hand in other works. A strong influence from Hugo van der Goes' art is found in this master's paintings, and it has been concluded that he spent at least part of his career in Ghent. The excellence of his imitative work shows what degree of perfection certain painters, lacking distinctive personality and individual inspiration, were able to achieve, thanks to the long and severe apprenticeship imposed by the guilds.

Apparently, no works by this master are found in the United States.

43.   DIPTYCH OF CHRETIEN DE HONDT

Antwerp, Musée Royal des Beaux-Arts
Cat. 1959, nos. 255, 256, 530, and 531

This small diptych shows the Virgin in a church and a Cistercian abbot at prayer. On the reverse of the panel of the Virgin is a *Salvator Mundi* in a niche, on a base which bears the date 1499. On the reverse of the abbot's portrait is another portrait of an abbot, clearly added over the original surface which was an imitation of marble, such as is sometimes found on the reverse of 15th century paintings.

The painter of this diptych is unknown. Based on this work, he has been given the conventional name of Bruges Master of 1499.

The *Virgin in a Church* is a late copy, with minor variations, of a work by Jan van Eyck, in the Berlin Museum. The coats of arms indicate that the principal portrait is that of Chrétien de Hondt and the other that of Robert Leclercq, 30th and 32nd abbots, respectively, of the Abbey of the Dunes, near

171

Master of 1499

Furnes, the former from 1495 to 1509 and the latter from 1519 to 1557. The panel of Chrétien de Hondt has many charming details: the opened Book of Hours is decorated with flowered borders characteristic of the workshops of miniatures, known as "Ganto-Brugeois", at the end of the 15th century. The abbatial crook is a jeweled masterpiece; a diptych is hung over the bed; the dresser, loaded with pewter tankards, and the high-backed chair decorated in a style simulating parchment, are elaborate and precise records of the furniture of the time; the three dogs of the canting arms of the abbot are found on the back of the chair and on the mantelpiece; the small dog sleeping near the abbot is, perhaps, also an allusion to his name (*hond* is Flemish for dog).

Physical data: Oak, arched panels, 12 1/4 x 5 3/4 in. (31.1 x 14.6 cm.) each (sight measurements); 14 5/8 x 8 5/8 in. (37.1 x 22 cm.) (including frames). Panels and frames made of one element with vertical grain. Overpaintings on the wing in grisaille of the *Salvator Mundi:* cloth background and face are colored and coat of arms on left are later additions. Red marbling painted on back of original diptych. Portrait of Robert Leclercq is obviously a later overpainting. Frames: those of the inside panels probably regilded in modern times; those of the outside probably have old paint, which may be original, and a molding and rosettes in "trompe-l'œil".

172

Master of 1499

Inscriptions: on the frame of the panel of the *Virgin:* SALVE · REGINA · MISERICORDIE, probably not original. On the panel of *Chrétien de Hondt,* on the consoles of the ceiling appear: C and H interlaced, the coat of arms of the abbot twice, and that of the abbey once. On the panel of *Christ:* the date 1499 on the base; the coats of arms of the two abbots; liturgical inscriptions: PRIMUS · ET · NOVISSIMUS · on the archway; P̄ (principium) and F̄ (finis), Ā (alpha) and ō̄ (omega) on the background; ASIA, EVROPA, AFRICA on the globe; *:Salvator mundi: Salva nos:* on the frame. Panel of *Robert Leclercq:* monogram CH on the frame, not original.

History: Acquired in 1827 from the last abbot of the Cistercian abbey of the Dunes, Nicolas de Roovere, by the Chevalier Florent van Ertborn; bequest of van Ertborn to the City of Antwerp, 1841 ([DELEN], 1958, no. 530).

Exhibitions: Bruges, 1902, no. 118; Dijon, 1951, no. 32; Amsterdam, 1951, no. 27; Brussels, 1951, no. 33; Bruges, 1953, no. 26; London, 1953-54, no. 20; Ghent, 1957, nos. 71-72.

Attributed to Memlinc in the *Messager des Sciences* (1829-30, pp. 61-62). BURGER (1861, p. 29) notes that the date 1499 nullifies this attribution, and suspects two hands. He points out that the *Virgin in a Church* reproduces a work by van Eyck. The same author (1869, p. 12) refutes the attribution to Cornelis Herrebout, who had been suggested by the monogram CH. HULIN DE

Master of 1499

Loo (1902, no. 118) believes that this diptych did not originally include the portrait of Robert Leclercq and that the date 1499 is that of the diptych in its original form, as it was painted for Chrétien de Hondt, whose monogram is CH. He thinks the portrait of Robert Leclercq was done by a later artist, the same one who was responsible for the overpaintings on the *Salvator Mundi*. WINKLER (1922, pp. 616-617) thinks the original painting was of Ghent origin. This is also the opinion of FRIEDLÄNDER (IV, 1926, no. 37), who believes it was done in the group influenced by Hugo van der Goes before he went to live in Bruges.

The panel of the *Virgin in a Church* is a copy of a painting by Jan van Eyck, in the Berlin Dahlem Museum (cat. 525c). It is of a slightly larger format than the Berlin work; therefore, the painter has included a larger part of the left-hand column and shows the Calvary above the rood screen in a more complete fashion. He added heavy jewels to the bodice of the Virgin, placed a flower-filled vase in the right foreground, and embellished the floor tiling; but the representation of the church still conforms to the original by van Eyck. LEJEUNE (1956, p. 38) points out that another copy of the van Eyck work, a drawing in the former Sir J.C. Robinson Collection, published by KÄMMERER (1898, p. 77), is akin to that of the Master of 1499. Still another copy, a little later, belongs to the collection of the Galleria Doria Pamphilj in Rome; it is generally attributed to Jan Gossaert and dates from the first years of the 16th century. WEALE (1908, pp. 137-38) had already pointed out several copies. LAVALLEYE (1, 1953, no. 30) notes a later copy, probably done in 1623, which also came from an abbey in Furnes (Madrid, Rodriguez Bauza Collection).

LEMAIRE (1950, *passim*) suggested recognizing the Church of Saint-Jean in Ghent, now the Cathedral of Saint-Bavon, as the church painted by van Eyck, and thought this to be an indication favoring its attribution to Hubert van Eyck. DE SMIDT (1957-58, pp. 75-83) proved this identification was not correct. LEJEUNE (1956, *passim*) identifies it as the former Cathedral of Saint-Lambert in Liège. This would justify certain iconographic peculiarities in this *Virgin in a Church* which the authorities have not been able to explain, such as the presence of two angels singing in the choir: according to the legend, angels sang near the tomb of Saint Lambert. LEJEUNE (1956, *passim*) also points out that the Saint John in the Calvary, who is clearly visible only on the copy by the Master of 1499, might enable a *Saint John* and its companion piece the *Virgin*, now in the porch of the Church of Saint-Jean-l'Evangéliste in Liège, to be identified as having originally belonged to the Calvary in the Cathedral of Saint-Lambert. This last identification is rather hypothetical.

The *Salvator Mundi* does not have the cruciferous halo. He is resting his foot on a globe divided by a T which bears the names of the three known continents: this is a simplified transposition of old monastic maps which showed the earth as a disc, surrounded by the ocean. A lighted candle is stuck onto the threshold of the niche. A candle of the same type is seen on the abbot's fireplace.

DELEN (1958, no. 531) dates the *Portrait of Robert Leclercq* around 1520, and attributes it to an anonymous Bruges artist.

174

GERARD DAVID

Active beginning in 1484, in Bruges and Antwerp(?)
Born in Oudewater (Holland). Died in Bruges in 1523

Gerard David probably received his initial training in Holland, perhaps with Ouwater, in Haarlem. His life may be traced through the public records: first, in Bruges, where he became a member, and then head, of the Painters Guild (1484 and 1501), and married the miniaturist Cornelia Knoop (1496); then, in Antwerp, where he was enrolled in the Painters Guild (1515); finally, once again in Bruges (1521), where he was buried in the Church of Notre-Dame (1523).

His first works seem to reflect an influence from the Haarlem School. Later, in Bruges, it was the influence of Memlinc (died in 1494) and, especially, of van der Goes (d. 1482) which was dominant. Still later, some of his works recall those of Quentin Metsys (whose works are datable from 1507) and may have been done in Antwerp, which had inherited the commercial supremacy of Bruges.

The only fully documented painting is the *Virgin with Angels and Saints* (1509) in the Museum in Rouen. Not so well documented is the *Justice of Cambyses* (cat. no. 44), which bears the date 1498. Art historians have grouped numerous other works, of varying quality, around these two paintings. The exportation of Flemish works of art reached its peak at the end of the 15th century, and the workshop of the last of the great Bruges Primitives was certainly an active participant. Several of his paintings, and especially those of two of his most important pupils, Adriaan Isenbrant and Ambrosius Benson, are still to be found in Spain today.

A certain coldness characterizes the style of Gerard David who was, however, a great colorist. Some of his compositions are reminiscent of miniatures. Several illuminations, moreover, are attributed to him.

Some twenty of the works of Gerard David or his workshop are in the United States, notably in Chicago, Cleveland, Detroit, Greenville (S.C.), New York, Philadelphia, Saint Louis, Toledo, and Washington.

44. THE ARREST OF THE DISHONEST JUDGE SISAMNES
Left half of THE JUSTICE OF CAMBYSES

Bruges, Stedelijk Museum voor Schone Kunsten (Groeningemuseum)
Cat. 1938, no. 40

Through a comparison of the two authenticated paintings by this artist and a study of records which may reasonably be considered as referring to them, this painting may be said to have been part of one of the principal works attributed

175

to Gerard David. The painting bears the date 1498; thus, it is, along with the *Virgin and Saints* in the Musée des Beaux-Arts in Rouen (cat. 554), the only other dated work by Gerard David. As a result, it is a basic picture for the study of this master. In addition, it is one of the first northern European works in which elements borrowed from the decorative repertory of the Italian Renaissance appear. It thus marks the end of the Gothic period of Flemish art which it is the purpose of this exhibition to reveal in its many phases.

The work belongs to a special group of paintings which emerged in the 15th century in the cities of Flanders and Germany, and which is known as "Pictures of Justice". These cities had gradually acquired, as collectivities, the privileges which had long been the prerogative of nobility. Among them were the right to have coats of arms and that of administering their own justice. Pride in having acquired these rights explains the considerable expenses approved by the cities, to engage, for example, the best painters to decorate their city council chambers (used as court rooms) with paintings such as this. Brussels possessed the first paintings of this kind known in Belgium, *The Justice of Trajan* and *The Justice of Herkenbald* by Roger van der Weyden. Louvain had Dieric Bouts paint *The Justice of Otto*, the last work of this master, now in the Musées Royaux des Beaux-Arts in Brussels (cat. 65-66). Bruges went to the best painter of the time, Gerard David. The theme chosen was that of *The Justice of Cambyses*. Scholars often drew from ancient literature the subjects for which the artist had to use a new iconography.

This painting shows the arrest of the dishonest judge, Sisamnes, who is still seated upon his chair of honor. King Cambyses gives the indictment of his wrongdoings by counting them on his fingers in the style of an orator of the Middle Ages. The small secondary scenes in the street show how Sisamnes allowed himself to be bought. Through the left arcade can be seen, at the edge of a square, the former house of the bourgeois in Bruges, the *Poortersloge*.

Another painting of the same size as the *Arrest* and also in the City Museum of Bruges, shows the punishment of Sisamnes, who was condemned to be skinned alive. These two paintings originally formed one work, divided only by a central wood strip in the frame (see illustration p. 178).

Physical data: Oak, 71 3/4 x 62 5/8 in. (182.3 x 159.2 cm.). Original frame. An examination of the vertical pieces of the frames proved that the two paintings originally formed one single work whose central dividing strip had been sawn in two, vertically (examination of wood structure made at the Institut Royal du Patrimoine Artistique, Brussels; JANSSENS DE BISTHOVEN, 1959, p. 17).
Inscriptions: date 1498 on the wall, over the judge's throne; various coats of arms on the upper part of the wall; fictious inscriptions on the edges of some of the costumes and in the medallion set into the wall on the left.

History: City Hall, Bruges, 1769, indicated as a work by Claeyssens (DESCAMPS, 1769, p. 306); taken by the French in 1794; recovered in 1815; placed in the Musée de l'Académie in 1827-28, then in the City Museum in 1930 (JANSSENS DE BISTHOVEN, 1959, pp. 23-25).

Exhibitions: Bruges, 1902, no. 121; Bruges, 1949, no. 21; London, 1949, no. 1; Bruges, 1951, no. 19; Venice and Rome, 1951, no. 15; temporarily loaned to the City of Lierre in 1953.

176

Gerard David

177

Gerard David

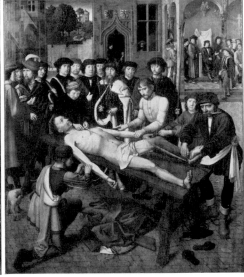

The panel on exhibition with its companion piece

It may be considered certain that *The Justice of Cambyses* was placed in the City Hall of Bruges upon its completion in 1498. There are no documents in the archives which indicate directly that this work was ordered from David, but the City accounts of 1498-1499 mention that Gerard David, who had already received various payments since 1487, notably for a *Judgment and Verdict of Our Lord,* was paid for having painted "a larger picture" which was placed in the council chambers (JANSSENS DE BISTHOVEN, 1959, pp. 21, 27, and 28). This document, already published by WEALE (1863, p. 230), inspired HULIN DE LOO (1902, no. 121) to put forward the hypothesis, since verified, that the two scenes originally appeared in one single painting. The document seems to furnish adequate evidence because it corresponds to the date which appears on the picture. The attribution to Gerard David was first proposed by WEALE (1863, pp. 223-224) and has been unanimously accepted by the specialists, with the exception of VAN DE WALLE DE GHELCKE (1949, p. 224), who has some reservations.

WEALE (1861, p. 55) first pointed out that one of the buildings shown resembled the *Poortersloge,* and recently JANSSENS DE BISTHOVEN (1959, p. 18, note 1) discovered a drawing which shows the building before its restoration in 1899-1903, in which it conforms to the representation shown by David. The coats of arms on the wall on either side of the judge's chair are, on the left, that of Philip the Handsome, and on the right, that of Philip the Handsome and his wife, Joan of Aragon. The medallions in the form of cameos which are set into the

178

Gerard David

180

Gerard David

wall probably represent, on the left, the myth of Hercules and Deianira (Ovid 9. 1; WEALE, 1861, p. 53), which is the origin of the horn of plenty and must signify here the peace and abundance which accompany the reign of justice, and, on the right, the myth of Apollo and Marsyas (JANSSENS DE BISTHOVEN, 1959, p. 19), which foreshadows the flaying of Sisamnes. GANS (1947, pp. 121-122) says this second medallion is a copy of an ancient one. JANSSENS DE BISTHOVEN (1959, p. 19) points out that it resembles the pendant worn by the young woman in a portrait by Botticelli in the Städelsches Kunstinstitut in Frankfort (cat. 936). According to MÜNTZ (1898, p. 480) and BODENHAUSEN (1905, p. 132), these two medallions are reproductions of cameos in the Medici Collection in Florence (it is known that the Medici had representatives in Bruges during that period). WEALE (1863, p. 228) suggested seeing the artist's portrait in the figure standing behind King Cambyses. There is a resemblance between this figure and a portrait of the painter in the *Recueil d'Arras*, as well as a self-portrait in the *Virgin and Saints* in the Musée des Beaux-Arts in Rouen (cat. 554) identified by BODENHAUSEN (1905, p. 161).

STRUBBE (1956, pp. 8-30) refuted the theory that the choice of the subject, *The Justice of Cambyses*, was an allusion to the condemnation in Bruges, ten years earlier, of a burgomaster and two aldermen who had been accused of corruption. The same author demonstrates that the painter was not inspired by the story of Cambyses as told by Herodotus, but rather by the version given by Valerius Maximus, a Latin author, in an anthology known in Bruges in Gerard David's time.

45. TRIPTYCH OF SAINT JOHN THE BAPTIST

Bruges, Stedelijk Museum voor Schone Kunsten (Groeningemuseum)
Cat. 1938, nos. 35-39

This altarpiece was ordered by an Ostend bourgeois living in Bruges, Jean des Trompes, in honor of his patron saint, John the Baptist. The central panel shows the most important act in the life of this saint, the Baptism of Christ in the Jordan. The donor is shown on the left wing with his son and St. John the Evangelist. His first wife and their four daughters are seen on the right wing with St. Elizabeth of Hungary. On the exterior of these wings, the Virgin and Child are painted on the left and the donor's second wife and their child are on the right, with Mary-Magdalene. This type of painting could only have been destined for a church: in 1520, four years after the donor's death, it was given to the Brotherhood of the Clerks of the Tribunal to be placed on the altar of their chapel in the Church of Saint-Basile in Bruges.

There is no inscription on the altarpiece relative to its author and no documents exist concerning its being ordered. However, specialists unanimously

181

Gerard David

attribute it to Gerard David and place its execution between 1500 and 1508, according to the portraits represented in the painting. It is a typical example of the works which owe their existence to bourgeois patrons of art in that period; moreover, it is one of the masterpieces of the early Flemish painting which reached the end of its development in Bruges at the very beginning of the 16th century.

> *Physical data:* Oak, central panel: 51 $^1/_{16}$ x 38 $^1/_{16}$ in. (129.7 x 96.6 cm.); left wing: 51 $^{15}/_{16}$ x 16 $^{15}/_{16}$ in. (132 x 43.1 cm.); right wing: 51 $^{15}/_{16}$ x 16 $^5/_8$ in. (132 x 42.2 cm.) (all sight measurements).
> Overpaintings have been detected in the central panel, especially in the sky, and on the outer sides, in the architectural setting, the shirt of the Christ Child, and the lower part of Mary-Magdalene's face (examination made at the Institut Royal du Patrimoine Artistique, Brussels; JANSSENS DE BISTHOVEN, 1959, p. 33).

> *History:* By a contract dated December 18, 1520, the heirs of Jean des Trompes gave the Brotherhood of the Sworn Clerks of the Tribunal in Bruges "a very beautiful and very precious painting with the representation of Saint John the Baptist" for the altar of the Clerks' chapel, on the condition that masses be celebrated for the soul of Jean des Trompes (Archives of the City of Bruges, *Registre des Procurations,* 1520-1521, fol. 108-109, ed. WEALE, 1864-65, pp. 294-297; verified by L. DEVLIEGHER: ed. JANSSENS DE BISTHOVEN, 1959, pp. 35-36 and 40-41). In 1606, the Clerks of the Tribunal refused to give the altarpiece to a grandson of Jean des Trompes who offered another painting in exchange (Archives of the City of Bruges, *Comptes de la chapelle des clercs assermentés du tribunal,* 1520-1623, fol. 230-231 and 238, ed. WEALE, 1863, pp. 284-287; verified by L. DEVLIEGHER: ed. JANSSENS DE BISTHOVEN, 1959, pp. 36-37 and 44-45). The triptych was taken by the French in 1794, returned in 1815, put in the Academy in 1827-28, then in the City Museum in 1930 (JANSSENS DE BISTHOVEN, 1959, p. 38). Cleaned by J. van der Veken in 1935 (JANSSENS DE BISTHOVEN, 1959, p. 39).

> *Exhibitions:* Bruges, 1902, no. 123; Amsterdam, 1946, no. 22; Bruges, 1949, no. 1; London, 1949, no. 3; Paris, 1952-53, nos. 7 and 8 (wings); Bruges, 1953, no. 28; London, 1953-54, nos. 8 and 10 (wings); Antwerp, 1954, no. 23 (wings); Madrid, 1958-59, nos. 21-24.

Neither the 1520 contract nor the decision by the Clerks in 1606 reveal the name of the painter of this triptych, but they do give the name of the donor. WEALE (1863, pp. 257-276) established that Jean des Trompes who was Magistrate of Ostend in 1498-1499, held official posts in Bruges, lost his first wife, Elizabeth van der Meersch, in 1502 and his second, Madeleine Cordier, in 1510. He had three children by his second wife and, since only one small girl is shown on the right outside wing with Madeleine Cordier, the painting was probably done before 1508. HULIN DE LOO (1902, p. 32, no. 123), FRIEDLÄNDER (VI, 1928, p. 78), and VAN PUYVELDE (1953, pp. 281 and 285) believe that only the outside wings were painted ca. 1508, while the central panel and inside wings were done before the death of the first wife in 1502. JANSSENS DE BISTHOVEN (1959, pp. 37-38) tends to believe that the altarpiece was ordered around 1503, the year in which the chapel of the Clerks was founded, with the idea of giving it for the chapel.

The attribution of this triptych to Gerard David is based strictly on style criticism. JANSSENS DE BISTHOVEN points out that MICHIELS (1845, p. 348) attributed it to Memlinc, WAAGEN (1863, pp. 182-183, note 1) to one of the

182

183

Gerard David

illuminators of the Grimani Breviary and later to Gerard Horenbaut, and WEALE (1861, p. 65) to the painter of *The Virgin and Saints* in the Musée des Beaux-Arts in Rouen (cat. 554), whom he shortly afterward identified as Gerard David (WEALE, 1864-65, p. 292). HULIN DE LOO (1902, p. 32, no. 123), BODENHAUSEN (1905, p. 145), FRIEDLÄNDER (VI, 1928, p. 78), LAVALLEYE (1936, p. 389), VAN PUYVELDE (1941, p. 33), and JANSSENS DE BISTHOVEN (1959, p. 39) all agree in its attribution to David.

HELD (1952, p. 89) notes an iconographic peculiarity: God the Father is surrounded by four small nude figures. He suggests they may be the souls of Holy Innocents or those of deceased children of the donors, and refers to it as an unusually early example of a kind of representation which became current in the 17th century.

The details of the landscape were painted with such care that a botanist has been able to identify the varieties of trees, Italian poplar, linden-tree, oak, a chestnut-tree whose trunk is covered with ivy, as well as numerous plants, wood strawberries, mallow, sorrel, shave-grass, swamp euphorbia, wild violets, plantain, dandelion, poppies, yellow iris, white dead-nettle, and fern (JANSSENS DE BISTHOVEN, 1959, pp. 33-34).

46. THE ANNUNCIATION

Detroit, Mich., The Detroit Institute of Arts. Acc. no. 27.201, cat. no. 50

This small painting is generally considered an early work of Gerard David, although some art historians feel inclined to place it at the end of his career.

As opposed to the Italians of the same period, who normally showed the Annunciation in the outside gallery of an aristocratic residence, the Flemish Primitives, at least from Roger van der Weyden on, generally placed the scene in the Virgin's bedroom or in a private chapel or oratory of her house (cf. cat. no. 28). The small picture on the wall shows Moses and the Burning Bush. This is one of the scenes of the Old Testament in which the Middle Ages saw a foreshadowing of the New: the Burning Bush, which burns without consuming itself, symbolizes the virginal motherhood of Mary. The majolica vase containing the lily, symbol of the Virgin's purity, is one of the many Italian objects imported through Bruges in that period. A prayer-stool similar to that of the Virgin is included in this exhibition as no. 162.

Physical data: Oak, 13 $^{11}/_{16}$ x 9 $^{3}/_{16}$ in. (35.1 x 23.3 cm.) (total surface).
History: Russian private collection (VALENTINER, 1927, p. 92); Van Diemen Galleries, New York, 1923 (R.K.D., The Hague); purchased from Van Diemen in 1927 for The Detroit Institute of Arts.
Exhibitions: New York, 1939, no. 76; Kansas City, 1940-41, no. 15; San Diego, 1957, no. 8.

184

Gerard David

185

Gerard David

VALENTINER (1927, p. 92), who was the first to publish the work, believes that its light tones reflect an influence from Quentin Metsys, and he places it between 1515 and 1520, after David's stay in Antwerp in 1515. FRIEDLÄNDER (VI, 1928, pp. 83, 91 and no. 175), on the other hand, considers it a work of the artist's youth, between 1484 and 1498. He thus places it in the same period as the *Virgin in an Apse* of the Epstein Collection in Chicago, the *Nativity* of the New York Metropolitan Museum (Friedsam Collection), the *Triptych of the Virgin* in the Louvre (cat. 2202b), the *Christ Nailed to the Cross* of the National Gallery in London (cat. 3067) and the corresponding wings of the Musée Royal des Beaux-Arts in Antwerp (cat. 179-180), in which he finds the same light colors and other characteristics of style. RICHARDSON (1944, p. 36, no. 50) was of the same opinion at first and dated the work around 1490; but he now considers it a late work by David, about 1520 (verbal statement). It seems more likely, however, that it is an early work of the artist, because it combines a Dutch influence in the faces and specific colors with such Eyckian characteristics as the conception of space in depth and the arrangement of the bedroom, which recalls van Eyck's *Marriage of Giovanni Arnolfini and Giovanna Cenami* in the National Gallery in London (cat. 186).

47. THE NATIVITY

Cleveland, Ohio, The Cleveland Museum of Art. Acc. no. 58.320

Authors agree in attributing this work to Gerard David and place it in his early period. It must be remembered in studying this picture that the balance of the composition was decidedly broken, probably as early as the 16th century, by the total overpainting of St. Joseph. This figure was originally appreciably smaller and thus more in the background.

In the right background is shown the Annunciation to the Shepherds. The column constructed of precious material which stands behind the donkey and the ox represents that against which the Virgin is supposed to have leaned at the time of the Nativity, according to the Apocryphal Gospels. The city rising in the background is intended to represent Bethlehem. However, it does not correspond to any particular city, although the presence of the round building relates it to representations of Jerusalem. It is interesting to note also that the city had already spread beyond its walls.

Physical data: Oak, 33 1/2 x 23 1/4 in. (85 x 59 cm.). The figure of St. Joseph is completely overpainted.
History: Russian private collection (BODENHAUSEN, 1905, p. 93, no. 3), 19th century; acquired in Russia by Richard von Kaufmann, Berlin (FRIEDLÄNDER, 1899, p. 14); Richard von Kaufmann sale, Berlin (Cassirer und Helbing), December 4, 1917, no. 78 (*Cicerone*, 1918, p. 26); acquired by Dr. Walter von Pannwitz (*ibidem*); Dr. Walter

Gerard David

187

Gerard David

von Pannwitz Coll., then that of Mrs. C. von Pannwitz, Hartekamp, no. 15; New York art dealer; purchased with funds from the Leonard C. Hanna, Jr. Bequest by The Cleveland Museum of Art, 1958 (FRANCIS, 1958, p. 227, note 1).
Cleaned in Berlin before 1905 (BODENHAUSEN, 1905, p. 93, no. 3).
Exhibitions: Berlin, 1898, no. 56; Rotterdam, 1939-40, no. 12; The Hague, 1945, no. 45; Bruges, 1949, no. 6.

In its style and composition this work is closely akin to two other paintings of the Nativity by Gerard David, that of the Friedsam Collection in the New York Metropolitan Museum of Art (Acc. no. 32.100.40 B) and, more especially, that of the Hungarian National Museum of Fine Arts (cat. 1336) in Budapest. As in the Budapest *Nativity*, its composition is derived from the Friedsam *Nativity* (BALDASS, 1936, p. 93). All the authors place the Cleveland panel in Gerard David's early period, but after the Budapest work (FRIEDLÄNDER, 1899, p. 14 and 1906, p. 33; BODENHAUSEN, 1905, p. 93, no. 3; CONWAY, 1921, p. 279; FRIEDLÄNDER, VI, 1928, no. 4 and p. 103; BALDASS, 1936, p. 93; BOON, 1938, p. 8). CONWAY (1921, p. 279) believes it could even have been painted before the artist left Holland. BOON (1938, p. 8), on the other hand, thinks that by the time he did this work, David had already lost direct contact with the art of the Dutch painter Geertgen tot Sint Jans and that the ties with that of Ouwater had weakened since the Budapest *Nativity*. BALDASS (1936, p. 93) views it as characteristic of David's second style, when the figures are still isolated and their faces borrowed from Geertgen, although new tendencies appear in the modeling and the drapery. In any case, this painting is, to him, later than the 1498 Justice panels in the Groeningemuseum in Bruges (cat. 40-41 and this cat. no. 44).

The figure of St. Joseph was entirely overpainted, probably as early as the beginning of the 16th century, presumably by an artist of the Bles group (BODENHAUSEN, 1905, p. 93), with the result that the balance in the composition is broken. A cleaning of the painting at the end of the 19th century or the beginning of the 20th century disclosed that this figure was originally placed more toward the background, forming a semi-circular group with the shepherd and the Virgin, as in the Budapest *Nativity*. Through the paint layers which now form the shoulder of St. Joseph, it also made visible the head of the original St. Joseph, bearded and very similar to the way he appears in the Budapest painting. BODENHAUSEN (1905, p. 93) thinks the overpaint might correspond to the portrait of an owner of the work at the beginning of the 16th century as was the case, only in an even much more ruthless manner, in a wing by Roger van der Weyden at the Galleria Sabauda in Turin (cat. 189; ARU and DE GERADON, 1952, no. 19). FRIEDLÄNDER (1917, no. 78) does not believe that St. Joseph has been overpainted, but he gives no reason for his position.

The motif of the Child resting on a portion of the Virgin's cloak is taken from the *Bladelin Altarpiece* by Roger van der Weyden in the Berlin Museum (cat. 535) (FRIEDLÄNDER, VI, 1928, p. 103). It is also found frequently in paintings of the Nativity by Memlinc. CONWAY (1921, p. 279) and SULZBERGER (1955, p. 178) suggest seeing a self-portrait of the artist in the young shepherd

188

Gerard David

kneeling at the extreme left. This suggestion seems all the more likely in view of the fact that the features of this shepherd are found, only more mature, in the *Virgo inter Virgines* altarpiece at the Musée des Beaux-Arts in Rouen (cat. 554), a work which documents authenticate and date in 1509, and in which David painted himself as the donor. Another self-portrait by David can presumably be seen in *The Arrest of Sisamnes* in the Stedelijk Museum in Bruges, being shown in this exhibition as no. 44.

48. THE VIRGIN CROWNED BY ANGELS WITH FOUR SAINTS

New York, N.Y., Duveen Brothers, Inc.

This work, unanimously attributed to Gerard David, is generally placed rather late in his career.

The Virgin is crowned as the Queen of Heaven by two angels and venerated by four saints, probably the four Evangelists. This representation of the Virgin is a kind of paraphrase of the vision of the Woman of the Apocalypse, "clothed by the sun, the moon at her feet and a crown of twelve stars on her head", although some elements like the crown, here a royal crown, are different.

> *Physical data:* Oak, 28 $^1/_8$ x 21 $^1/_2$ in. (71.5 x 54.7 cm.) (total surface). Cradled panel.
> *History:* Prince Juan de Bourbon (grandson of Charles IV, King of Spain) Coll.; Count of Santa Maria Coll., Madrid; on loan at the Prado for many years (DOUGLAS, 1946, p. 161); Duveen Brothers, Paris and New York, since 1937 (FRIEDLÄNDER, XIV, 1937, p. 106).
> *Exhibitions:* Detroit, 1941, no. 15; New York, 1942, no no.; New York, 1946, no. 3; Bruges, 1949, no. 19; Indianapolis, 1950, no. 20; London, 1953-54, no. 125; Bordeaux, 1954, no. 24.

This painting was published shortly before the second world war by FRIEDLÄNDER (XIV, 1937, p. 106), who includes it among the additions to the catalogue of Gerard David's original works. RICHARDSON (Cat. Detroit Exhib., 1941, no. 15) dates the work in David's Bruges period, but after 1500. The Italian influence which DOUGLAS (1946, p. 163) detects in the angels and in the Virgin's crown prompted him to view it as one of the latest among David's important works. VAN GELDER (1949, p. 254) also considers this painting as an example of the later works of the artist.

Gerard David probably found inspiration for this painting in the lost work of Hugo van der Goes, a *Deipara Virgo Foretold by the Prophets and the Sibyls*, known from a description by Jerome Busleyden, who had it in his house in Malines, and through a copy painted by Ambrosius Benson in the Musée Royal des Beaux-Arts in Antwerp (cat. 262).

The four figures venerating the Virgin have been identified as four Doctors of the Church by BROCKWELL (Cat. London Exhib., 1953-54, p. 40, no. 125) and

189

Gerard David

190

Gerard David

by DOUGLAS (1946, p. 161) who, moreover, views them as portraits. But, instead of the vestments of bishop, archbishop, cardinal, and pope which characterize the Doctors of the Church, the Saints in this painting wear the simple tunic and robe usually worn by Christ's apostles and disciples. Their facial characteristics also correspond to the traditional way in which the four Evangelists are represented, especially the two unbearded figures. The one at the extreme left seems to be St. John and the one on the right resembles St. Luke as he appears, for example, in the painting by Roger van der Weyden preserved in the Museum of Fine Arts of Boston (cf. this catalogue no. 7). The Virgin holds a rose in her hand, like the *Virgin of the Rose,* also by David, in the Colegiata del Sacro Monte in Granada (LAVALLEYE, 2, 1958, no. 59 and pl. VIII).

A late, exact copy of this composition was sold at auction by Sotheby and Co. in London at the Count Greffulhe sale on July 22, 1937, as no. 58 (photograph in the R.K.D., The Hague).

49.   CHRIST THE SAVIOUR

New York, N.Y., Nicholas M. Acquavella Galleries

This painting is generally considered a work of Gerard David and placed relatively early in his career.

The iconographic type of Christ resurrected, showing His wounds, is rarely found in Flemish painting of the period. Christ's face here is closely akin to the type described by an apocryphal document of the Middle Ages, the so-called Lentulus Letter.

Physical data: Oak, 18 $^{13}/_{16}$ x 13 $^{3}/_{4}$ in. (47.8 x 35 cm.) (total surface).

History: Private collection, Madrid (LAVALLEYE, 1, 1953, p. 9); Nicholas M. Acquavella Galleries, New York, since 1954.

Exhibitions: None known.

This painting remained unpublished until a few years ago. LAVALLEYE (1, 1953, pp. 9-10), who published it for the first time, rightly notes that the type of Christ in this painting is very similar to that in the *Baptism of*

191

Gerard David

Christ by David, done between 1502 and 1507, in the City Museum of Bruges (cat. 36-39) (shown in this exhibition as no. 45) and the *Resurrection* in the right wing of a triptych, painted about 1500, in the Robert Lehman Collection in New York. He places the Acquavella *Christ* in the same period as the latter work. Another bust of Christ by David, quite similar to this one, but apparently done rather late, is in the John G. Johnson Collection in Philadelphia (cat. 330) (LAVALLEYE, *ibidem*); but there the Saviour is blessing and His hands are not pierced with wounds. FRIEDLÄNDER, in 1946, and VALENTINER, in 1954, also attributed the work to Gerard David in written statements to its owners. FRIEDLÄNDER dates the painting about 1500.

This is one of the devotional images which the Passion of Christ so widely inspired among Flemish artists at the end of the Middle Ages. But here, instead of a representation of Christ suffering and crowned with thorns, as He was often shown by Dieric and Aelbrecht Bouts and their workshop, or of Christ Blessing, as Memlinc painted Him, Gerard David represented Christ resurrected and showing with serenity the wounds on His hands.

50. THE CRUCIFIXION

Greenville, S.C., Bob Jones University Art Gallery. Acc. no. 75

Recently acquired by Bob Jones University after having belonged to a European private collection, this painting remained unpublished until the last few years. It is recognized today by several authorities as a work by Gerard David.

This *Crucifixion* shows the Virgin supported by St. John at Christ's right, and a three-quarter back view of Mary-Magdalene kneeling in front of Christ. In the middle distance, on His left, is the group of Jews, normally placed in the foreground, balancing the group of Christ's followers. The city of Jerusalem is represented here like a Flemish city of the 15th century, surrounded by walls with gates in the form of high towers.

> *Physical data:* Oak, 38 ¹⁵/₁₆ x 30 ⁹/₁₆ in. (99 x 77.6 cm.) (total surface).
> *History:* T.H. Ward Coll., London; acquired by Bob Jones University in 1955.
> *Exhibitions:* None known.

This painting was published as a work of Gerard David for the first time a few years ago by MARLIER (1956, p. 11). Several art historians had already attributed it to the Bruges master in written statements to the President of Bob Jones University (FRIEDLÄNDER and VALENTINER in 1952; MARLIER, SCHARF, SUIDA, and WESCHER in 1955). VALENTINER saw the influence of Geertgen in the group in the background and believed, as a result, that the painting dated from David's early years in Bruges. This opinion was shared by SUIDA.

192

Gerard David

193

Gerard David

However, MARLIER (1956, p. 11) judges that the monumental character of the composition, its classical balance, and the placing of the figures on a diagonal reveal a direct, or indirect, contact with Italian art, and that it thus belongs to the artist's later period.

The monumental style of this composition, especially in the draperies, brings it close to other works of the middle or final period of Gerard David's career: the *Saint Anne Altarpiece* of the Widener Collection in the National Gallery in Washington (1507), the *Altarpiece of the Virgin* in the Palazzo Bianco in Genoa (before 1515) and the *Descent from the Cross* of the Frick Collection in New York (late period). The figure of Christ is very close to that in the *Calvary* by David in the Palazzo Bianco in Genoa, which also dates from about 1515.

COMSTOCK (1957, pp. 204-205), following SUIDA (written statement, 1955), compares this composition, and particularly the view of Jerusalem in the background, to the *Crucifixion* of the Thyssen Collection at the Schloss Rohoncz, Castagnola - Lugano, and relates the Virgin and St. John to their counterparts in the *Crucifixion* in the New York Metropolitan Museum (Acc. no. 09.157) and the *Descent from the Cross* in the Frick Collection. The Greenville work must also be compared with the *Crucifixion* in the Berlin Museum (cat. 573) which has the same general composition, and where the group in the middle distance on the right is almost identical. The stiffness of execution and the crudity of color lead however to the hypothesis that this painting is a work of David's workshop or even his school.

A late copy of the Greenville *Crucifixion*, attributed to Marcellus Coffermans, is in the John G. Johnson Collection in Philadelphia (cat. 395).

JUAN DE FLANDES

Active in Simancas in 1496, Salamanca in 1505, and Palencia in 1506
Died in Palencia before December, 1519

Documents from the court of Queen Isabella of Castile include mention of a painter named Juan de Flandes (i.e. John of Flanders) in the service of the Queen in 1496 and from 1498 until Isabella's death in 1504, after which it is known that he continued to work in Spain. The true name of this painter is unknown, but his Spanish surname reveals that he came from Flanders. Moreover, this origin corresponds to the style of works authenticated as being by this artist.

It is known through documents that Juan de Flandes received payments for works executed for Queen Isabella in 1496 (Simancas) and from 1498 until 1504, the year of the Queen's death; further, that he received an order to paint an altarpiece for the chapel of the University of Salamanca in 1505 and, in 1506, to do an altarpiece for the high altar of the Cathedral of Palencia. The only

194

authenticated works by him which still exist are a fragment of the predella in Salamanca, and the paintings in Palencia. It is through a comparison of style with these last works that he has been assigned the great majority of the small panels of the *Life of Christ and the Virgin,* intended for the *Oratorium* of Queen Isabella of Castile. Of the twenty-eight known panels in this series, twenty-five are attributed to Juan. Of the three remaining scenes, two are said to be by Michel Sittow, according to a document, and the third is attributed to him on a stylistic basis. This document does not, however, give the name of the painter who did the other twenty-five panels. If these can really be attributed to Juan de Flandes, this artist demonstrates a rather clear kinship with the Flemish miniaturists of the end of the 15th century.

Juan de Flandes also manifests a certain influence from Hugo van der Goes.

51.   CHRIST CARRYING THE CROSS

San Francisco, Calif., M.H. de Young Memorial Museum. Acc. no. 47-8

This interesting painting is preserved in the de Young Memorial Museum in San Francisco under the name of Juan de Flandes. It has not yet been the subject of a study which would either sustain that attribution or invalidate it.

The strange trefoil form of this panel raises the question of the use for which it was originally intended. The picture has an unpainted border on its whole periphery which could correspond to a lost original frame; it could also correspond to the framing of a painting as part of an altarpiece or of any other piece of religious furniture. It might have been one of the Stations of the Cross, which began to appear in that period; however, the presence of the Crucifixion in the background seems to nullify this hypothesis.

Physical data: Oak, 18 1/2 x 19 1/2 in. (47 x 49.5 cm.) (total surface). Trefoil panel.
History: A. Mayer Coll., Carlsbad, Czechoslovakia; Oscar Bondy Coll., Vienna; Baron Stummer von Tavarnok Coll., Vienna (R.K.D., The Hague); Frederick Mont Coll., New York; gift of Mr. and Mrs. George T. Cameron to the M.H. de Young Memorial Museum, San Francisco, 1947.
Exhibitions: None known.

The technique of this panel is Flemish, but the faces and the costumes are not usually found in Flemish paintings of the late fifteenth century. It could very probably be a picture executed either by a Flemish painter working in some other country or a foreign artist working in Flanders who would have assimilated the technique used there. The present attribution of this painting takes into account the first of these two hypotheses, because Juan de Flandes, who was originally from Flanders, worked in Spain, and that in the beginning his technique was still completely Flemish. Notwithstanding certain characteristics in common with the small panels of the *Life of the Virgin and Christ,* painted by Juan for Queen

195

Juan de Flandes

Isabella the Catholic between 1498 and 1504, which reflect certain similarities in the facial types and clothing, the San Francisco panel deviates from the style of Juan de Flandes' works. It is much more detailed, its composition is more crowded, and the modeling is more precise. These style differences appear very clearly in comparing the *Christ Carrying the Cross* in San Francisco with the two other paintings of the same subject which are authenticated by documents as having been done by Juan de Flandes, one in the Kunsthistorisches Museum in Vienna (cat. 226) and the other in the Cathedral of Palencia. Moreover, according to the costumes, it would be difficult to date the San Francisco painting earlier than 1510-1515, and the works painted by Juan de Flandes after 1505 are of stylistic and technical characteristics more and more close to the Spanish manner.

On the other hand, the San Francisco painting displays many similarities of composition, facial characteristics, modeling, and style with the *Christ Carrying the Cross* attributed by FRIEDLÄNDER (1929, p. 249) and WINKLER

196

(1931, p. 178 and illustration p. 117) to Michel Sittow, which is now in the Pushkin Museum in Moscow (Inv. 601). These points of similarity are, however, not sufficiently precise to permit the attribution of the San Francisco panel to Sittow. At best they can serve as an indication in orientating the further attribution of this painting.

One other element must be taken into consideration in classifying this work: the group of figures seen mostly from a back view at middle-distance on the right brings to mind the Italian paintings of the early Renaissance; such groupings had great success among the painters known as the Antwerp Mannerists, around 1515-1530. A similar group is shown, for example, in the right middle ground in the central panel of the triptych of the *Adoration of the Magi* in the Musée Royal des Beaux-Arts in Antwerp (cat. 208). The composition of the *Christ Carrying the Cross* in San Francisco is, however, much more static than that of the Antwerp Mannerists. For this reason it seems equally difficult to classify it within that school. It seems reasonable to believe that a painting of such a fine quality will be soon properly identified.

MICHEL SITTOW

Active in Bruges, Toledo, Copenhagen, Malines, Valladolid, and Tallinn from 1482 to 1525
Born in Tallinn ca. 1469. Died in Tallinn in 1525

The Flemish artist Master Michiel, painter for Queen Isabella the Catholic, was finally identified only some twenty years ago as Michel Sittow, an artist who came from Tallinn in Esthonia. Numerous documents have supplied detailed information on this painter's life and activity.

Michel, son of a painter of Dutch origin, "Clawes van der Suttow", was born in Tallinn ca. 1469. In 1482, he went to Bruges where he probably enrolled in the workshop of Memlinc, whose influence on his style was preponderant. In 1492, or perhaps even earlier, he became painter for the Spanish Queen, Isabella the Catholic, for whom he painted, in collaboration with Juan de Flandes, an *Oratorium* showing scenes from the Life of the Virgin and Christ. It is known through records that Sittow was commissioned to do two of these panels, *The Ascension of Christ* (Brocklesly Park) and *The Assumption of the Virgin* (Paris, Quesnet Collection). In 1501, he worked for the Queen in Toledo. In 1507, he returned to Tallinn, where he obtained his mastership and was married. He probably stayed there until 1514, when he went to Copenhagen to the court of Christian II, whose portrait he painted. In 1515, he worked in Malines for Margaret of Austria, and in Spain, especially Valladolid, for Ferdinand of Aragon. The following year he entered the service of Charles V. In 1518, he was once again in Tallinn, where he remarried and where, in 1525, he became dean

197

of the Guild of Saint Canut. He died in Tallinn in December of that same year.

Portrait painter and court painter, Michel Sittow is one of the best examples of the wide influence of Flemish art, especially that of Bruges, at the end of the 15th century. Attracted from the Baltic by the reputation of the Flemish School, he went to Flanders for his training, assimilated the Flemish style and technique, and then spread them across Europe.

52. CATHERINE OF ARAGON AS THE MAGDALENE

Detroit, Mich., The Detroit Institute of Arts. Acc. no. 40.50, cat. no. 645

This portrait, unanimously attributed to Michel Sittow, called Master Michiel, is characteristic of the portraits of royalty done by this artist in several countries of Europe, only a few rare examples of which remain today.

Mary-Magdalene, holding the perfume vase, is shown here with the features of Catherine of Aragon (1485-1536), Infanta of Spain, youngest daughter of Ferdinand II of Aragon and Isabella of Castile. In 1502 Catherine became the young widow of Arthur, Prince of Wales, and later the first wife of Henry VIII and the mother of Mary Tudor. Such portraits of women in the guise of religious figures, most often as Mary-Magdalene and sometimes also as the Madonna, were not uncommon at the beginning of the 16th century.

Physical data: Oak, 12 x 9 $^{15}/_{16}$ in. (30.5 x 25.2 cm.) (sight measurement).
History: Berlin art dealer, before 1930 (WINKLER, 1930, p. 248); August Berg Coll., Portland, Oregon (RICHARDSON, 1940, p. 83); Clendenin J. Ryan Coll., New York (*ibidem*); M. Knoedler and Co., New York, 1940; gift of The Detroit Museum of Art Founders Society to The Detroit Institute of Arts, 1940. Restored in 1955.
Exhibitions: Malines, 1958, no. 84.

This portrait was attributed for the first time to Michel Sittow by WINKLER (1930-31, p. 248 and 1931, p. 178), who recognized the model as the same one found in the *Portrait of a Lady* in the Kunsthistorisches Museum in Vienna (cat. 1489) and the *Virgin and Child* in the Museum Dahlem in Berlin (cat. 1722). FRIEDLÄNDER (1915, col. 180) had already identified the Vienna model as Catherine of Aragon by comparing historical data about a certain Master Michiel, a Flemish painter who worked at the court of Isabella of Castile, with a detail of the costume, the letter K alternating in the necklace with the rose of England and the letter C attached to the neck of the dress. GLÜCK (1933, pp. 106-107) also accepts this identification of the subject in the Vienna portrait, and this, although not supported by any documents, seems very reasonable. There is documentary evidence that Master Michiel executed the portraits of several members of the immediate family of the Infanta of Spain and that the latter greatly admired the artist's works, which she had known at the court of her mother,

198

Michel Sittow

Queen Isabella the Catholic. The presence of the Tudor rose on the cover of the perfume vase in the Detroit *Magdalene* (RICHARDSON, 1958-59, p. 81), as well as the knob of the cover where two C's face to face may perhaps be recognized, both give support to the identification of the model in the Vienna, Berlin, and Detroit paintings as the daughter of Queen Isabella. This identification has, however, been contested by WEINBERGER (1948, pp. 248-251), who cannot bring himself to recognize Catherine of Aragon in the Vienna portrait.

The type of clothing places the painting at the end of the 15th and the beginning of the 16th centuries. The firm and precise style of the work is, moreover, considered characteristic of the artist's first period, while he was still under Memlinc's influence (RICHARDSON, 1958-59, p. 82). GLÜCK (1933, p. 107) believes that Michel Sittow painted it just after 1504, at the same time as a portrait of Henry VII in the National Gallery of London (cat. 416), which was done at the time of a trip the artist might have made to England after the death of Queen Isabella in 1504. Catherine of Aragon was then the young

199

Michel Sittow

widow of the Prince of Wales. BALDASS (1935, p. 78), on the other hand, because of the close kinship of style between this portrait and the works of Gossaert, especially the Virgin of the *Carondelet Diptych* in the Louvre (cat. 1996-1998), dated 1517, suggests placing the date of execution of the *Magdalene* ca. 1520. Thus, he comes near the dating of WEINBERGER (1948, p. 248), who places the Vienna portrait about 1515.

53. A YOUNG MAN IN A RED CAP

Detroit, Mich., The Detroit Institute of Arts. Acc. no. 58.383, cat. no. 1316

This work has been part of the catalogue of Michel Sittow, known as Master Michiel, for only twenty years. It may be a self-portrait of the artist. In its penetrating sensitivity and the vigor of its modeling, this *Young Man* can be compared to the best portraits of the beginning of the 16th century.

Physical data: Oak, 6 $^7/_{16}$ x 5 $^1/_{16}$ in. (16.4 x 12.9 cm.) (total surface). Cradled panel.
History: Private collection, Genoa (FRIEDLÄNDER, VIII, 1930, p. 36); Paul Bottenwieser, art dealer, Munich and then New York, 1929; Julius H. Haass Coll., Detroit, from 1929 *(Pantheon,* 1929, p. 104); Mrs. Lillian Henkel Haass Coll., from 1940 (JOHANSEN, 1940, p. 35, no. 14); gift of Mr. and Mrs. Henry Ford II to The Detroit Institute of Arts, 1958.
Exhibitions: New York, 1939, no. 241.

First published as an early work of Gossaert, perhaps painted at the time of his trip to Italy in 1508-1509 (*Pantheon,* 1929, p. 104; FRIEDLÄNDER, VIII, 1930, pp. 36 and 162, no. 67), this portrait was later definitely recognized by authorities as a work by Michel Sittow. HULIN DE LOO and VALENTINER (cited by FRIEDLÄNDER, XIV, 1937, p. 112) were the first to recognize his hand, and FRIEDLÄNDER (*ibidem*) soon came over to their opinion, as did POST (1941, p. 685).

Those who have discussed the painting generally agree in dating this portrait in the very early years of the 16th century based, among other reasons, on the style of dress. RICHARDSON, who had first considered it an early work of Sittow, done about

200

1500, when the artist was still in Spain (1939, pp. 108-109), now views it as a work of his mature period, after he had disassociated himself from the firm and precise style inherited from Memlinc (1958-59, p. 82). FRIEDLÄNDER (VIII, 1930, pp. 36-37 and 162, no. 67), who had placed it either in 1508 or 1512 and had attributed it to Jan Gossaert, did not modify that dating even when he rectified his attribution. For WEINBERGER (1948, p. 251), the work dates from the first decade of the 16th century and could even have been painted in Tallinn around 1510. VALENTINER (1939, no. 241) places it around 1512.

The very simple clothing leads to the conclusion that, in contrast to other models of Michel Sittow, this one is not a personality of the court, but an ordinary bourgeois. The model is probably Italian according to FRIEDLÄNDER (VIII, 1930, pp. 36-37), who bases his opinion on the Genoese origin of the painting. RICHARDSON (1939, pp. 108-109), however, thought him very probably Spanish, as in another *Portrait of a Man in a Red Cap,* preserved in the Museo d'Arte Antica in the Castello Sforzesco in Milan (cat. 285; Cat. Florence Exhib., 1947, pl. 6) under the name of the Master of the St. Ursula Legend, but which the same author, following VALENTINER, attributes to Michel Sittow. More recently, RICHARDSON (1958-59, p. 83) suggested seeing a self-portrait of the artist in the Detroit painting. The type of head-dress, a kind of soft cap, is rarely found in Flemish paintings of the period. Perhaps it is a slightly whimsical kind of head-gear worn by artists, as RICHARDSON suggests. Whatever it is, this head-dress is the same as that found in the Milan portrait previously cited.

HIERONYMUS BOSCH

Active mostly in 's-Hertogenbosch (Brabant), beginning in 1480-81
Probably born in 's-Hertogenbosch. Died in 1516

Hieronymus Bosch, also called Hieronymus van Aken (Aachen = Aix-la-Chapelle), the city from which his family probably originated, was enrolled as a painter in the guild of 's-Hertogenbosch as from 1480-81. He is cited several more times in the public records of that city until his death.

The study and classification of Bosch's production are not easily accomplished because his art is so individual and so very different from the other Flemish Primitives. In addition, none of his works are dated, and even though several are signed, his signature was imitated as early as the 16th century as were, in that period, certain of his compositions. Several of Bosch's works of very fine quality are preserved in the Prado in Madrid, almost all of which came to it from Philip II, King of Spain. Some drawings are also attributed to this artist.

Most of Bosch's paintings are animated by numerous small figures of a fantastic nature, who move with full freedom, brought to life by a skilled brush, fiery and overflowing with fantasy. Bosch sometimes moralizes when he paints

Heaven, Purgatory, and Hell, and separates the good people from the evil. The influence of Bosch was felt again later, for example, in the work of Pieter Bruegel the Elder (died in 1569), who engraved several of his compositions.

Hieronymus Bosch occupies a place apart from the other Flemish Primitives. His extremely personal art requires that he be classified alone, outside the Bruges, Ghent, Brussels, and Antwerp Schools of his period.

Several of the works of Bosch and his school or his followers are found in the United States, notably in Boston, Indianapolis, New Haven, Princeton, Philadelphia, San Diego, and Washington.

54. TRIPTYCH OF THE LAST JUDGMENT

Bruges, Stedelijk Museum voor Schone Kunsten (Groeningemuseum)
Cat. 1938, no. 208

This triptych is scarcely known because the authorities on Hieronymus Bosch have generally restricted themselves to citing it as a product from his workshop or even as an imitation. It did not appear in any exhibition between 1907 and 1953. Friedländer, however, included it as an original in his catalogue of the works of Hieronymus Bosch. The painting is characteristic of the artist's style, and it is in particular an example of the prodigious imagination which Bosch displays.

The subject of the triptych is a Last Judgment which is depicted with considerable freedom. Christ as Judge of the Last Judgment is seated on a sphere of light in the upper part of the central panel. He is the Christ showing His wounds but He is not flanked by the usual intercessors, the Virgin and Saint John. The fires which illuminate the far distance in the central panel and the right wing probably evoke the terrors of the end of the world, while scenes of the torments of Hell occupy the rest of these two panels. In the foreground of the left wing are shown visions of Paradise, in the middle ground is represented the fountain of life, and in the far distance is outlined a mounting wave of the Chosen. Curiously enough, illustrations of various proverbs are mixed into all these scenes.

Recently a *Crowning with Thorns* was discovered on the reverse of the wings (see illustration p. 205). It is, unfortunately, in very poor condition.

Physical data: Oak, arched triptych, center: 39 $^1/_{16}$ x 23 $^{13}/_{16}$ in. (99.2 x 60.5 cm.); left wing: 39 $^3/_{16}$ x 11 $^5/_{16}$ in. (99.5 x 28.8 cm.); right wing: 39 $^3/_{16}$ x 11 $^1/_4$ in. (99.5 x 28.6 cm.) (sight measurements). On the reverse, in grisaille and in very bad condition, a *Crowning with Thorns* has recently been brought out by cleaning (JANSSENS DE BISTHOVEN, 1959, p. 13, note 1).
Inscription in Gothic writing in the lower right corner of the central panel: *Jheronimus bosch*. On the blade of the knife, a letter in the form of an **M** (or a **B**).

202

Hieronymus Bosch

History: Appeared at sale of Collection of Emile Gravet, Paris (Drouot), May 8, 1906, 4, no. 2; Seligman Coll., Paris, 1907; acquired from that collection in 1907 by Auguste Beernaert, who gave it to the City of Bruges through the Friends of the Museums (HOSTEN and STRUBBE, 1938, no. 208).

Exhibitions: Bruges, 1907, no. 218; Ostend, 1953, no. 1; Venice, 1954; Madrid, 1958, nos. 17-19; Bruges, 1959, no. 4.

This triptych was attributed to Hieronymus Bosch when it was in the Seligman Collection (Cat. Bruges Exhib., 1907, no. 218), then to an imitator of Bosch by LAFOND (1914, pp. 59-60), and to Henri met de Bles by MAETER-LINCK (1908, pp. 145-156). FRIEDLÄNDER (V, 1927, p. 100) considers it an original work by Hieronymus Bosch. The most recent justifiable opinions, those of HELD (1952, p. 89) and JANSSENS DE BISTHOVEN (1959, p. 15), without being as definite, characterize it as a work either by the master himself or, at least, painted in his workshop. BALDASS (1943, p. 29) thinks it is the work of a follower. TOLNAY (1937, p. 104) and COMBE (1946, p. 50) qualified it as an imitation and have not included it in Bosch's production. Recently BALDASS (1959, p. 32) pointed out that this composition implies the existence of the *Last Judgment* in

203

204

Hieronymus Bosch

the Akademie der bildenden Künste in Vienna.

The authorities are inclined to recognize the subject as a Last Judgment. JANSSENS DE BISTHOVEN (1959, pp. 11-16) points out that many familiar motifs of Hieronymus Bosch can be seen in this painting, especially from the three principal works by this master, all preserved in the Prado in Madrid: *The Garden of Delights, The Hay Wagon,* and *The Seven Deadly Sins.* These details are rather far removed from a Last Judgment and thus give a quite unusual character to this Bruges triptych. The vision of the end of the world, in the central panel, even includes illustrations of some Flemish proverbs (HOSTEN and STRUBBE, 1938, no. 208). Preparations

Detail of outside wings

can also be seen for a skinning, which is supposed to be one of the punishments of Hell (ROST, 1956, pp. 513-516). The letter M, or B, seen on the blade of the large knife was commented on, notably by BAX (1949, pp. 300 and 324), who thinks it might be the initial either for *Mundus,* the earthly power who punishes wrongdoers, or for *Bosche,* standing for 's-Hertogenbosch. According to JANSSENS DE BISTHOVEN (1959, p. 14), however, none of these hypotheses seem convincing.

The grisaille on the reverse, a single composition covering the two wings, is badly damaged. To the extent it is still possible to judge, it appears to be of an excellent quality and worthy of the hand of Hieronymus Bosch, just as do the other paintings of the triptych.

205

55. FRAGMENT OF A LOST COMPOSITION (INTEMPERANCE?)*

New Haven, Conn., Yale University Art Gallery. Acc. no. 1959.15.22

This fragment of a lost composition is unanimously accepted by authorities as an original work by Bosch. It is generally classified in his mature period.

The exact subject of this small panel has not yet been determined with certainty. Various interpretations have been suggested, but none can be definitely accepted as long as the original composition to which this fragment belonged remains unknown.

Physical data: Oak, 14 $^3/_{16}$ x 12 $^3/_8$ in. (36 x 31.5 cm.). Cradled panel. The absence of both the raised edge and the unpainted border on the entire periphery of the panel leads to the conclusion that it is only a fragment. Some changes from the preliminary drawing are visible.

History: Sir Felix Clay Coll. (incorrectly spelled "Clary" in several publications), Great Britain, sold in London (Christie's) on May 11, 1928, no. 31 (TOLNAY, 1937, p. 90, no. 9); acquired by Brace (?) (Frick Art Reference Library, New York); Malmedé, art dealer, Cologne, 1935 (FRIEDLÄNDER, XIV, 1937, p. 101); still there in 1936 (BALDASS, 1943, p. 235 and 1959, p. 228); Katz, art dealer, Dieren (R.K.D., The Hague); E. and A. Silbermann Galleries, New York; Mr. and Mrs. Louis M. Rabinowitz Coll., Sands Point, Long Island, N.Y. (VENTURI, 1945, pp. 63-64); bequest of Mr. and Mrs. Louis M. Rabinowitz to the Yale University Art Gallery, 1959.

Exhibitions: Rotterdam, 1936, no. 51; Grand Rapids, 1940, no. 5; Muskegon, 1941; New York, 1955, no. 8; New Haven, 1956, no. 2.

The specialists agree in considering this small panel to be a fragment of an original work by Hieronymus Bosch. They classify it, along with the *Ship of Fools* in the Louvre (cat. 4004), in the mature period of the artist ([HANNEMA], 1936, p. 32, no. 51; FRIEDLÄNDER, XIV, 1937, p. 101; TOLNAY, 1937, p. 90, no. 9; BALDASS, 1938, pp. 68 and 69; IDEM, 1943, p. 235 and 1959, p. 229; VENTURI, 1945, pp. 63-64; COMBE, 1946, p. 82, no. 40). BALDASS (1938, pp. 68 and 69, note 2; 1959, p. 82) is of the opinion that the Yale fragment must date from the same period as the *Prodigal Son* in the Boymans-van Beuningen Museum in Rotterdam (cat. 51) and the *Death of the Miser* in the National Gallery in Washington (Kress Coll.), and a little before the triptych of the *Temptation of Saint Anthony* in the Lisbon Museum (cat. 231), which is placed between 1490 and 1505.

The close kinship of style and composition between this little panel and the *Ship of Fools* in the Louvre prompted BRAND PHILIP (verbal statement reported in the catalogue of the Amsterdam Exhib., 1958, p. 81, *sub* no. 72) to conjecture that both might have been part of the same altarpiece. In addition, as in the *Ship of Fools*, symbolic details play an important role here (BALDASS, 1943, p. 70). The fact that the picture is only a fragment of a composition makes it difficult to determine the subject of the work to which it originally belonged.

---

* *This entry has been prepared on the basis of data collected by Mr. Colin Eisler for the Corpus of the Flemish Primitives in New England museums (to be published soon).*

Hieronymus Bosch

Several interpretations have been suggested. HANNEMA (1936, p. 32, no. 51) and TOLNAY (1937, p. 90, no. 9) suggest it may be a fragment of an episode in the story of the Prodigal Son. BALDASS (1943, pp. 22 and 235; 1959, pp. 26 and 229) believes it is more likely a fragment of a representation of two of the Deadly Sins, Lust and Intemperance, and thinks it might have belonged to a painting cited in the inventory of the collection of Marghareta Boge in Antwerp in 1574, by which date the square table of the *Seven Deadly Sins,* now in the Prado Museum (cat. 2822), was already in the possession of Philip II: *een tafereel van*

Hieronymus Bosch

Jeronimus Bosch wesende van de VII doodsonden ("a painting by Hieronymus Bosch, of the seven Deadly Sins") (Tolnay, 1937, p. 90, no. 9). Bax (1949, p. 199) calls it an allegorical satire with happy people celebrating May or Summer. Werner (1960, p. XVIII) views it as an allegory of drunkenness and Venturi (1945, pp. 63-64) thinks it may come from the proverb "more are drowned in a goblet than in the sea". Combe (1946, p. 82, no. 40) does not accept any of these interpretations and simply refers to it as a "fragment of a lost composition". This seems, in fact, the most logical, since it is not known to which work this fragment really belonged. Tolnay (1937, p. 90, no. 9) believes, moreover, that Bruegel must have known this painting, because the Carnival figure in the *Combat of Carnival and Lent* in the Kunsthistorisches Museum in Vienna (no. 716) seems to him to have been inspired by the figure straddling the cask in the Yale painting.

The coat of arms on top of the tent can be identified in Renesse (1900, p. 254) and Rietstap (n.d., p. 172) as being that of the de Bergh family in 's-Hertogenbosch and The Hague. Brans (1948, p. 44) believes the coat of arms is that of the young man shown in the tent and that it alludes to the corruption of nobility.

56. ECCE HOMO

Indianapolis, Ind., The Clowes Fund, Inc. Cat. no. 6

This *Ecce Homo* is one of the two examples of this composition from the hand of Hieronymus Bosch. The other, better known in the literature about Bosch, belongs to the John G. Johnson Collection in Philadelphia. The Indianapolis example, like the one in Philadelphia, is considered by the authorities as an original by the artist. Several of them even view this one to be of a superior quality to that in the Johnson Collection.

The way in which the *Ecce Homo* is presented is very exceptional, as much in its composition, shown as a continuous frieze instead of a centered and limited group, as in the imagination reflected in the numerous figures surrounding Christ.

Physical data: Oak, 24 $^3/_{16}$ x 20 $^1/_2$ in. (61.5 x 52 cm.) (total surface).
History: A. and E. Silbermann Galleries, New York (John G. Johnson Collection files, Philadelphia); Dr. George Henry Alexander Clowes Coll., Indianapolis, since 1940.
Exhibitions: Detroit, 1941, no. 3; Indianapolis, 1950, no. 7; Indianapolis, 1959, no. 6.

The two known examples of this *Ecce Homo*, those of the John G. Johnson Collection in Philadelphia (cat. 352) and of Indianapolis, are identical in their essential elements of composition. Only the central column, the twin of that just next to Christ, no longer appears on the Philadelphia painting since a cleaning of this panel in 1938. In addition, the wall in the foreground is absent in the

Philadelphia painting, which must have been shortened at the lower end, because the painted surface extends right to the bottom edge of the panel. The Indianapolis picture thus probably discloses the original aspect of the composition.

In written statements to the owner of the Indianapolis *Ecce Homo*, certain specialists (TIETZE and TOLNAY, 1940) expressed the opinion that this version is superior to that in the Johnson Collection. RICHARDSON (1941, p. 17), the first to publish the work, concurs in this opinion. VALENTINER (written statement)

Hieronymus Bosch

says both are originals by Bosch, but makes no distinction between their quality. LAFOND (1914, p. 43), who did not know the Indianapolis painting, thought it difficult to make a statement either for or against an attribution of the Philadelphia composition to Bosch himself. BALDASS, who had first (1943, p. 250) classified the Philadelphia painting among the original works by Bosch, later (1959, p. 244) hesitated to attribute it to him with certainty. He does not mention the version in Indianapolis.

Opinion is divided on the date which should be assigned to this work. Since no date has been given to the Indianapolis painting, it is necessary to refer to those proposed for the Philadelphia example. The latter is placed by BALDASS (1917, p. 178; 1943, p. 250; 1959, p. 244) in the early period of Bosch, before a different composition of the *Ecce Homo* by Bosch in the Städelsches Kunstinstitut in Frankfort (cat. 1577). TOLNAY (1937, p. 92, no. 31) and COMBE (1946, pp. 23 and 83, no. 43) place it in the artist's middle period. COMBE *(ibidem)* regards it as an isolated work in his production, the only remaining witness, probably, of a group of vanished works which must have belonged to the same level of stylistic development. FRIEDLÄNDER (V, 1927, pp. 91-92), on the other hand, thinks the *Ecce Homo* in the Johnson Collection must be placed after that in Frankfort, in spite of its apparently archaic space conception.

Several more or less faithful copies of this composition are noted by LAFOND (1914, p. 43). BALDASS (1959, p. 244) points out a drawing in the Crocker Art Gallery in Sacramento (SWARZENSKI, 1955, p. 4), which shows this scene as part of a large composition of the *Carrying of the Cross*. He sees in this drawing, however, a compilation of motifs borrowed from different works by Bosch and probably coming from the hand of a follower.

57.   THE LAST JUDGMENT

New York, N.Y., Private Collection

This *Last Judgment* is considered by some specialists as an original work by Hieronymus Bosch, and by others as a good copy by one of his close pupils.

As in other representations of the Last Judgment by Bosch and his imitators, this one illustrates in detail the punishments inflicted on the Damned according to the kind of sins they had committed. At least three of the seven Deadly Sins, Greed, Lust, and Sloth, are easily recognizable. However, the way in which the punishments are shown, especially the tangle of bodies in the center of the composition, completely distinguishes this picture from others by Hieronymus Bosch of the same subject. Four angels call with their trumpets to the resurrected at the four corners of the universe, while the twelve Apostles aid Christ. Heaven and the Ascension of the Chosen are shown at the upper left, while Hell is seen at the upper right.

210

Physical data: Oak, 33 $^7/_{16}$ x 37 $^3/_8$ in. (84.9 x 95 cm.) (total surface). Cradled panel. Signature in the lower right corner: *Jheronimus bosch.*

History: Collection of the Infante Don Sebastian de Bórbon y Braganza, Madrid (Cat. Pacully sale, 1903, p. 49, no. 17); exhibited at former asylum of Pau, belonging to heirs of Don Sebastian, 1876, no. 374 (LAFOND, 1914, p. 58, note 1); Emile Pacully Coll., Neuilly, sold in Paris (G. Petit), May 4, 1903, no. 17; E. Pacully sale, Paris (Drouot), July 5, 1938, no. 12 (*Pantheon*, 1938, p. 269); acquired by present owner around 1938. Cleaned around 1938-39.

Exhibitions: Bruges, 1902, no. 288.

This painting has been known since the Exhibition of Flemish Primitives in Bruges in 1902. It was then published, and later republished, by FRIEDLÄNDER (1903, p. 169 and V, 1927, p. 149, no. 87) as a very good old copy or a product of Bosch's workshop. HULIN DE LOO (1902, p. 77, no. 288), who shares this opinion, finds the style of this painting similar to that of the copy of the Lisbon *Temptation of Saint Anthony* preserved in the Musées Royaux des Beaux-Arts in Brussels (cat. 50). LAFOND (1914, pp. 55 and 58) considers it, along with the

211

triptych in the Vienna Academy (cat. 579-581) and a painting from the school of Cranach the Elder in the Museum Dahlem in Berlin (cat. 563), as one of the three reductions, variations, or copies of a lost *Last Judgment* ordered by Philip the Handsome from Hieronymus Bosch in 1504. He views the New York one as a copy, undoubtedly done shortly after Bosch's death, by one of his pupils or direct imitators, other than Pieter Huys. TOLNAY (1937, p. 104, no. 49), who does not accept the work as an original either, also dates it around 1520. COMBE (1946, pp. 49-50 and 69, note 165) regards it as an imitation, probably of the 16th century, and detects several details borrowed from Bosch's works, particularly from the Vienna *Last Judgment,* the *Temptation of Saint Anthony* in the Museu Nacional de Arte Antiga in Lisbon, and *Hell* of the *Hay Wagon Triptych* in the Prado, as well as from an engraving of the same subject by Alart Du Hameel. However, since the 1902 exhibition, several authors consider it an original by the artist (FIERENS-GEVAERT, 1902, p. 175; LEPRIEUR, 1903, pp. 33-34; BOUYER, 1903, p. 295). HYMANS (1902, p. 80) only attributes it to Bosch with reservations, but does find it an excellent work. Eventually, after its cleaning, FRIEDLÄNDER (written statement to the owner, 1939) also agreed to the attribution of the work to Bosch himself; but, in contrast to COMBE (cf. above), he does not find motifs borrowed from other works by Bosch. In any case, the signature in the lower right corner of the picture is not sufficient to authenticate it as an original work by the artist, because similar ones are found on numerous copies and imitations of Bosch's works.

The general composition of this *Last Judgment* has been compared several times to that of an engraving of the same subject by Alart Du Hameel (1449? - ca. 1509) (LAFOND, 1914, pl. opposite p. 82 and p. 118, no. 2; FRIEDLÄNDER, V, 1927, p. 149, no. 87). The authorities either view the work as inspired by that engraving (TOLNAY, 1937, p. 104, no. 49; COMBE, 1946, pp. 49-50), or consider the engraving as a free copy of a creation by Bosch (BALDASS, 1943, p. 30). Several elements of the composition of the New York painting, especially the background landscape, are also found in the center of the *Last Judgment* engraved by Jeronimus Cockx from a lost triptych by Bosch (LAFOND, 1914, pl. opposite p. 88 and p. 119 no. 12). A late copy of the New York *Last Judgment,* with some variations in detail, belongs to a private collector in Brussels; it was exhibited in Rome in the Palazzo Barberini in the *Mostra del Demoniaco nell'arte* in 1952 (photograph at the Centre National de Recherches Primitifs Flamands, Brussels).

212

Hieronymus Bosch

DRAWING AND WOODCUT

DIERIC BOUTS
For biography, see p. 101

58. PORTRAIT OF A YOUNG MAN

Northampton, Mass., Smith College Museum of Art. Acc. no. 1939.3

This drawing, done with a silverpoint on paper, has been considered by all authorities as an original, dating from the second half of the 15th century. The drawing is very close, in its spirit and style, to the works of Dieric Bouts. Its composition, as well as the subject's costume, is almost identical with that of a portrait preserved in the National Gallery in London which bears the original date 1462 and is unanimously considered as being from the hand of Dieric Bouts. Most specialists consider the Northampton drawing to be also by Dieric Bouts. It would then be the only known drawing by this painter. Some see in it a self-portrait of the artist. Others attribute it to a follower of Dieric Bouts. All are unanimous in placing its execution around 1462-1470.

Physical data: Silverpoint drawing on paper, with an ivory ground, $5\,^7/_{16}$ x $4\,^7/_{32}$ in. (138 x 107 mm.). An examination under the microscope revealed that the drawing is absolutely original, except in three places on the shoulder and the sleeve where hatching has been added, probably in graphite (supplementary note in the *Smith College Museum of Art Bulletin,* XXXVIII, 1958, p. 7).

History: Dr. Henri Wellesley Coll., Oxford, sold in London (Sotheby's), June, 1866, no. 709; Frederick Locker-Lampson Coll., Rowfant, Sussex, sold in London (Christie's), December 20, 1918, no. 142; Henri Oppenheimer Coll., London, sold in London (Christie's), July 13-14, 1936, no. 221; P. and D. Colnaghi and Co., London; Ludwig Rosenthal Coll., Bern; Schaeffer Galleries, New York; acquired by the Smith College Museum of Art in 1939.

Exhibitions: London, 1927, no. 504; San Francisco, 1940, no. 9; Cambridge, Mass., 1941; Montreal, 1944, no. 1; Cambridge, Mass., 1948-49, no. 5; Rotterdam-Paris-Brussels, 1949, no. 13; Philadelphia, 1950-51; Worcester, 1951-52, no. 4; Montreal, 1953, no. 1; New York, 1954, no. 33; Brussels-Delft, 1957-58, no. 32.

This drawing was originally attributed to Memlinc, perhaps, as VORENKAMP (1939, re-edited in 1958, p. 1) observes, by analogy with the almost identical portrait painted by Dieric Bouts (London, National Gallery, cat. 943) which bears the date 1462 and had formerly been attributed to Memlinc. CONWAY (1921, p. 245) still continued to attribute the drawing to Memlinc's workshop. POPHAM (II, 1921, p. 23, no. 11) was the first to compare it to the 1462 painting in the National Gallery, which has long been recognized as a work by Dieric Bouts. A little later, the same author (1926, p. 8) suggested attributing the drawing to Dieric Bouts. SCHÖNE (1938, p. 88, no. 7) considers it as definitely being an original drawing from the hand of Dieric Bouts, done in view of the execution of a portrait painted about the same period as the one in the National Gallery, but from a different model. He points out that it is the

213

only known drawing by this artist. TOLNAY (1943, p. 130) and TIETZE (1947, p. 8) share his opinion, but the former dates it ca. 1462 while the latter places it around 1462-1470. MONGAN (1949, p. 14) dates it around 1470, in the same period as Dieric Bouts' *Justice of Emperor Otto*. PANOFSKY (1953, p. 316, note 5) was the first to oppose the attribution to Dieric Bouts. He considers it a self-portrait because of the way in which the eyes are drawn, and he dates it around 1470 because of the hair style and hat. Since he believes it to be an original drawing, and not a copy, it seems impossible to him to assign it to Dieric Bouts, because the artist would already have been an older man by that time. He attributes it to a follower of Bouts. BOON (1957-58, no. 32) does not consider it to be a self-portrait, but does believe it is the work of Dieric Bouts. However, he does not agree with the generally accepted date of 1462 because he says a high hat such as worn by the young man was not known until around 1467.

214

Drawing and Woodcut

HUGO VAN DER GOES
For biography, see p. 116

59.   AN EPISODE IN THE STORY OF JACOB (also called THE GOOD SHEPHERD)

New York and Paris, Wildenstein and Co., Inc.

This drawing does not represent the Good Shepherd, but an episode in the story of Jacob, a shepherd in the service of Laban, as told in the Book of Genesis (30.25-43). Jacob waters the flock in a fountain after having put some peeled rods in the watering-place and, by this artifice, obtains speckled lambs. Since

215

Laban had promised to leave to him the speckled lambs, Jacob ended up by obtaining for himself the greatest part of the flock.

The composition of this scene is inscribed in a circle: the drawing is probably a design or cartoon (that is to say, the model) for a stained-glass roundel, such as was made at that time for churches and also houses. Two examples may be seen in paintings being shown in this exhibition: the *Mass of Saint Gregory* by Roger van der Weyden (cat. no. 10) and the *Virgin* of the *Diptych of Martin van Nieuwenhove* by Memlinc (cat. no. 31).

This drawing could be the work of a pupil or a follower of Hugo van der Goes who used, for the figure of the shepherd, a composition by this master which also derives from the story of Jacob.

> *Physical data:* Sepia ink on cream paper, 9 x 7 in. (228 x 178 mm.) (sight measurement). Non-original inscription near the upper edge: *hugues.*
> *History:* André de Hevesy Coll., 1935; Wildenstein and Co., Inc., New York, 1956.
> *Exhibitions:* Paris, 1935, no. 198; New York, 1956, no. 1.

FRIEDLÄNDER (IV, 1926, p. 62) attributes this drawing to a pupil of Hugo van der Goes. POPHAM (1932, p. 64) compares it to designs for roundels in domestic stained-glass windows, which were done by artists of his school. The same author points out that the figure of the shepherd is derived from that in a drawing of *Jacob and Rachel* preserved in the Christ Church Library in Oxford. He considers the latter drawing to be very probably from the hand of Hugo van der Goes and, in any case, certainly contemporaneous with this master. POPHAM *(ibidem)* thinks the Wildenstein drawing was done by one of Hugo van der Goes' pupils or followers, but not the same one who did the *Kneeling Lady* (being shown in this exhibition as no. 61) in The Pierpont Morgan Library in New York.

60.   SAINT GEORGE AND THE DRAGON

Washington, D.C., National Gallery of Art. Acc. no. B 17724

This work is considered by the authorities as an original 15th century drawing. Some attribute it to Hugo van der Goes.

The drawing illustrates an episode in the story of Saint George which is found in the Golden Legend. The Saint, having wounded the dragon, tells the princess to tie her belt around the monster's neck and it will follow her like a dog from then on.

> *Physical data:* Pen and sepia on paper, 8 1/16 x 6 1/2 in. (205 x 165 mm.).
> Original inscription on the harness of the horse: . IORGE + I . Non-original inscription at lower left: *Mr Rogier.*

216

Drawing and Woodcut

History: Heimsoeth sale, May 5, 1879, no. 99; A. von Lanna Coll., Prague, 1899; A. von Lanna sale, June 6-7, 1910, II, no. 33; Prince of Liechtenstein Coll.; acquired by Lessing J. Rosenwald for the National Gallery of Art in 1948.

Exhibitions: None known.

Like many drawings, this one bears an apocryphal signature: *Mr Rogier,* for Roger van der Weyden. KÄMMERER (1899, p. 106) was the first to publish this drawing, but with only a limited credit as to the attribution to Memlinc, which was given to it at that time. CONWAY (1921, p. 245), however, considers it a product of Memlinc's workshop. FRIEDLÄNDER (IV, 1926, pp. 62-63) says it is very probably an original from Hugo van der Goes' early period. BOON (1950-51, p. 94) does not accept this attribution and believes the drawing could be of French origin.

217

61.   A KNEELING LADY

This drawing is generally considered by the specialists as a 15th century work by a follower of Hugo van der Goes who could, perhaps, have taken his inspiration from a composition by this painter.

The high head-dress in the shape of two horns from which hangs a light veil was in style around the middle and during the second half of the 15th century.

Physical data: Pen and sepia on paper, 9 $^1/_2$ x 7 $^5/_{16}$ in. (242 x 186 mm.).
History: Sir Charles Greville Coll.; Earl of Warwick Coll.; Charles Fairfax Murray Coll.; acquired by The Pierpont Morgan Library in 1910.
Exhibitions: New York, 1934; Princeton, 1937, no. 9; Hartford (Conn.), 1938; San Francisco, 1940, no. 41; Montreal, 1953, no. 4.

218

Drawing and Woodcut

WINKLER (1922, pp. 612-613) compares this drawing to three others which might have belonged to the same sketchbook, and places the artist among the followers of Hugo van der Goes, around 1480 to 1500. POPHAM (1928, pp. 176-177) compares these drawings to the small drawings for stained-glass roundels by a follower of van der Goes, the Master of the Story of Tobit. Later, POPHAM (V, 1932, p. 64, no. 10) says the *Kneeling Lady* in New York can be seen in one of the round drawings in the Kupferstichkabinett in Berlin (cat. 539B), in the series of the *Life of Joseph* which was inspired by the Master of the Story of Tobit. FRIEDLÄNDER (IV, 1926, p. 81) and BOON (1950-51, pp. 90-91) consider the *Kneeling Lady* as the work of a follower of Hugo van der Goes, but BOON *(ibidem)* does not accept the comparison made by POPHAM (V, 1932, p. 64, no. 10) to the drawings for stained-glass windows in Berlin, and he dates the drawing between 1490 and 1500.

SIMON MARMION

Active in Amiens from 1449 to 1454, in Valenciennes from 1458 to 1489
Born in Amiens(?). Died in Valenciennes in 1489

Miniaturist and painter, he is named, beginning in 1449, in numerous documents of the cities of Amiens, Lille (1454), Tournai, where he was enrolled in the Painters Guild in 1468, and, especially, Valenciennes. No signed or duly documented works by him have come down to us. To him is attributed the altarpiece in the Abbey of Saint-Bertin in Saint-Omer (Berlin Museum and London National Gallery) dedicated in 1459 by the Abbot Guillaume Fillastre, as well as several illuminated manuscripts (notably in Brussels and Leningrad). Starting from these facts, his catalogue has been considerably enlarged on the basis of stylistic criteria. It is likely that he was trained in the French School and then strongly influenced by the Flemish painters, especially Dieric Bouts, to the extent that he may be classified among them.

There are some dozen works in the United States which are ascribed to him or to his workshop, in Louisville, New York, Philadelphia, and Washington.

62. PIETA

Cambridge, Mass., Fogg Art Museum, Harvard University
Acc. no. 1941-343

This *Pietà* is attributed to Simon Marmion and can be compared to two paintings in the United States which are attributed to this artist, a *Crucifixion* in the John G. Johnson Collection in Philadelphia and a *Pietà* in the

219

Robert Lehman Collection in New York. This is the only drawing known which is considered as having been done by this artist.

Physical data: Silverpoint on paper prepared with an ivory ground, 6 x 4 ¹/₂ in. (153 x115 mm.). Non-original inscription in the lower left corner: *Peter van Lint.*
The sheet must have been cut down at the right edge (WISHY, 1959, no. 20).

History: Lewis Gilbertson Coll., 1926; Henry Oppenheimer Coll., 1932; Oppenheimer sale, London (Christie's), July 10-14, 1936, no. 269; acquired by the Fogg Art Museum, 1941. Cleaned after the Oppenheimer sale (1936).

Exhibitions: London, 1927, no. 503; London, 1932, no. 637; Philadelphia, 1950-51, no. 14; Detroit, 1951, no. 1; Pittsburgh, 1951, no. 129; New York, 1959, no. 20.

POPHAM (1926, p. 21), the first to publish this drawing, considered it a copy of a lost work by Simon Marmion. Subsequently, after 1936, a cleaning of this drawing revealed its unsuspected qualities. This prompted MONGAN (1942, pp. 115-120) and WISHY (1959, no. 20) to consider it one of the rare and finest original drawings of the Franco-Flemish School from the end of the 15th century which are in the United States. The two specialists believe it is certainly from the hand of Simon Marmion, by comparison with the *Crucifixion* in the John G. Johnson Collection in Philadelphia (cat. 318), which was done for the Abbey of Saint-Bertin in Saint-Omer, and which is considered as a key work of Simon Marmion.

VRANCKE VAN DER STOCKT

Active in Brussels, 1444-1495
Died in Brussels in 1495

In 1444, he inherited the workshop of his father, Jan van der Stockt. In 1464, he succeeded his teacher, Roger van der Weyden, as painter of the City of Brussels. He also worked in Hal in 1460 and in Bruges in 1468. There are no known works by him which are signed or duly documented. Some drawings, as well as paintings, are attributed to him.

He is often identified as being the Master of the Redemption of the Prado, after a triptych of this subject preserved in Madrid. Other paintings

220

in the style of Roger van der Weyden are attributed to him, although more general terms such as "follower of van der Weyden", would often seem more suitable for those works.

Three paintings preserved in American collections are attributed to this artist, in New York, Oberlin, and Rochester.

63. CHRIST AMONG THE DOCTORS

New York, N.Y., The Pierpont Morgan Library. Cat. I, no. 226

This drawing is generally attributed to Vrancke van der Stockt. It shows the Virgin and Saint Joseph as they find the Christ Child in the Temple in a theological discussion with the Doctors.

221

Physical data: Pen and brown ink over traces of black chalk on salmon-tinted paper, 9 ^{1}/$_2$ x 6 ^{15}/$_{16}$ in. (241 x 176 mm.).
History: Lord Palmerston Coll.; Charles Fairfax Murray Coll.; acquired by The Pierpont Morgan Library in 1910.
Exhibitions: None known.

Bock and Rosenberg (I, 1930, p. 7) attribute this drawing to the same hand that was responsible for *The Descent of the Holy Ghost*, a drawing in the Berlin Kupferstichkabinett (cat. 5427). Wescher (1938, p. 3) also believes it related to the Berlin work as well as to a series of other drawings which he attributes to the Master of the Redemption of the Prado. He judges the author of these drawings to have been a Brussels artist who specialized in decorative painting, such as mural painting. He thinks he was an artist who, as the head of a studio, would often have had to do rapid compositions for the use of his assistants and, moreover, would have been in contact with German art. Vrancke van der Stockt fills all these conditions exactly, and Wescher concludes from this that these drawings are evidence in favor of the thesis of Hulin de Loo (XXIV, 1926-29, col. 70-72), who suggested that the Master of the Redemption of the Prado and Vrancke van der Stockt were one and the same person.

64.   EXERCITIUM SUPER PATER NOSTER II

Mons, Bibliothèque Publique. Cat. no. 190

This book is a rare and precious example of the type called xylographic book which, in the first half of the 15th century, constituted a transitional step between illustrated manuscripts and printed books. Xylographic books were printed by means of woodcuts on which the text and illustrations were engraved, an application of the process of wood engraving, which had been known for only a short time. In the period of the Dukes of Burgundy, the Southern Netherlands were one of the principal production centers for these books, much less expensive than manuscript books. Considered then as works of little value, these books must have been numerous. They have now almost all disappeared, and there are scarcely a hundred known in the world. This work is the only one preserved which was printed in Flemish. It was probably produced in a Brussels workshop. Its text, commentaries on the Lord's Prayer, was written by an Augustine canon in Brussels, Henric Uten Bogaerde, who had latinized his name as Pomerius. The illustrations were engraved from drawings by Vrancke van der Stockt. The book was printed between 1447 and 1450.

Physical data: Paper, xylographic book, 8 folios, 11 x 8 ^{1}/$_4$ in. (280 x 210 mm.). Incomplete. Binding from the Romantic period.
History: Unknown.
Exhibitions: Brussels, 1935, no no.; Brussels, 1953, no. 86.

222

First published by CHATTS (1844). DE BACKER (1924) described it and LEBEER (1938, pp. 15-54 and 1953, pp. 189-217) stressed its importance, identified its authors, and was able to fix its date within narrow limits. The copy is incomplete, but an exact idea can be had of what it was originally like thanks to another copy, also incomplete, in the Bibliothèque Nationale in Paris. It is fortunate that the pages missing from the Mons copy are present in the Paris one. These two copies belong to the second edition of the *Exercitium Super Pater Noster*, published some twenty years after the appearance of the first edition. LEBEER (1938) made a comparison between this book and another one also written by Pomerius, the *Spirituale Pomerium*. The author demonstrated that Vrancke van der Stockt had done the illustrations in the latter book and he determined that the artist was also the author of the models for the illustrations in the *Exercitium* in Mons. He dates this second edition between 1447 and 1450; thus, a little after the *Pomerium*, whose execution was not as successful. He believes, further, that the execution of this *Exercitium* can be traced to Brussels.

Drawing and Woodcut

224

Drawing and Woodcut

MASTER OF THE SAINT BARBARA LEGEND
For biography, see p. 127

65. EPISODES IN THE LEGEND OF SAINT BARBARA

New York, N.Y., The Pierpont Morgan Library. Cat. III, no. 127

This drawing is considered a preliminary study from the hand of the Master of the Saint Barbara Legend in preparation for a painting illustrating that legend. The painting, part of which still exists, was a triptych. The drawing corresponds to the composition of the left half of the central panel of this triptych, panel which is preserved in the Musées Royaux des Beaux-Arts in Brussels. Recently, the Reverend Bollandist Baudouin de Gaiffier discovered the text of the version of the legend which was followed by the painter (see this catalogue, entry no. 25). Thanks to this discovery, he was able to identify and explain all the iconographic elements of this drawing. It can be seen that the artist conformed to even the slightest details of this literary text.

The episodes of the legend which are illustrated in this drawing are the immediate continuation of those shown in the left wing of the triptych, the panel which is preserved in Bruges and is being shown in this exhibition as no. 25. On the left, Saint Barbara descends from the tower and then comes outside to observe the progress being made in the work which her father ordered. She looks at the painted and carved decorations, among which are representations of the sun, the moon, and the stars. These can be found on the roof of the small shelter housing the bath which her father, Dioscorus, had built for his daughter. An angel descends from heaven and comes to the tower to explain to Barbara the mystery of the Incarnation. A little later the Incarnate Word appears to Barbara in the window in the form of a young child. The angel continues his discourse, teaching Barbara about the suffering which Christ had to undergo in order to save the world, and Barbara sees the body of the Child covered with wounds, in the window on the right. Barbara, wishing to receive baptism, goes to the thermal pavilion. She first has a conversation with an envoy of Origen, who has come to complete her instruction (on the right). Then, lead by an angel (the angel is not mentioned in the literary text), Barbara traces a small sign of the cross on a marble column of the pavilion and she makes an imprint of her right foot on the tile. Kneeling, she miraculously receives baptism by the hands of Saint John the Baptist, under the eyes of the Holy Trinity, Christ and God the Father (undoubtedly the Dove also, but it is not clearly seen), represented here, rather unusually, behind Saint John the Baptist.

Physical data: Pen and brown ink on paper, 11 5/16 x 5 in. (287 x 127 mm.). Non-original inscription in brown ink on the lower right: *Lucas van Leyden.* Modern inscription in dark brown ink on lower left: *Rijmsdijk's Museum.*
History: Jan van Rijmsdijk's Coll.; Charles Fairfax Murray Coll.; acquired by The Pierpont Morgan Library in 1910.
Exhibitions: New York, 1919.

225

FRIEDLÄNDER (1924-25, p. 21, note 1) was the first to connect this drawing with another one now in the Louvre (no. 22.665); he believed the two drawings were a preparatory work for a diptych which was not realized. This composition, however, has been used for a triptych of which two panels are preserved (see cat. no. 25). Furthermore, since the discovery by de GAIFFIER (1959, pp. 3-23) of the literary version of the Saint Barbara Legend, which the painter clearly followed, it has become evident that the New York drawing represents the second quarter of the story and that the Louvre drawing represents the following part

of the legend. The two drawings have different dimensions and proportions; this make it difficult to reach any conclusion as to their interdependance and their relationship to the triptych.

WESCHER (1938, p. 5) pointed out the closeness of this drawing to some drawings preserved in Oxford (Vasari Society, VIII, pl. 15-18).

FLEMISH, 15th Century

66. A YOUNG LADY STANDING

Ghent, Private Collection

This drawing is probably an old copy after a drawing of the Flemish School of Memlinc's period. If there was an original, it is not known. It seems to be a portrait. The young woman's clothes and head-dress are in the fashion of the second half of the 15th century. As far as it is known this drawing has not yet been published.

Physical data: Pen and ink on paper, 8 1/4 x 3 5/16 in. (210 x 85 mm.) Humidity spot on the skirt.
History: H. Hamal Coll.; De Backer Coll., before 1953.
Exhibitions: Ghent, 1953, no. 3; Malines-Brou, 1958, no. 210.

Drawing and Woodcut

According to the owner, this drawing was formerly attributed to Jan van Eyck, but is considered by FRIEDLÄNDER and WINKLER as a copy from a lost original of around 1470-1480 which was done by someone in Memlinc's entourage. It had been formerly suggested that this might be a portrait of Jacqueline of Bavaria. The shape of the sleeves and the style of head-dress bring this drawing close in time to the period of execution of *A Saint Preaching* by the Master of the View of Sainte-Gudule in the Louvre in Paris (Inv. 1991) of ca. 1470-80, where two young women are wearing head-dresses of the same type. This characteristic head-dress is also found in the tapestry *Esther and Ahasuerus* from the Institute of Arts in Minneapolis (this cat. no. 151) where it is worn by two of Esther's attendants.

FLEMISH, 15th Century

67.   SAINT JAMES THE MINOR

New York, N.Y., The Pierpont Morgan Library. Cat. I, no. 225

This drawing represents Saint James the Minor, recognizable by his attributes, the book and a fuller's staff, a kind of bent club.

It probably belonged to a series of the twelve Apostles of which there is a replica on paper in the Albertina in Vienna: this series shows six seated apostles, as is the one on exhibition, and six standing; the name of the apostle is written in Gothic letters above each of them. The complete series of Vienna and also the New York drawing are thought to be copies of the 15th century after lost originals by Jan van Eyck. The drawing from The Pierpont Morgan Library, on parchment and not on paper as are those of Vienna, is regarded as being of a higher quality than the latter.

Physical data: Brush drawing on parchment in pale greenish-brown with some pen work; edges and folds of garments partly outlined in gold; touches of red on lips, flesh tone on cheeks; 5 1/4 x 3 3/8 in. (136 x 86 mm.).

History: W. Russell Coll.; Charles Fairfax Murray Coll.; acquired by The Pierpont Morgan Library in 1910.

Exhibitions: New York, 1919; State University of Iowa, 1951, no. 4.

The drawing from New York was first attributed to Petrus Christus when it was in the Fairfax Murray Collection (Cat. of this collection, 1905-1912, I, no. 225). WINKLER (1916, p. 297, note 2) was the first to point out the resemblance of the New York Saint James the Minor with the same apostle in the series of the twelve Apostles in the Albertina in Vienna (cat. 1928, nos. 1-12)

227

Drawing and Woodcut

which were previously attributed to Israel van Meckenem and to identify this series as copies of lost originals by Jan van Eyck. FRIEDLÄNDER (I, 1924, p. 126) states that these lost originals must be attributed to Jan van Eyck and dates them ca. 1430. This attribution was accepted by BENESCH (1928, p. 3, nos. 1-12). This last author considers that the Vienna copies were themselves done in the 15th century. BALDASS (1952, p. 284) supposes that the originals were used as models for small sculptured pieces, perhaps for the decoration of a reliquary and he places the lost originals between 1430 and 1434.

Another apostle on parchment also exists in corresponding dimensions to the one in New York: it is a Saint Paul which is almost identical to the drawing of the same Saint in the series in Vienna. It measures 5 ³/₄ x 3 ¹/₈ in. (146 x 78 mm.) and was on the art market in Paris in 1927 (BENESCH, 1928, no. 2). It was sold with the Graupe Collection in Berlin on May 12, 1930 (no. 70). WINKLER (1931, p. 258) points out another series of twelve Apostles which also derive from the Jan van Eyck originals; it is an incomplete series of which there are some examples in the Musée du Louvre in Paris and in the Musée Bonnat in Bayonne.

228

Drawing and Woodcut

JEAN DE VALENCIENNES

Active in Bruges from 1378 to 1386

The appellation "van Valenchine" - from Valenciennes - which is found in the accounts of the City of Bruges, leads to the supposition that this artist might have been a native of that town or had worked in Valenciennes which was an important artistic center in the second half of the 14th century. The presence of a Jean de Valenciennes is attested to in Bruges in 1364. In fact, at this date his name appears in the list of jurors of the Corporation of Painters and Sculptors. It is likely that this artist is the same as the one who, in 1379, directed the sculpture atelier which worked on the decoration of the façade of the City Hall of Bruges. The accounts again refer to activities of Jean de Valenciennes in 1382 (notably at the Ducal Palace of Bruges) and in 1386 (the Aldermanic room of the Bruges City Hall). Some have identified the sculptor Jean de Valenciennes who worked on the tympanum of the Portal de la Mar of the Cathedral of Palma de Mallorca, after the death of Pere Morey in 1394, with the artist of same name whose activities are referred to in Bruges.

68. ZACHARIAH AND THE ARCHANGEL GABRIEL
TRISTAN AND ISEULT
Two corbels from the City Hall of Bruges

Bruges, Gruuthuse-Museum. Inv. II, nos. 404-405

These two historiated corbels were formerly on the façade of the City Hall in Bruges where they served to support statues. The statues were destroyed at the time of the French Revolution in 1792 but the corbels remained in place until 1854, when they were removed to a museum during the restoration of the building. Copies replaced them on the façade. There is a documentation on the history of the construction of the City Hall which allows the dating of the corbels about 1379. It may be supposed that they are the work of the sculptor Jean de Valenciennes or his workshop.

The interpretation of the subject matter of these two corbels is uncertain. It is generally considered that one represents Zachariah and the Archangel Gabriel who announces to the incredulous old man that he will have a son, the future Saint John the Baptist. The other corbel may represent an episode of the Celtic(?) legend of Tristan and Iseult. The protagonists of this love story have drunk the magic philtre which Brangien (the personage shown apart at the right) has given them by mistake.

229

These two corbels are very important for studying the style of sculpture in Flanders at the end of the 14th century. Very few examples of sculpture in the Netherlands during the 14th century still remain but there are enough to prove that Claus Sluter may have received there the basic training which he used in creating the new style.

Physical data : Limestone, 11 ⁷/₁₆ x 21 ¹/₄ x 9 ⁷/₈ in. (29 x 54 x 25 cm.) and 10 ⁵/₈ x 15 ⁵/₁₆ x 9 ⁷/₈ in. (27 x 39 x 25 cm.), not including the 5 ⁷/₈ in. (15 cm.) of plain stone block intended to be sunk into the wall. Traces of old polychromy. Damage to the face of Zachariah; the right hand of Brangien is missing as well as part of her nose.

History: The historiated corbels are visible, but not identifiable, on a view of the façade of the City Hall of Bruges made before the French Revolution and on a drawing by E. Vermote in 1813, after the Revolution and before the mid-19th century restoration (Janssens de Bisthoven, 1944, p. 20). This data supports the identification of these corbels with those known to have been carved and polychromed about 1379 for the City Hall which was erected on the site of the former House of the Aldermen, demolished in 1376, as attested by communal accounts published by Janssens de Bisthoven (1944, pp. 9-11 and 70-73). In 1854, at the time of the restoration of the City Hall, sixteen corbels including the present two, were removed and placed in the Cloth Hall, then in the Lapidary Museum of the Gruuthuse (Janssens de Bisthoven, 1944, pp. 43-44).

Exhibitions: Ghent, 1956, nos. 125 and 128.

It seems likely that these corbels were put in place and polychromed in 1379. In that year the accounts of the construction mention payments to the sculptor Jean de Valenciennes as head of a workshop. Moreover, it is possible that these corbels were made in that sculptor's workshop as Janssens de Bisthoven (1944, pp. 36-43) believes. This author further observes that the renowned sculptor Jean de Marville worked in Bruges at the same period (1376) for Philip the Bold. Janssens de Bisthoven wonders whether Jean de Marville did not work in the atelier of Jean de Valenciennes in 1379. From 1380 Jean de Marville was at Champmol at the service of Philip the Bold and after

230

1385, he was assisted by Claus Sluter. The two corbels of Bruges do indeed present a certain kinship of style with the sculptures of the Chartreuse of Champmol. Many authorities in this field have stressed the affinities of style which exist between these corbels and the statues of prophets as well as the historiated corbels of the old portal of the City Hall of Brussels which can be dated 1385-1390 according to BERGIUS (1937, pp. 96-102), or more probably before 1385 according to ROGGEN (1945-1948, pp. 29-38). In that case they could be youthful works of Claus Sluter. The corbels of Bruges may be compared, furthermore, with the ones of the former City Hall of Malines, presumed works of Jan van Mansdaele, which date from 1383-1385 (SQUILBECK, 1933, pp. 329-333).

BRUSSELS, beginning of the 15th Century

69-70. THE THREE YOUNG GIRLS AND THE MIRACULOUS BIRD
THE PAYMENT OF THE WORKMEN BY THE THREE YOUNG GIRLS
Two scenes from THE ALTARPIECE OF THE MIRACULOUS FOUNDATION
OF THE CHURCH OF HAKENDOVER

Hakendover, Church of Saint-Sauveur

These two groups belong to the oldest of the large carved altarpieces in wood preserved in Belgium: they are two of the twelve scenes which recount the history of the miraculous foundation of the church at Hakendover. The first one represents the bird bringing to the three young girls a message from God indicating the place where they should build the church, while the other shows the

231

three young girls paying the workmen after the completion of the church. The altarpiece also includes twenty-four statuettes of apostles and saints, a Crucifixion, and a figure of Christ the Saviour. When open, this altarpiece measures 19 ft. 4 in. (5.90 m) in width. It no longer has its original polychromy.

The name of the artist of this monumental work as well as the date of its execution are unknown. The specialists who have shown great interest in the piece as much for its outstanding qualities as for its rarity, have placed its date of execution at the beginning of the 15th century and consider it related to the art of Brabant.

Physical data: Applewood(?) (MAERE, 1920, p. 83), *The Three Young Girls:* 14 9/16 x 11 x 8 1/4 in. (37 x 28 x 21 cm.); *The Payment of the Workmen:* 14 15/16 x 13 3/4 x 5 7/8 in. (38 x 35 x 15 cm.). Polychromy and gilding completely taken off. The enclosing structure is of oak. On the back it bears the large letters cut with a chisel F V M T and M(?) (MAERE, 1920, p. 97, note 2). Good state of preservation. Traces of the original polychromy at the back.

History: In the course of his official visits to Hakendover, the dean of Tirlemont noted in 1715 that there was on the altar "a piece of very old but very decorative furniture" and in 1723 that this furnishing "which decorates the high altar represents, in sculpture, the history of the miraculous foundation of the church" (Archives de l'Archevêché de Malines, *Visitationes decanales,* cited by MAERE, 1920, p. 74, notes 3-4). From the reports in the Archives de la Commission Royale des Monuments it is learned that in 1852 the altarpiece still had its polychromy but in a bad state; that it was entrusted in the years 1853-1856 to the restorer Sondervorst of Tirlemont; that in 1875 it was in good condition but that its original arrangement had been modified (R. M. Marijnissen graciously made available for the catalogue the information he has assembled). In 1864 it no longer had any polychromy and the *Crucifixion* was missing (WEALE, 1864, nos. 142-176). About 1880 a cast was made of all the sculptures of the altarpiece and this cast has preserved the head of Saint Gertrude wearing a fluted bonnet, which has since disappeared. The group of

The Virgin and Saint John at the Crucifixion, which existed in 1894 (DESTRÉE, 1894, p. 78) disappeared shortly thereafter; it is no longer to be seen in a photograph of the altarpiece made in 1896 (DE KONINCK, 1896, pl. III). In 1919-1920 van Uytvanck of Louvain restored the altarpiece; he did not know of the existence of the cast (MAERE, 1920, pp. 80-82).

Exhibitions: Malines, 1864, nos. 118 and 121 (1st edition), nos. 170 and 173 (2nd edition).

WEALE (1864, nos. 90-124), PIOT (1867, pp. 236-237), Jean ROUSSEAU (1877, pp. 27-33), BETS (1882, p. 33), and Henri ROUSSEAU (1891, pp. 29-33), with slight variations, placed the altarpiece in the second half of the 14th century. WAUTERS (1882, p. 66) on the contrary, placed it much later, in the second half of the 15th century. MAERE (1920,

232

pp. 86-97) made the most complete analysis of the altarpiece, placed it at
the end of the 14th or very early in the 15th century, and discerned the
hands of a principal artist and of assistants, the two groups in this exhibition
being by the principal master. He compared the *Hakendover Altarpiece* with
the stone tabernacle of the Church of Saint-Martin in Hal, dated 1409. In
spite of the difference of material, he found such a close relationship between
the two works, notably in the heads of the group in *The Payment of the
Workmen* at Hakendover and of the personages in *The Washing of the Feet* at
Hal that he was tempted to believe them by the same artist. He thought the
Altarpiece of Hakendover to be contemporary with that of Saint Clare in the
Cologne Cathedral. The sculptured canopies of Hakendover seemed to him to
come from the same Brabantine workshop as those of the *Altarpiece of the
Passion* of Grönau in Lübeck, but the figure sculpture of Grönau was made
by a German artist. Nevertheless he notes certain analogies without drawing
any conclusion. The Christ of *The Crowning with Thorns* at Grönau, for
example, wears a long shirt with flaring cuffs on the sleeves as seen in the
costumes of the young girls at Hakendover. DEVIGNE (1932, p. 104) dates the

233

Sculpture

Hakendover Altarpiece from the first quarter of the 15th century. GERSTENBERG (1933, p. 164) places it about 1410. ROGGEN (1934, pp. 108-121) proposes to date it much later, after 1432, giving later examples of the same details of costume and hair style. On the other hand, he bases his argument on two points: first, the choir at Hakendover has the right proportions to accommodate this wide altarpiece and he deduces that the altarpiece is later than the construction of the choir in 1425; and second, a written account of the miraculous origin of the construction of the church was sent to Rome for official recognition in 1432; as the iconography of the altarpiece conforms so closely to that of the written account, he deduces that the altarpiece is later than 1432. DUVERGER (1935, p. 43, note 97) refutes these two arguments: nothing proves that the new choir was not built on the same plan as the earlier one; there probably existed a version of the story, older and perhaps similar to that which was sent to Rome in 1432.

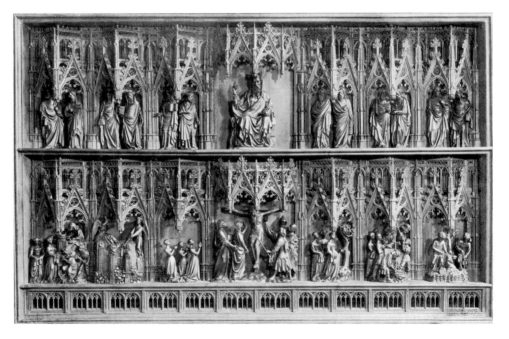

Central part of the altarpiece

234

Sculpture

FLANDERS (GHENT ?), middle of the 15th Century

71. SAINT PETER
Bracket for a beam

Ghent, Museum voor
Oudheden der Bijloke
Inv. no. 855

This large block of wood carved with the figure of Saint Peter under a canopy is a support for a beam, that is, a short beam which projects from the wall and adds support to the long beam that extends across the ceiling of a room. It formerly decorated the House of the Corporation of the Tanners at Ghent.

This sculpture is dated in the 15th century, starting from the presumed date of the construction or decoration of the House of the Tanners.

> *Physical data:* Oak, 51 $^3/_{16}$ x 15 $^3/_8$ x 4 $^3/_4$ in. (130 x 39 x 12 cm.); the figure: 29 $^1/_2$ in. (75 cm.). Some damage to the canopy on the right side.
>
> *History:* Still in place in the House of the Corporation of the Tanners in 1857; removed in or before 1883; sold by Verhulst, Ghent, and acquired by the City (Cat. Exhib. Ghent, 1913, no. 1107).
>
> *Exhibitions:* Ghent, 1913, no. 1107; Ghent, 1956, no. 132; Ghent, 1958, no. 15.

According to CLAEYS (1906, no. 406) the communal accounts show that about 1451 the construction of the House of the Corporation of the Tanners was begun.

CASIER and BERGMANS (I, 1914, pp. 59-60) consider this sculpture to be a work from the Ghent School of the middle of the 15th century.

Sculpture

BRABANT(?), ca. 1470-1480

72.   SAINT MARGARET OF ANTIOCH

Bruges, Gruuthuse-Museum
Inv. II, no. 66

This graceful figure represents Saint Margaret. The origin of this sculpture is not known but the style allows the assumption that it was produced in the Southern Netherlands and very likely in Brabant. Stylistic features and costume would seem to date the execution of the figure about 1470-1480. On the sculpture are preserved several pieces of a former polychromy, notably at the back on the mantle of red textile enriched with gold. In 15th century documents, that material is called *drap d'or* ("gold cloth").

Saint Margaret is shown standing on the dragon which she overcame by the sign of the cross. The dragon still holds in its jaws a fold of the Saint's mantle. The hands are lost; they perhaps held a cross and a book or this last attribute only since the Saint wears a cross in the form of a pendant suspended from her neck. The court mantle which rises very high behind the head and was held together in front by two buckles linked by a small chain, as well as the headdress in the form of a crown, recall that Margaret was the daughter of a king.

> *Physical data:* Oak, 34 5/8 in. (88 cm.). Traces of polychromy and gilding which may be original. The hands are lost.
>
> *History:* In 1882 in the Collection of Jules Frésart in Liège (DE RODDAZ, 1882, ill. p. 247).
>
> *Exhibitions:* Copenhagen, 1931, no. 316.

236

This sculpture has never been the subject of a specialized study. Style and costume seem to indicate that it was made about 1470-1480.

BRUSSELS, ca. 1475-1480

73. THE LEGEND OF SAINT LEONARD
Three scenes of the right wing of THE ALTARPIECE OF SAINT LEONARD

Léau, Church of Saint-Léonard

These three scenes, comprising all together seventeen figures, occupy the right compartment of the carved altarpiece which has for its subject the story of Saint Léonard. The left compartment presents a group of similar importance. The central compartment, higher than the others, has lost its sculptured group. These three compartments are decorated with sculptured canopies of architectural form as are seen in all the altarpieces of this kind, but those of the *Altarpiece of Saint Leonard* are among the most remarkable of their type. The work is that of a Brussels workshop as indicated by the mallet mark of that city. The artist's name is unknown. This anonymous sculptor worked about 1475-1480, to judge by the style of the sculpture and by the costumes of the figures. This dating is confirmed by a church account which mentions the altarpiece in the year 1475. The altarpiece must have been commissioned to decorate the chapel of Saint-Leonard which had just been added to the church for the pilgrims who were attracted in great numbers by the renown of the miraculous statue and of the relics of Saint Leonard. Other items of value completed the furnishing of this chapel from 1481 to 1484, notably a large chandelier and a brass closure surmounted by statues, commissioned from Renier van Thienen in Brussels, an embroidered antependium which was acquired in Lierre, and a new reliquary, the work of a goldsmith of Louvain.

The sculptures shown in this exhibition represent three scenes of the legend of Saint Leonard, a hermit who lived in the 6th century: Saint Leonard, in his humility, refusing the mitre, symbol of episcopal rank; the king requesting the Saint to pray for the queen who has been seized with the pangs of childbirth in the midst of the forest during a hunting party; Saint Leonard in prayer with the king and the queen who is assisted by her ladies in waiting. Several of the personages wear the high bonnet characteristic of the period about 1470-1480; the queen and her attendants wear the tall hennin of the same period.

Physical data: Oak, the three groups together: 22 ^{1}/$_4$ x 32 ^{11}/$_{16}$ x 11 ^{13}/$_{16}$ in. (56.5 x 83 x 30 cm.); average height of the figures: 16 ^{9}/$_{16}$ in. (42 cm.). Polychromed and gilded. In a good state of preservation. The polychromy and gilding are probably not original; they do not seem to cover an older polychromy. City mark of Brussels, a mallet, on the back of each of the three principal groups. Inscription in pencil(?) on the gilding under the right arm of Saint Leonard in prayer: *G. Luyten 1873 16 xb* (result of an examination made in April 1960 on the occasion of the conservation of this group at the Institut Royal du Patrimoine Artistique in Brussels).

237

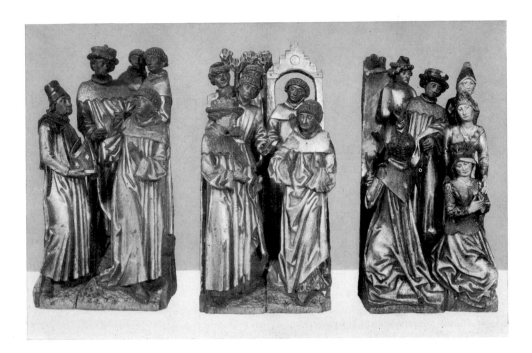

History: The financial records of the church for the year "of the St. John" 1478-79 mention the following for the month of September 1479: *Item Aert dy moelder ghegeven van onse liever vrouwen bielden te makene ende van dat hy bij kerckmeesters te Bruesele ghegaen was om die tafele van Synte Leenaerts. Int Jaer voerleden ghegeven ter goeden rekenynghen 5 gulden* (Archives ecclésiastiques du Brabant, register 1215, fol. 238. Noted by PIOT, 1860, pp. 58-59; transcribed for this catalogue at the Archives Générales du Royaume in Brussels, April 15, 1960, no. 75827). The inscription on the gilding, dated December 16, 1873, perhaps refers to a restorer at that date.

Exhibitions: Brussels and Delft, 1957-1958, nos. 74 and 75: two statuettes (the person offering the mitre and the Saint listening to the request of the king) which were then shown at the Musées Royaux des Beaux-Arts in Brussels in 1958 as an exchange for the loan of a painting to Léau.

The text in the accounts for 1479 may be translated as follows: "Item, given to Master Aert de Maelder for having made images of Our Lady and for having been to Brussels at the request [(or) to see] the members of the church council for that altarpiece of Saint Leonard. In the past year given on account 5 florins".

In spite of its lack of precision this document comes to the support of the indications given by the style and by the costumes to place the sculptures ca. 1475-1480. The record does not specify in what capacity Master Aert de Maelder acted. He seems to have been a painter rather than a sculptor because, on the one hand, this name (*maelder* = painter) could as well be a description of his occupation as a surname, and on the other hand, there is the evidence in the church accounts, several years later, in July 1483, that a certain Aert di scilder (*scilder* = painter) was paid for having furnished a design (TARLIER and WAUTERS, II, part 2, 1887, p. 62). This document is in the Archives Générales

238

du Royaume (Archives ecclésiastiques du Brabant, register 1216, fol. 89 v°, accounts for 1482-83). It is possible that Aert de Maelder and Aert di scilder are the same artist, a painter. In this case the account of 1479 probably refers to the execution of a pattern for the altarpiece, that is to say, a drawing which could be realized by the sculptor, or to the polychromy of the altarpiece, or even to the execution of painted wings, now lost, for the carved altarpiece.

ROGGEN (1937, pp. 276 and 280) draws attention to the manifest influence of the style of Dieric Bouts on the author of these sculptures. It is not to be disputed that by their elongated silhouettes, their controlled but very expressive gestures, and the gravity of their expressions, the personages of these sculptures recall those of the paintings of Dieric Bouts, notably the *Last Supper* (Louvain, Church of Saint-Pierre) of which the wings are shown in this exhibition (no. 17) and more especially the *Justice of Otto* (Brussels, Musées Royaux des Beaux-Arts, nos. 65-66). The pose of the person offering the mitre and that of Saint Leonard moved to pity by the anguish of the king are very close to attitudes found in the *Proof by Fire* of the *Justice of Otto*. This panel was finished and exhibited in the City Hall of Louvain by 1473; it is after this time that the altarpiece of Léau might be dated. The church record of 1479 seems to lend support to this dating. PIOT (1860, pp. 58-59), who discovered the record but did not publish it in full, gave the following interpretation, which seems erroneous: "The members of the church council went to Brussels in order to make a payment to Aert de Maelder for his altarpiece of Saint Leonard". In addition, this author, considering Aert de Maelder as the sculptor of the altarpiece, suggested identifying him with a certain Arnould de Diest, who, some twenty-three years earlier, in 1455-56, had delivered to the church at Léau some carved canopies. DESTRÉE (1894, pp. 164-169) and ROUSSEAU (1896, p. 20) and, after them, most of the specialists in this field have based themselves on this double error. Following in their wake ROOSVAL (1933, p. 137) has believed himself able to give to the activity of this Arnould de Diest and to his workshop a whole series of altarpieces at present in Sweden as well as that of Vemö in Finland. This confusion must be cleared up and the name of Aert de Maelder abandoned as that of a sculptor. The suggestion of BAUDOUIN (1957, no. 75) which proposes to identify Aert de Maelder with a painter of Louvain named Arnoul Raes the Younger is only an hypothesis. The sculptor of Léau may in time be reconstructed from his works.

The altarpiece of Saint Leonard at Léau may be compared with that called of Claude de Villa in Brussels (Musées Royaux d'Art et d'Histoire) which might be by the same hand.

Brussels city mark
(Geel Altarpiece)

239

The Altarpiece of the Passion at Geel. The arrows indicate the four carvings on exhibition

240

Sculpture

BRUSSELS, ca. 1480-1500

74-77. SAINT VERONICA, THE CENTURION LONGINUS and
TWO ANGELS from THE ALTARPIECE OF THE PASSION

Geel, Church of Sainte-Dymphne

These four statuettes belong to a Crucifixion group which occupies the central compartment of a large altarpiece of the Passion. Saint Veronica presents the veil on which was imprinted the Holy Face. Longinus, the Centurion, is suddenly illuminated by faith and he points with his uplifted right hand to the Christ. The two angels soar in the air near the cross. The whole altarpiece measures 8 ft. 6$^1/_2$ in. (2.60 m.) in height by 9 ft. $^1/_2$ in. (3 m.) in width; it comprises forty figures like the ones in this exhibition as well as seventy-four smaller figures on consoles and under canopies at the sides of the three main groups. The intricately carved canopies are admirable in workmanship. The altarpiece still retains its painted wings.

The author of this altarpiece is not known. That he was from Brussels is apparent from the mark of that city (the mallet) impressed on the back of the sculptured groups. To judge by the style, the work was executed in the last twenty years of the 15th century. Its workmanship is of such exceptional quality as to class the altarpiece among the best of its kind.

Such altarpieces in wood, replete with many carved figures and rich architectural detail, brilliantly painted and gilded, enjoyed a very great vogue at this period. Brussels and Antwerp were the principal centers of production of such works, many of which were exported, notably to the Scandinavian countries where they are still found in great numbers.

Physical data: Oak, *Veronica:* 22 $^1/_{16}$ in. (56 cm.); the *Centurion:* 23 $^1/_4$ in. (59 cm.); the *Angels:* 3 $^{11}/_{16}$ in. (22 cm.), with wingspread of 14 in. (35.5 cm.). Polychromed and gilded. The state of preservation is good in so far as the sculpture is concerned. The polychromy and gilding are not old save for the flesh parts and the veil of Veronica which have large crackles showing them to be old, if not original. City mark of Brussels, the mallet, accompanied by another in the form of a Greek cross with split extremities on the back of two of the principal groups (found in 1959 during the restoration of the altarpiece at the Institut Royal du Patrimoine Artistique in Brussels, MARIJNISSEN and SAWKO-MICHALSKY, 1960, pp. 147-149, 152).

History: The presence of the altarpiece in the church is attested for the first time about 1825 by the request of a collector, Chevalier Florent van Ertborn, who addressed the members of the church council with a view to acquiring the altarpiece (KUYL, 1863, p. 129).

Restored in 1850-1855, principally the polychromy (Archives de la Commission Royale des Monuments, MARIJNISSEN and SAWKO-MICHALSKY, 1960, pp. 143-149). Restored in 1958-60 at the Institut Royal du Patrimoine Artistique in Brussels.

Exhibitions: None known.

It is reasonable to suppose that a work so monumental in size and so difficult to transport was made for the church in which it has been since 1825 at least. The iconography of neither the carved altarpiece nor the painted wings give any assistance on this point. The saints which figure on the exterior of the

241

Sculpture

242

Sculpture

wings give no indication either: they are Saints Anthony, Nicholas, George, Barbara, Catherine and Hadrian (Van Herck, 1951).

The discovery of the city marks in the form of a mallet places the execution of the altarpiece in a Brussels workshop. The other mark in the form of a Greek cross with split extremities is not yet identified, but the one found on an altarpiece in Vemö, Finland, also accompanied by the city mark of Brussels, may be identical to it (Roosval, 1933, p. 137, who refers to Meinander, 1908). de Borchgrave d'Altena (1948, p. 14) notes a relationship between the first *Altarpiece of the Passion* at Strengnäs, Sweden, called *Strengnäs I,* with the *Altarpiece of the Passion* at Geel. It is evident that the types of the personages and in particular of the female figures (of which the Saint Veronica offers an excellent example) are the same on both altarpieces, to such a degree that it would seem permissible to see in the two works products of the same workshop if not of the same hand. The altarpiece of *Strengnäs I* also bears the Brussels city mark. Roosval (1933, p. 141) discovered that this retable was ordered by Bishop Conrad Rogge which places the date of the commission between 1479 and 1501. d'Hulst (1953, pp. 143-144) proposed to attribute the paintings of the altarpiece in Geel to the workshop of the Master of the View of Sainte-Gudule.

If the second *Altarpiece of Strengnäs,* called *Strengnäs II,* is an Antwerp product as Roosval believes, it cannot be by the same hand or from the same workshop as the *Altarpiece of the Passion* at Geel as this author suggests (1933,

243

p. 141, note 2). D'HULST (1953, pp. 143-144) concludes that they come from the same workshop but he places it in Brussels because the painted wings of the two altarpieces are to be attributed, according to him, to the workshop of the Master of the View of Sainte-Gudule. As for the sculptured portions of the two altarpieces, as far as it is possible to judge from inadequate photographs, there is a wide difference in style between them.

BRUSSELS, ca. 1490

78-79. THE VIRGIN and SAINT JOHN from a CALVARY GROUP

Louvain, Collegiate Church of Saint-Pierre

These two monumental statues of the Virgin and of Saint John belong to a large Calvary group which dominates the choirscreen under the triumphal arch at the entrance of the choir of the Collegiate Church of Saint-Pierre in Louvain. Formerly numerous, such ensembles are rarely preserved today and the case of Louvain is truly exceptional, especially because it has retained its original arrangement: the Crucifix and the statues of the Virgin and of Saint John which flanked it are set up in a narrow base in the form of an altarpiece, ornamented on the side toward the nave with three statues of saints (Gregory, Paul and Jerome) and on the side toward the choir with three paintings in grisaille (Saints Ambrose, Henry and Augustine). The Calvary group has been taken down temporarily while the church is being repaired. The choirscreen has been heavily restored but the group is preserved almost intact with its old, perhaps original, polychromy. This Calvary is considered by art historians as one of the masterpieces of Flemish sculpture of the 15th century and the most beautiful work of its kind still existing in Belgium.

A date about 1490 seems possible for this Calvary group because it surmounted the choirscreen which was apparently being finished at that time. Several authorities have proposed an attribution to Jan Borman but with insufficient reasons, it would seem. On the other hand, it is reasonable to place its execution in Brussels. The influence of the art of Roger van der Weyden is still manifest in this work of about a quarter of a century after the death of the painter. The sculptures are to be compared in particular with the *Crucifixion* by van der Weyden in the Prado Museum in Madrid and also with the same artist's *Crucifixion* in two panels in the John G. Johnson Collection in Philadelphia.

Physical data: Oak, the *Virgin:* 70 ⁷/₈ in. (180 cm.); *Saint John:* 70 ¹/₈ in. (178 cm.). Old polychromy, restored.

244

Sculpture

History: In 1667 DE PARIVAL (cited by STEPPE, 1952, p. 84) speaks with admiration of the
great crucifix above the choirscreen of the Church of Saint-Pierre in Louvain. He notes
that, a short time before, it had been cleaned, repainted and gilded. The Calvary is to
be seen in a painting of the 17th century by Henri van Steenwyck the Younger, in the
Musées Royaux des Beaux-Arts in Brussels (cat. 448) (STEPPE, 1952, p. 82).
Restored in 1953 at the Institut Royal du Patrimoine Artistique, Brussels, when
numerous superimposed layers of modern paint and gilding were removed, and missing
parts filled in.
Exhibitions: Louvain, 1945, nos. 26 and 27; Brussels, 1951, no. 195; Brussels, 1954,
no. 147; Antwerp, 1954, no. 213.

This Calvary is often attributed to Jan Borman (Cat. Exh. Antwerp, 1954,
no. 213, and Louvain, 1954, nos. 26-27) or to his workshop (Cat. Exh. Brussels,
1954, no. 147). STEPPE (1952, p. 83, note 16) considers this possible. Recently
the Calvary was catalogued among Nicolas Gerhaert's work and dated 1440-
1450 (FLIEDNER, 1858, p. 197), but the attribution to a Brabant sculptor from
ca. 1490 is more probable. The activity of Jan Borman took place ca. 1479-1520.
Only two carved altarpieces done by him are preserved, but it is known that he also
made large sized figures such as the Crucifixion group for Diest in 1494 which
unhappily does not exist any more. The archives of the Church of Saint-
Pierre, destroyed in 1914 and in 1940, revealed nothing on the subject of the
execution of the choirscreen and of
its Crucifixion group. VAN EVEN
(1895, p. 355) claims that the screen
was erected in 1488 but he seems to
deduce this from the fact that it is
known, by an act of the Louvain city
council of January 9, 1489, that a
metal caster was charged with making
a monumental door in brass to be
placed under this choirscreen, undoubtedly in the central arch. This
would prove that at that date the
screen was built. The 1489 document
specifies that Jan Borman the Elder
and Jan Borman the Younger, resid-
ents of Brussels, were charged with
delivering a design for this door
(undoubtedly a model in wood)
(STEPPE, 1952, p. 83). MOLANUS (VAN
EVEN, 1884, p. 339), who wrote in
1575 and had searched the archives
of the church, claimed that this door
was placed in 1493. From this data
it is possible to conclude that the
Calvary on the choirscreen was in
place about 1490 but nothing is known
about the attribution.

246

BRUSSELS, before 1491-93 (?)

80. SAINT MARY-MAGDALENE

Brussels,
Musées Royaux d'Art et d'Histoire
Inv. no. 2992

This statue of the Magdalene is one of the most beautiful of its kind. Its origin in Brussels is attested to by a city mark and it is dated in the late 15th or early 16th century.

Mary-Magdalene is one of the Saints most familiar to art historians of the 15th century: in numerous scenes of the Passion of Christ she takes a rank immediately after the Virgin and Saint John. The discovery of some of her relics in Provence in 1449, contributed to her popularity and her representations in painting or sculpture were from this time on increasingly numerous. Mary-Magdalene is characterized by her elegant clothing, which follow the fashion of the times very closely.

Physical data: Oak, 22 $^{1}/_{16}$ x 5 $^{1}/_{2}$ x 3 $^{15}/_{16}$ in. (56 x 14 x 10 cm.). Oval base. Stamp mark in the form of a leaf and traces of a citymark in the form of a mallet (for Brussels) under base, now concealed by an added modern base (DESTRÉE, 1894, pp. 136-137).

History: René Desmotes Collection, Paris; given by this collector in 1890 to the Musées Royaux d'Art et d'Histoire, Brussels.

Exhibitions: Brussels, 1888, no. 1485; Brussels, 1905, no. 73.

DESTRÉE (1894, p. 137) noted the resemblance of the Brussels Magdalene to one in Paris (Musée de Cluny) which also bears the mallet mark of Brussels; the two are very close in the facial types, the hair

arrangement with braids, the style of the draperies and even the little base. He dates both figures in the second half of the 15th century. ROLLAND (1939, p. 89) dates the present figure at the end of the 15th century. DE BORCHGRAVE D'ALTENA (1947, p. 14) attributes this figure as well as that in the Cluny Museum to Jan Borman, although he erroneously denies the presence of the Brussels city mark (1952, pp. 4-6). The coiffure of Mary-Magdalene and even her face are similar to those in a misericord of the choirstalls in Diest dating ca. 1491-1493; they might have been made by the same sculptor and date from the same period. The choirstalls in Diest are sometimes attributed to Jan Borman.

BRUSSELS, ca. 1491-1493

81-84. A MARINE KNIGHT, A SLEEPING MAN,
        A MAN PUSHING A DOG IN A WHEELBARROW,
        A LAME BEGGAR ON CRUTCHES
        Misericords from choirstalls

Diest, Church of Saint-Sulpice

These four small sculptures decorate the consoles attached to the undersides of the movable seats of choirstalls. These were called "misericords" because they provided merciful support when the divine office requested long standing.

The choirstalls of the Church of Saint-Sulpice in Diest, to which these seats belong, are considered to be the most beautiful in Belgium. Some of the sculptures for these stalls were delivered in 1493. The name of the sculptor is unknown, but some authorities propose that of Jan Borman of Brussels.

The sculptural decorations of misericords are sometimes purely decorative but very often they are of a satirical character. At times they are inspired by proverbs or folklore, as is the case at Diest for the man pushing a dog in a wheelbarrow and the sleeping man, or by popular types as the lame beggar on crutches, or by legendary types as the marine knight.

248

Physical data: Oak, 11 ¹³/₁₆ x 24 ¹³/₁₆ in. (30 x 63.5 cm.).

History: The accounts of the church for 1482 mention the travel expenses of two canons to Louvain, Malines and Herentals to see choirstalls. The accounts of 1493 mention a payment for the transport by water of sculptures for stalls: *Item ghegeven en betaelt eenen scepman, van beelde te voeren van den gestoelte... op den lesten dach september in den jare 1493, 4 st.* (RAYMAEKERS, 1856, pp. 497-499).

A manuscript chronicle in Latin, the *Chronicon Diestiensis* of Henri van Gorrichem (died 1536) known in a manuscript translation of 1669 by Van Zurpele, claimed that the stalls bore the date of 1491 (manuscript in the Archives of the City of Diest, published by RAYMAEKERS, 1856, p. 324, note 5). In 1818 the backs and the prayer-desks of the stalls were sold to an English collector (VAN DER LINDEN, 1936, p. 80). The church preserves the other parts.

Exhibitions: None known.

The church accounts prove that the acquisition of the stalls was envisaged in 1482. It is known that in 1483 the church ordered a choirscreen from Antoon Keldermans which was put in place in 1488. The cost of this work may have delayed the ordering of the stalls. It is possible that the stalls did bear the date 1491, probably on one of the parts sold in 1818 (which do not belong to the Victoria and Albert Museum in South Kensington, London, as stated in an inventory in 1906, p. 11). The entry in the accounts of 1493 reads in translation: "Given and paid to a boatman for having transported the images of the stalls... the last day of September 1493, 4 st.". This indicates that at this date the work was going forward with the installation of the stalls.

VAN WEDDINGEN (1935-36, p. 55) proposes seeing in these stalls a work of Jan Borman or of his atelier because of their quality and from the fact that this sculptor is known to have made a large Crucifixion group for the church at this period, which was placed over the choirscreen under the triumphal arch (but is no longer in existence). This proposal is taken up by DE BORCHGRAVE D'ALTENA (1942, p. 14).

249

Sculpture

The iconography of the choirstalls at Diest is that which is often found on furnishings of this sort but in this case it is particularly rich in varied themes. The misericord of the man sleeping on a cushion placed on a table may be a representation of laziness. GRAULS in a lecture, noted that it might also illustrate the proverbs "Inactivity is the cushion of the devil" and "A good conscience is the best cushion" (VAN WEDDINGEN, 1935, pp. 58-66). The misericord of the man pushing

a dog in a wheelbarrow is an allusion to stupidity or foolishness. The theme is that of the fable of La Fontaine "The Miller and his Ass". It is interesting to note that the man wears a hood edged with bells which, about that time, became typical of "fools". The subject of the beggar with crutches and of the knight with the fish tail are found at this same period in the works of Hieronymus Bosch. Combats of marine knights were popular; they appeared in the program of the festivals organized on the occasion of the reception of Philip the Good at Bruges in 1440 and at Ghent in 1458, where were to be seen in the river Lys, near the bridge close by the meat market "sea knights swimming in the water and fighting with each other" as reported by an eye witness, Georges Chastellain (CHASTELLAIN, *Chronique,* 1454-1458, edited by KERVYN DE LETTENHOVE, III, 1864, p. 414).

BRUSSELS, end of the 15th Century

85. SAINT GERTRUDE OF NIVELLES

Etterbeek (Brussels), Church of Sainte-Gertrude

This beautiful statue of an abbess reading represents Saint Gertrude of Nivelles, daughter of the Mayor of the Palace, Pepin of Landen (and so great-grand aunt of the Emperor Charlemagne) who, with the help of her mother, founded the abbey of Nivelles in Brabant in the 7th century.

The name of the sculptor is unknown but since the statue bears the city mark of Brussels, it is certain that it was carved in a workshop of that city. It survives in a good state of preservation but unfortunately has lost the polychromy which should complete it as was usual in the 15th century with all

250

sculptures in wood and even in stone. It is one of the most beautiful statues dating from the end of the 15th century.

Physical data: Oak, 47 $^{11}/_{16}$ in. (121 cm.). City mark of Brussels, the mallet, under the base. The carved top of the crozier and some parts of the pages of the book are missing. Hole for a tenon on top of head. In the hollows of the folds of the drapery, some traces of gesso and color.

History: Found in 1935 in the attic of the modern Church of Sainte-Gertrude of Etterbeek (Brussels), and identified shortly after by Armand Godfrin, a young art historian who died during the war without having had the opportunity to publish his exceptional find (DEQUID, 1949, p. 44).

The polychromy of the statue, very much damaged, was removed at the time of its discovery. Later on, in 1946, it underwent a treatment of conservation at the Institut Royal du Patrimoine Artistique. Very little polychromy was left except in a few folds of the drapery (these evidences have been preserved).

Exhibitions: Brussels, 1953, no. 42; Louvain, 1959, no. 15.

The origin of this statue is unknown. The mallet mark shows that it came from a Brussels workshop. In form and style, it is related to the statue of *Saint Anne Carrying the Virgin and Child* in the Church of the Dominicans at Louvain. DE BORCHGRAVE D'ALTENA (1949, p. 42) dates the figure about 1490 and compares it in excellence with notable statues of the end of the 15th century such as those at Louvain in the Church of Saint-Jacques, a *Saint Hubert*, a *Saint Lawrence* and a *Saint Fiacre*. Likewise comparable is the *Saint James* in the chapel of the cemetery of that church. But the names of the authors of these sculptures are not known. DE BORCHGRAVE D'ALTENA (1952, pp. 93-94) proposes the name of Jan Borman for the *Saint Gertrude* and many other statues. The authentic works

251

of Jan Borman prove that he was a great artist but do not seem to permit the attribution to him of the *Saint Gertrude* and a number of other statues too generously assigned to him.

The identification of the statue as *Saint Gertrude of Nivelles* is based on its iconographic details: the veil, the crozier and the open book with the rules of her order indicate that the subject is an abbess. Little mice can usually be seen climbing up the staff of Saint Gertrude's crozier - on this statue it is lacking - for she was considered a protectress against these rodents. The identification of the statue as being *Saint Gertrude* is supported by the fact that she is the patroness of the church in which the statue was found.

BRUSSELS, end of the 15th Century

86-89. THE FLAGELLATION, THE CARRYING OF THE CROSS, THE DESCENT FROM THE CROSS, THE ENTOMBMENT

Brussels, Musées Royaux d'Art et d'Histoire. Inv. nos. 866-869

These four scenes, which apparently come from the Church of Saint-Pierre in Louvain, must have belonged to a sculptured altarpiece which had for its

252

subject the *Passion of Christ*. They bear the city mark of Brussels. The date of their execution may be placed in the last quarter of the 15th century.

Physical data: About 18 ⁷/₈ x 14 ¹/₈ in. (48 x 36 cm.) each. City marks of Brussels: mallet, compass(?), and mark in the form of a grill on the back of the groups. Part of polychromy still present. Additional linen support for the group of *The Carrying of the Cross*.

History: Acquired from the Church of Saint-Pierre at Louvain in 1861.

Exhibitions: None known.

The male physiognomies are of a distinctive type: wide faces with short noses and drawn-in lips on toothless mouths. The pose of the Mary-Magdalene in the *Descent from the Cross* resembles that of the Magdalene of the 1483 paschal candlestick of Léau, shown in this exhibition (cat. nos. 103-104).

It is known that the altarpiece on the high altar of the Church of Saint-Pierre in Louvain comprised eight sculptured groups which were set in two rows one above the other; they represented the *Passion of Christ* and were polychromed and gilded. This high altar was destroyed early in the 19th century (VAN EVEN, 1895, pp. 351-352).

It could be accepted that the four groups belonged to this high altar; they should then be dated 1441 (DESTRÉE, 1894, p. 117). It should however be pointed out that the guarantee of the Brussels "métier" of "The Four Holy Crowned Martyrs", expressed by the mallet city mark, may not have been introduced before 1455, although DESTRÉE (1894, p. 132) is more definite. Judging from the style of the sculptures a date at the end of the century seems more acceptable.

253

90.   A KNEELING ANGEL

Bruges, Gruuthuse-Museum

This *Angel* and its companion piece in the Jan Van Herck Collection, Antwerp, also shown in this exhibition (cat. no. 91) probably flanked a lost

central subject. Their origin is not known. They date probably from the end of the 15th century. They may come from a Bruges workshop.

Physical data: Oak, 16 $^1/_8$ x 10 $^1/_4$ in. (41 x 26 cm.). The wings are lost, leaving only their bases. Several fingers are missing.
History: First published by CASIER and BERGMANS (I, 1914, p. 55).
Exhibitions: Ghent, 1913, no. 1068; Copenhagen, 1931, no. 67.

The former identification of the figure as the Angel of an *Annunciation* is difficult to accept since the discovery of a companion piece, noted by KONRAD (1928, pp. X-XI). The comparison of the two angels leaves little doubt that they belong together. It is not known what these kneeling angels enframed. A smaller sized work from the parish church of Gestel-Meerhout (prov. Antwerp) representing four angels carrying a medallion on which the monogram of Christ is to be seen (reproduced by JANSEN and VAN HERCK, 1949, fig. 50) gives an idea of the original purpose of these angels. This comparison also applies to the *Two Flying Angels* of the Saint John's Hospital, Bruges (cat. nos. 94-95 in this exhibition).

CASIER and BERGMANS (I, 1914, p. 55) and KONRAD (1928, pp. X-XI) suggest the piece is from a Brussels workshop. The latter author dates it in the second third of the 15th century. Its companion piece was considered as made in a Bruges workshop at the end of the 15th century (see notice no. 91), and this identification necessarily includes that of the Bruges *Angel*.

Sculpture

BRUGES(?), end of the 15th Century

91. A KNEELING ANGEL

Antwerp, Jan Van Herck Collection

Companion piece to the *Kneeling Angel* from the Gruuthuse-Museum in Bruges which is included in this exhibition as no. 90. Their origin is not known. They date probably from the end of the 15th century and may come from a Bruges workshop.

> *Physical data:* Oak, 16 1/2 x 9 7/8 in. (42 x 25 cm.). The wings are lost, leaving only their bases. Several fingers and the left foot are missing.
>
> *History:* In 1880 in the Collection of Eugène Van Herck, Antwerp; later passed into the Collection of Jan Van Herck at Antwerp.
>
> *Exhibitions:* Brussels, 1880, no. B 312; Malines, 1883, no. 1037; Ghent, 1913, no. 1070; Antwerp, 1930, no. A 51; Antwerp, 1948, no. 18; Antwerp, 1959, no. 29.

KONRAD (1928, pp. X-XI) believes this *Angel* and its companion piece came from a Brussels workshop. The relationship of this *Angel* to its companion piece and their original use are discussed under no. 90. JANSEN and VAN HERCK (1949, p. 66, no. 146) and the Catalogues of the Antwerp Exhibitions of 1948 (no. 18) and 1959 (no. 29) place its origin in a Bruges workshop and date it at the end of the fifteenth century.

BRABANT, end of the 15th Century

92. A KING OF JUDAS from a TREE OF JESSE(?)

Léau, Church of Saint-Léonard

This personage with a curious posture may have belonged to a large *Tree of Jesse* on the branches of which it is likely he was seated with legs hanging down. Prophets and kings especially are found in Trees of Jesse, which represent

255

the ancestors and predecessors of Christ sprung from the stock of Jesse. This figure which seems originally to have had a crown must be one of the kings. His short tunic, bordered with bells, is not incompatible with such an identification: in the 15th century, bells were sometimes used on the edges of ceremonial costumes or even of liturgical vestments.

The characteristics of style and the costume of the figure lead to a dating toward the end of the 15th century among the products of Brabant which were so abundant at that time.

Physical data: Oak, 36 ⁵/₈ in. (93 cm.). Several wooden bells are lacking: they were all around the hem of the tunic. There are four holes for pegs on top of the hat. The empty right hand probably held a staff. A slot in the back, at the height of the right wrist, indicates that the statue was borne on a supporting bar coming from the left and not extending to the right.

History: In the Church of Saint-Léonard at Léau before 1901 (PRENAU, 1901, p. 26).

Exhibitions: In several exhibitions before 1901 (PRENAU, 1901, p. 26); Léau, 1924; Antwerp, 1948, no. 264.

The figure was first considered as representing a prophet (PRENAU, 1901, p. 26), then as David dancing before the Ark (SANDER PIERRON, 1924, pp. 101-108). The latter identification was still used in 1948 (Cat. Exhib. Antwerp, 1948, no. 264) but according to RÉAU (II, 1, 1956, p. 269) David danced naked before the Ark. DE BORCHGRAVE D'ALTENA (1939-40, p. 263) proposes to see in this figure a personage from a *Tree of Jesse* of large size, which seems the most likely interpretation. He must be a prophet or a king of Judas (the holes on top of the hat probably indicate that he was wearing a crown). Nevertheless, no sculptured *Tree of Jesse* of large size exists in Belgium and none is mentioned. RÉAU (II, 2, 1957, p. 137) notes one at Gisors (Eure) in France, which measured 49 ft. in height and dated from the 16th century. Several examples of the end of the 15th century or the beginning of the 16th century are known in painting and stained-glass.

In the 15th century, bells were not peculiar, as later, to the costumes of "fools". They are to be seen hanging

256

from the belt of the ceremonial dress of Lysbeth van Duvenvoorde by a Dutch Master of about 1435 (The Hague, Mauritshuis, on loan at the Rijksmuseum, Amsterdam). They were used to ornament "dancing belts" *(ceintures à danser)* as evidenced by the accounts of the Dukes of Burgundy (BEAULIEU and BAYLÉ, 1956, p. 96, note 7). They are to be seen bordering the short tunic, like that of the figure from Léau, of the king on the altarpiece of the *Martyrdom of Saint George* by Jan Borman, dated 1493 (Brussels, Musées Royaux d'Art et d'Histoire) where are also shown the fringed belt and the boots of the Léau costume.

The presence of the head of a Moor on the front of the hat is not easily explained. It has lead Count VON SALM (in a verbal communication) to suggest that the personage might be a morris-dancer *(Moriskentänzer)* such as found in German art, notably in the sculptures of Erasmus Grasser in Munich. Morris-dancers are not known in any Flemish work of art of the 15th century still preserved, but this motif has been used, since they are found decorating the enamel objects mentioned in the Inventory of Charles the Bold prepared in 1467 (DE LABORDE, Part 2, II, 1851, nos. 2649 and 3586).

BRABANT(?), second half of the 15th Century

93. COMPASSIONATE GOD

Liège, Musée Diocésain

This group of God the Father seated and holding before Him the body of the dead Christ, is a *Dieu de Pitié,* an iconographic subject corresponding to that of the Virgin of Mercy *(Vierge de Pitié).* It is possible that the group originally included the dove of the Holy Ghost. In that case, this group should be called a Holy Trinity or, more precisely, the Throne of Grace. This group probably belonged to the central part of an altarpiece. It seems related to sculpture of the second half of the 15th century in Brabant.

Physical data : Oak, 15 ³/₄ x 8 ⁷/₈ x 4 ¹/₈ in. (40 x 22.5 x 10.5 cm.). Traces of gilding and polychromy. Base painted green and besprinkled with red and white flowers.

257

History: Origin unknown.
Exhibitions: Brussels, 1935, no. 1552; Verviers, 1959, no. 60.

It has been stated that this group was formerly flanked by two statues of saints (Cat. Exhib. Brussels, 1935, no. 1552) or by a *Virgin and Child and Saint Catherine* (Cat. Exhib. Verviers, 1959, no. 60).

The curule chair used as a throne is quite common in this period. The clasp on the cope of God the Father in the form of a diptych is noteworthy and can be seen occasionally in Flemish Primitive painting; it is mentioned more than once in the account books of the Dukes of Burgundy but apparently none is preserved in Belgium.

FLANDERS(?), 15th Century

94-95. TWO FLYING ANGELS

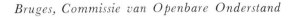

Bruges, Commissie van Openbare Onderstand

These two large figures of flying angels perhaps once decorated an altar. Their origin is unknown and, if they are classified as related to the art of Flanders, it is because they were found in Bruges.

> *Physical data:* Oak, 31 ½ in. (80 cm.) each. The wings are lacking. The hands are much damaged. The polychromy is not original.
> *History:* Found in the storerooms of the Public Assistance Commission of Bruges.
> *Exhibitions:* Bruges, 1939 (no cat.).

These two flying angels may have been set around a Marianum or any other similar work. It is possible to have an idea of their original purpose by comparing them with a small sized work surrounded by four angels at the parish church of Gestel-Meerhout (prov. Antwerp) (JANSEN and VAN HERCK, 1949, fig. 50).

258

FRANCO-FLEMISH, ca. 1500

96.   CHRIST SEATED ON CALVARY

San Francisco, Calif.,
M.H. de Young Memorial Museum
Acc. no. 6545

Christ crowned with thorns, seated on a pile of stones or on a stone seat during the preparations for the Crucifixion: such a representation of Christ, known from 1400 on, is found especially in the late years of the 15th century and early years of the 16th century. The example from the de Young Memorial Museum in San Francisco is very likely a sculpture from the Southern Netherlands or from the North of France. The dating ca. 1500 seems acceptable.

> *Physical data:* Oak, 52 ¹/₄ in. (134 cm.). Traces of polychromy. Damages at the base. A part of the left foot missing. Two holes in body: at neck and abdomen.
> *History:* Acquired at Lille; given to the Museum by M.H. de Young in 1897.
> *Exhibitions:* None known.

This type of Christ is not to be confused with the Ecce Homo which represents Christ shown to the people, in derision after the Flagellation and the Crowning with Thorns. Here the scene takes place on Calvary as is shown by the small skull on the base. Legend reports that the skull of Adam reappeared on the ground at the foot of the cross at the moment of the death of Christ. The scene here represented is furthermore not the Merciful Christ *(Christ de Pitié)* such as was generally shown according to the vision of Saint Gregory (see this cat., no. 10), for then Christ should

259

bear the wounds of the Crucifixion. MÂLE (1922, pp. 94-97) designates this iconographic type "Christ Awaiting His Death". In Flanders and in Brabant the type is sometimes called *Christus op de koude steen* ("Christ on the cold stone") for He is always seated on rocks or a slab of stone.

NETHERLANDS, ca. 1490-1510

97. A SCENE OF CHARITY

Brussels, Musées Royaux d'Art et d'Histoire. Inv. no. 3251

This group of three persons probably belonged to an altarpiece which had for its subject *The Seven Works of Mercy*. The woman

dispensing charity wears the costume of a widow; her robe is unbelted and her face is framed by a kind of wimple called "barb" which is attached to her veil. The alms are received by a figure in tattered clothing (sometimes identified as a man) carrying on her shoulders a small sleeping child which is bound to the bearer's head by a cloth.

This sculpture is perhaps from Brabant in the Southern Netherlands. It could as well be from a workshop in the Northern Netherlands. It can be dated about 1490-1510.

260

Physical data: Oak, 13 $^9/_{16}$ x 10 $^{15}/_{16}$ x 2 $^1/_{16}$ in. (34.5 x 27.7 x 5.2 cm.) thick.

History: Comtesse Dubois de Prelle Collection; came into the Musées Royaux d'Art et d'Histoire, Brussels, in 1895.

Exhibitions: None known.

DE BORCHGRAVE D'ALTENA (1934, pp. 64-66) believes the work to be from Brabant and dates it about 1500. He calls attention to the iconographic detail of the child carried on the shoulders of another person and gives several examples in paintings, notably *The Works of Mercy* by the Master of Alkmaar (Amsterdam, Rijksmuseum, cat. 1538). In the 15th century a notable example is in the *Crucifixion* attributed to Joos van Gent (Ghent, Cathedral of Saint-Bavon) and in *The Works of Mercy* by the Master of the View of Sainte-Gudule (Castagnola-Lugano, Galleria Schloss Rohoncz).

BRABANT (ANTWERP ?), ca. 1500

98.   THE BAD(?) THIEF from a
CRUCIFIXION GROUP

Kontich,
Rev. Josse Van Herck Collection

The tormented figure hanging from a tau-shaped cross is probably the Bad Thief from a sculptured Crucifixion group. He has the bound eyes and the drooping head which generally differentiate him from the Good Thief who looks at Christ. The sculpture seems to date from ca. 1500 and might belong to the Antwerp School.

Physical data: Walnut (JANSEN and VAN HERCK, 1949, p. 65, no. 126), 15 $^5/_{16}$ x 6 $^1/_2$ in. (39 x 16.5 cm.). The right foot is lacking. Probably detached from an altarpiece.

History: In the Van Herck Collection before 1911.

Exhibitions: Malines, 1911, no. 63; Antwerp, 1948, no. 57.

This figure was identified as the Good Thief by JANSEN and VAN HERCK (1949, p. 65, no. 126) and in the Cat. Exhib. Antwerp, 1948, no. 57. The Good Thief is usually to be seen on the right side of Christ and most of the time differs from the Bad Thief by

261

a young and beardless face as well as a more resigned attitude. The Bad Thief is more tormented, often blindfolded and turns away from Christ. It is therefore possible that the statuette from Kontich should be the Bad Thief.

BRABANT, ca. 1500

99. THE ANNUNCIATION

Brussels, Musées Royaux d'Art et d'Histoire. Inv. no. 1006

This *Annunciation* is a scene detached from a sculptured altarpiece. Altarpieces are made up of separate elements juxtaposed within a case called a *huche*. These elements fit together and are held by pegs. It is thus possible to take them apart. This was done in the 19th century by antique dealers and collectors to isolate the figurines or the small scenes which could be used separately more advantageously. These sculptured elements are recognizable for their trompe-l'œil setting, their lack of thickness and their sharply sloping ground. Thus isolated, these fragments often have a very great charm, as is the case with this *Annunciation*.

The work has the characteristics of the altarpieces of Brabant. It is to be dated around 1500.

Physical data: Oak, or walnut (?) (DESTRÉE, 1894, p. 161), 19 ¹/₁₆ x 11 ³/₁₆ x 6 ¹/₈ in. (48.5 x 28.5 x 15.5 cm.). Traces of polychromy in the draperies of the canopy. The right hand and the top of the Angel's staff are lacking.

History: Hagemans Collection; entered the collections of the Musées Royaux d'Art et d'Histoire in Brussels in 1861.

Exhibitions: Brussels, 1958 (no no.); Liège, 1959, no. 26.

DESTRÉE (1894, pp. 161-162) notes a similar scene on the altarpiece of Villers-la-Ville, a Brabantine work. He places the Brussels *Annunciation* at the beginning of the 16th century.

The style of the neckline of the dress of the Virgin indicates the end of the 15th or the beginning of the 16th century. The curtain of the bed is lifted in order to reveal the figurine of a lion which is on top of the bed post.

262

BRABANT, ca. 1500

100. JOINT-COVER with **SAINT ANTHONY HERMIT**

Louvain,
Musée d'Art Chrétien de l'Université Catholique

This long carved beam is a joint-cover (called *mauclair*) which concealed the meeting of the two valves of the door of a church, a chapel, or some monastic building. It probably comes from the Carthusian monastery or Chartreuse of Louvain of which the buildings were erected around 1500, a very acceptable date for this sculpture.

The personage represented is Saint Anthony Hermit, called also Saint Anthony Abbot, recognizable from the flames of Saint Anthony's fire which springs up under the Saint's feet, from his homespun robe with a hood, from his tau-formed walking stick from which is suspended a small bell and from the book of the Rule of the Order of Saint Anthony. The cult of the Saint reached its height at the end of the 15th century and the beginning of the 16th century: most of the monuments on which he appears date from this period.

Physical data: Oak, 152 x 7 ⁷/₈ x 7 ⁷/₈ in. (386 x 20 x 20 cm.).

History. According to an unverified local tradition, it came from the Carthusian monastery of Louvain.

Exhibitions: None known.

It is known that the buildings of the Chartreuse of Louvain were erected after December 10, 1489: the authorization for the erection of a Carthusian monastery was granted on that date. The church, begun in 1498, was completed in 1499 and consecrated in 1501. A second cloister was begun in 1503 (VAN EVEN, 1895, pp. 487-89).

This *mauclair* is to be compared, among others, with that still in place in the Church of Saint-Léonard at Léau, dating from the same period.

263

METALWORK

BRABANT, ca. 1476

101-102. TWO STATUETTES
from the TOMB OF ISABELLA OF BOURBON, DUCHESS OF BURGUNDY

Amsterdam, Rijksmuseum. Cat. 1915, no. 213

It has been demonstrated with virtual certainty that these two brass statuettes and eight others, which belong to the Rijksmuseum in Amsterdam, originally decorated the sides of the tomb of the young Duchess Isabella of

264

Bourbon, first wife of Charles the Bold, who died in 1465. This tomb was in the church of the Abbey of Saint-Michel in Antwerp. It was erected in 1476 (or 1478) through the efforts of her daughter, Mary of Burgundy. Both the church and the tomb disappeared in the 18th century, except for the recumbent statue which is now preserved in the Cathedral of Notre-Dame in Antwerp. Old drawings and documents show that this tomb corresponds to the type, surrounded by a procession of mourners, which Philip the Bold, first Duke of Burgundy, had chosen for his tomb in Champmol. The tombs of Louis de Male in Lille and of Joan of Brabant in Brussels, were executed according to this same model by order of Philip the Good in 1454-1455 and 1458-1459, respectively. However, for these tombs the hooded mourners were replaced by members of the families of these princes dressed in costumes of the period. Isabella's tomb in Antwerp also had its gallery of twenty-four family portraits showing her ancestors. To the extent that it is possible to judge from drawings made before the destruction of the tomb and from the ten statuettes in the Rijksmuseum in Amsterdam, it appears that the creator of the Antwerp tomb more or less faithfully copied the statuettes on the tombs in Lille and Brussels. He reproduced them, however, in reversed positions (as they would be seen in a mirror) and modified certain details of the poses and costumes. These statuettes no longer showed the same persons they were supposed to represent in Lille and Brussels, but were given new identities. The reason for inverting the poses has never been satisfactorily explained. It may have been done to deviate further from the two earlier tombs in order not to confuse the public and to make the new identities more acceptable. Whatever his original intent, the creator of this tomb in Antwerp achieved figurines full of life and personality. Some of them are of such moving beauty that Dürer, Rubens and Rembrandt copied them and on occasion imitated them in their works.

The talented caster who made the statuettes of the tomb in Antwerp has remained anonymous, along with the artist who drew the models from the tombs in Lille and Brussels. The prototype of the male statuette was the figurine of Philip the Good on the tomb of Joan of Brabant in Brussels. The collar of the Order of the Golden Fleece has been removed from this figure, and a crown has been added. The female statuette has not been identified.

Physical data: Cast brass, man: 21 5/8 in. (55 cm.); woman: 22 13/16 in. (58 cm.).

History: Acquired by the City of Amsterdam in 1691, along with eight other statuettes, from Pieter de Vos in exchange for a life annuity of one hundred and fifty florins. Pieter de Vos had probably inherited them from his father, Simon de Vos, who died in 1681 (SIX, 1896, p. 402).

Exhibitions: Amsterdam, 1873, nos. 413-422; Amsterdam, 1877, no. 604; Dinant, 1903, nos. 5(?) and 8(?); Paris, 1947 (the female figure), no. 107; Dijon, 1951, nos. 146 and 149; Amsterdam, 1951, nos. 223 and 226; Brussels, 1951, nos. 205 and 208.

WAGENAER, SCHELTEMA and DE VRIES, in the last century, believed that the statuettes in the Rijksmuseum came from the former Amsterdam City Hall (SIX, 1896, p. 402). PINCHART (V, 1866, p. 131) was the first to see that they had come from a tomb. He thought they had belonged to the destroyed tomb of

Duchess Joan of Brabant in Brussels, made by Jacques de Gérines in 1458-1459. DE ROEVER (1888, p. 209) pointed out the resemblance of these statuettes to those on the destroyed tomb of Louis de Male, which was also by Jacques de Gérines, dating from 1455-1456. Since the latter tomb was still intact in 1691, when the statuettes were already in Amsterdam, they cannot have come from that tomb. He does think, however, that they were done by Jacques de Gérines. DESTRÉE (1894, p. 207) said they could not have come from the Brussels tomb which was not destroyed, he says, until 1695. He suggested that they could have come from the tomb of Isabella of Bourbon in Antwerp, but he was not familiar with its actual appearance. The same author (Cat. Dinant Exhib., 1903, no. 5) thinks the drawings for these statuettes may have been done by Roger van der Weyden and that Jean Delmer could have made the wooden model. KONRAD (II, 1923, p. 195) was the first to identify these statuettes as the mourners of the tomb of Isabella of Bourbon in Antwerp, from which some of the statuary had already been removed by 1678 as is shown in an engraving (KONRAD, 1928, pp. 30-34). He presents as his principal arguments the fact that the recumbent figure is in the same style as the small statuettes and that Dürer, who certainly visited the Abbey of Saint-Michel in Antwerp, also made a drawing based on one of the statuettes now in Amsterdam (Notebook of Drawings by Albrecht Dürer, British Museum, London). LINDEMAN (1941, pp. 49-50) took up KONRAD's hypothesis and compared the statuettes to the precisely drawn copies and the sketches from the tombs in Lille and Brussels. He concluded from this that the creator of the tomb in Antwerp had plagiarized from Jacques de Gérines. LEEUWENBERG (1951, pp. 13-59) found the number and names of the mourners of the tomb of Isabella of Bourbon in a work by Papebrochius, an author of the end of the 17th century: they represented the ancestors of that princess. Thus, Philip the Good must not have been among them and even though a statuette resembles him it was intended to represent another person. This explains why the collar of the Order of the Golden Fleece was not put on the Amsterdam figure. ROGGEN (1955-56, p. 179) analyses this very complex question and argues in favor of the thesis of KONRAD-LINDEMAN-LEEUWENBERG.

DEVIGNE (1932, pp. 104-107), on the other hand, believed the statuettes should be attributed to Jacques de Gérines because of their resemblance to those of the tomb in Lille. She did not accept their being identified as the mourners of the tomb in Antwerp which Jacques de Gérines could not have done since he died in 1463. They must be identified as the statuettes on the tomb in Brussels which had already lost some of its mourners by 1602 (Notebook of Drawings by Succa, 1602, Brussels, Bibliothèque Royale). GAVELLE (1935, pp. 127-128) also said the statuettes in Amsterdam should be attributed to Jacques de Gérines, but since he found that one statuette (one of those in this exhibition) resembles the one of Philip the Good on the tomb in Brussels, but without the collar of the Order of the Golden Fleece, he dated these statuettes before the founding of that Order in 1430. Therefore, he suggested that they had decorated an unknown tomb which was made by Jacques de Gérines. He believes the statuettes were designed by Jan van Eyck and Roger van der Weyden. According

266

to this hypothesis the statuettes from this tomb, the ones now in Amsterdam, would have been the prototypes for the statuettes in Lille and Brussels instead of being their replicas.

KONRAD (1928, p. 31) places the execution of the tomb of Isabella in 1476 because, according to him, Mary of Burgundy had ordered this work for her mother's tomb before her father's death and her marriage to Maximilian. This author made reference to the archivist Donnet who had apparently published documents from the archives which reported this fact, but he gave no bibliographical reference and it has not been possible to find his source. All the authorities who have studied the question of these statuettes and the tomb in Antwerp have given 1476 as its date of execution, but do not indicate the source of their information. VAN DEN NIEUWENHUYZEN (1957, pp. 58-59) places the execution of the tomb two years later, in 1478, thus one year after the Joyous Entry of Mary of Burgundy into Antwerp (June, 1477). He does not specify the documents in which he found this information. In 1566, the tomb was pillaged by the Calvinists and the statuettes were removed except for the three which remained in place until the 18th century. The tomb was then demolished and the recumbent figure was first put in the Musée Royal des Beaux-Arts in Antwerp and later removed to the Cathedral in Antwerp (DE BOSSCHERE, 1909, pp. 68-71).

Four 15th century silverpoint drawings, two now in the Boymans-van Beuningen Museum in Rotterdam and the other two destroyed in 1940 with the Koenigs Collection in The Netherlands, are very similar to certain statuettes of these tombs. These drawings have been the subject of many publications. They have been considered as originals by Jan van Eyck or Roger van der Weyden. They have been viewed as copies made from the figures on the tombs or made for the people illustrated by these figures. LEEUWENBERG (1951, p. 24) rejects their attribution to Jan van Eyck and considers them copies made from the tombs. PANOFSKY (1953, p. 200, note 3, p. 291 and 291, note 4, pp. 438 and 477-478) supports the rejection of their attribution to van Eyck and places them, as did LEEUWENBERG, between 1450 and 1460; but he believes they were done in preparing the iconography of the tombs and were made from original portraits at the beginning of the 15th century. He attributes them to Roger van der Weyden's workshop.

RENIER VAN THIENEN

Active in Brussels from 1465 to 1494
Died before June 1498

Lived in Brussels where he was appointed as communal counsellor and second burgomaster.

The accounts of the Abbey of Saint-Jacques-sur-Coudenberg and of the Court of the Dukes in Brussels, those of the Church of Saint-Léonard in Léau

267

and of the Abbey of Averbode mention several orders which were made to him between 1465 and 1494, of lighting devices, choirscreens, paschal candelabra and copper buttons for the duchess' coach. Of these works exist only today the paschal candelabrum of Léau of which two statuettes are exhibited here (cat. nos. 103-104)

and a statuette of Saint Leonard which belonged to a lighting fixture in the same church. There were also identified as coming from his workshop, three lions in brass which belonged at the base of a lost object and which are identical to the lions which carry the paschal candelabrum of Léau.

In the last years of his life it is difficult to differentiate him from his son who had the same first name and was also a metalworker of repute.

103-104. SAINT MARY-MAGDALENE and SAINT LEONARD
Statuettes from a
PASCHAL CANDELABRUM

Léau, Church of Saint-Léonard

These two statuettes belong to the paschal candelabrum in the Church of Saint-Léonard. This candelabrum is one of the largest in Europe after that in Durham (England), one of the most famous, and the only authenticated work of the metal caster Renier van Thienen. It is, moreover, the only one of its kind preserved in Belgium. Entirely cast in brass, this candelabrum weighs approximately 1800 pounds and is 18 ft. 5 in. (5.60 meters) high. It is decorated with a Calvary of which the cross is attached to the central stem which bears the paschal candle. The figures of the Virgin, Saint John, and Mary-Magdalene are on the branches like

268

Metalwork

tapers. The statuette of Saint Leonard dominates the lectern of the Exultet on the lower part of the candelabrum.

According to the church accounts, this imposing work was ordered in 1482 and the artist himself came to supervise its installation in November, 1483.

The paschal candle on top of the candlestick is compared in the divine service for Holy Saturday to the pillar of fire which guided Israel by night. It is for this reason that paschal candlesticks were made very high.

Physical data: Cast brass, *Mary-Magdalene:* 24 $^7/_{16}$ in. (62 cm.); *Saint Leonard:* 12 $^9/_{16}$ in. (32 cm.). Some damage, namely to the hands of Mary-Magdalene. The upper part of the crozier held by Saint Leonard has disappeared.

History: The accounts of the Church of Saint-Léonard for the year 1482-1483 mention: *Item verdinct te make-ne teghen meester Reynder van Thienen, gheelgieter te Bruysele, enen candelare staende sal inden hoghen coer na tenoer ende na die maniere van synte Peters te Lovene ende na tenoer enen selegrave (or selegrane) daer af ghemaect es daer af coste sal ellic C libras XV rynsche gulden ende op dit vorseid werck es betaelt L rynsche gulden* (Archives Générales du Royaume, archives ecclésiastiques, no. 1216, fol. 93, ed. Tarlier and Wauters, 1887, p. 231; reviewed and corrected for this catalogue at the Archives Générales du Royaume, May 13, 1960, no. 76119). The church accounts for 1483-1484 mention in November, 1438: *Item gecocht teghen meester Reynder van Thienen, wonende te Brueselle, enen luminaris inden hogen choer, wagende XVIIIc ende XXXIX^z libras cost ellic hondert XV^z rijnsgulden compt tsamen op IIc LXXXV rijnsgulden dair af die meesters van Leeuwe den selven Reynder voirseid betaelt hebben ter sommen van vijftich Rijnsgulden in aflaghe der sommen voirseyd. Ende van momboiren nu ter tijt wesende, hebben hem noch betaelt, doen hij den luminaris opden achten dach van dezer maent stelde, den selven Reynder voirseid LV rijnsgulden.* (Arch. Gén. du Royaume, arch. eccl., no. 1216, fol. 115 rº and vº, studied but

269

not published, by Piot, 1855, p. 282; transcribed for this catalogue at the Archives Générales du Royaume, May 13, 1960, no. 76119).

Exhibitions: Malines, 1864, no. 219 (1st ed.) and 241 (2nd ed.); Liège, 1881, Section IV, no. 139; Brussels, 1888, no. 812; Brussels, 1905, Section III, no. 3; Deurne - Brussels, 1957, no. 302 (only the statuettes).

The translations of the foregoing accounts are as follows: "Agreement made concerning this item with Master Renier van Thienen, brass caster in Brussels, for him to make a candelabrum which will be installed in the large choir according to the type and in the fashion of the one in Saint-Pierre in Louvain and according to the purport of a *selegrave* (?) which was made of it and it will cost fifteen Rhenish florins per hundred pounds and on this work, fifty florins have been paid"; "Item purchased from Master Renier van Thienen, living in Brussels, a lighting fixture in the large choir, weighing 1839 $^1/_2$ pounds, costing, per each hundred, 15 $^1/_2$ florins, making the total sum of 285 Rhenish florins of which the members of the council of the church of Léau have already paid to the said Renier a sum of 50 florins to be deducted from the said sum. And the present churchwardens have also paid to the same Renier when he installed the lighting fixture, the 8th of this month, the sum of 55 florins".

Thus, the basic facts are clear: the paschal candelabrum was installed on November 8, 1483; it weighed a total of 1839 $^1/_2$ pound and cost 285 Rhenish florins, calculated as was ordinarily done for this kind of work according to the weight of the metal; the work was made to resemble a candlestick which was in the Church of Saint-Pierre in Louvain. These documents are typical contracts of the period. It was common to make reference to similar existing objects which were not necessarily the work of the same artist. It appears that the similarity concerned the general form more than the details of its execution. No

The entire paschal candelabrum

270

Metalwork

two objects are preserved which are absolutely identical.

The artist was Renier van Thienen the Elder. This is confirmed by a notation in the accounts for 1484-1485 of an expense of six *sols* during the stay in Léau of Master Renier's son (PIOT, 1855, p. 283). This account appears in register 1216 on folio 136, vº.

COLLON-GEVAERT (1951, pp. 256-257) thinks that Jan Borman may possibly have made a wooden model for this paschal candelabrum. SQUILBECK (1953, pp. 268-271) points out that among the numerous documents which exist concerning the orders received by Renier van Thienen none mention the name of an artist who might have been assigned to make the "master" or model. Documents discovered in the archives by DUVERGER (1946, p. 131) prove that Jan Borman made the wooden model of the recumbent figure of Mary of Burgundy for her tomb in Bruges. However, it is not known whether the caster of that tomb was Renier van Thienen the Elder (who did the paschal candelabrum) or his son (DUVERGER, 1939, p. 31). In fact, there is actually no sound reason for attributing the design of the paschal candelabrum to Jan Borman. WAUTERS (1887, p. 62) thinks that Aert de Maelder, whom he believes did the carved altarpiece of Saint Leonard (part of which is shown in this exhibition as no. 73), made the model for another lighting fixture ordered from Renier van Thienen by this same church in Léau for the chapel of Saint-Leonard. The only part of the latter work which still exists is a statuette of Saint Leonard in a Dutch private collection. FREDERIKS (1943, p. 124) finds a kinship of style between the statuettes of these two candelabra by Renier van Thienen and the above mentioned carved altarpiece of Saint Leonard. The references cited by the various authors are not precise enough, and no well founded conclusion can be drawn from them.

BRABANT, last quarter of the 15th Century

105. LECTERN

Tirlemont, Church of Saint-Germain

Belgium still possesses many Gothic lecterns in brass. This one is among the most beautiful examples from the end of the 15th century. The name of its creator is unknown although it has sometimes been attributed to Renier van Thienen or to Jan van Thienen.

The reading desk of the lectern is supported by a pelican, symbol of Christ, poised on top of a globe which represents the world.

Objects of this kind were made by casting different pieces in a wooden mold and then assembling them. For one single figure, an eagle for example, it was sometimes necessary to assemble a dozen pieces which had been cast separately. The same process was employed for all secondary parts such as shafts, finials, and statuettes. The pattern, or model, in wood was made by a sculptor.

Nothing is known about the artist who designed this lectern or the metal-worker who made it.

Physical data: Brass, 73 1/4 x 26 3/4 in. (186 x 68 cm.) ; base: 21 5/8 in. (55 cm.) in diameter. Restorations: The book-stand placed on the pelican's tail is modern; of the six statuettes, only those of Saint John and Saint Mark(?) are old, the four others are modern *(Commission Royale des Monuments (...). Résumé (...), 1908, pp. 103-104).* There are indications on the base which suggest that it was originally supported by lions or dogs which have disappeared.

History: This lectern has probably always belonged to the Church of Saint-Germain. In 1908, a report on its restoration pointed out that four of the six statuettes of the base were missing and that the sculptor van Uytvanck had prepared figures intended to replace them *(Commission Royale des Monuments (...). Résumé (...), 1905,* pp. 352-353 and 1908, pp. 103-104).

Exhibitions: Brussels, 1880, no. A 546; Brussels, 1888, no. 798; Bruges, 1902, no. E 13; Brussels, 1905, Section III, no. 6; Brussels, 1953, no. 33.

Specialists are unanimous in placing the execution of this lectern in the last quarter of the 15th century. PINCHART (1882, p. 98) tended to think it was a little later than the lectern in the church of Chièvres, dated 1484. DESTRÉE (1905, p. 77) thought it was very similar to the lectern made in 1465 by Renier van Thienen for the Church of Saint-Jacques-sur-Coudenberg in Brussels which is now lost but is described in the contract (PINCHART, 1863, p. 59). TAVENOR-PERRY (cited by SQUILBECK, 1953, p. 269) believes it can be attributed to Renier van Thienen himself. It was recently said to have been made by Jan van Thienen, but with no reason given for this attribution (Cat. Brussels Exhib., 1953, no. 33). SQUILBECK (1953, p. 269) thinks it is not possible to name the artist because, even if the style does not negate an attribution to Renier van Thienen, it is still not proved. This author points out that the "métier" of metalwork, for the city of Brussels alone, included twenty-five masters, and that metalwork was also flourishing in many

272

other cities in the Netherlands. He adds that especially in this kind of work, imitations were very common and sometimes were even called for in the contract.

BRABANT, second half of the 15th Century

106. BRACKET-SCONCE

Louvain, Church of Saint-Jacques

A German traveller, Dr. Jerome Münzer (Monetarius), during a trip through the southern part of the Netherlands in 1455, noted that there were more than four hundred brass chandeliers, both large and small, in the Cathedral of Antwerp (MONETARIUS, ed. CISELET and DELCOUR, 1942, p. 57). All the churches in Belgium were well provided with lighting devices of every type, and many of them still exist. This bracket-sconce is a good example. It probably dates from the second half of the 15th century and belongs to the Church of Saint-Jacques in Louvain, also remarkable for other works of art of the same period.

Physical data: Cast brass, 16 $^7/_8$ in. (43 cm.). Identification mark in the form of a bell engraved on the shield.
History: Unknown.
Exhibitions : Malines, 1864, no. 232 (1st. ed.) and 254 (2nd ed.) ; Brussels, 1888, no. 835 ; Deurne - Brussels, 1957, no. 206.

This object was probably made originally for the church in which it is still preserved. The identification mark in the form of a bell is perhaps that of the caster; it has not yet been identified. Two other bracket-sconces of this kind are in the same church and they also have a small shield under the drip-pan (one of the shields has disappeared but its stud is still

273

visible). DE BORCHGRAVE D'ALTENA (1939-40, p. 287) suggests that these three bracket-sconces may have belonged to the same piece, perhaps a lectern. Even if it is evident that they were part of one series, it seems difficult, nevertheless, to believe that they belonged to the same object because they differ in their dimensions (14 $^5/_8$ in., 17 $^1/_2$ in., 20 $^1/_8$ in.; 37 cm., 45 cm., 51 cm.), the details of their decoration, the shape of the stems, and even the shape of the drip-pans.

BRUGES, second half of the 15th Century

107. CHANDELIER

Bruges, Saint John's Hospital

This brass chandelier belongs to a type of which there is conserved a fairly great number of examples dating back to the second half of the 15th century or the beginning of the 16th century. It has sixteen branches. Its decoration, a *Virgin*

274

and Child in Glory, at the top, and the branches of vine forming the arms of the light, indicate that it was used in a church. It possesses a suspension ring and another ring at the base to allow maneuvring in the same way as all the chandeliers in houses; it probably had a system of pulleys which allowed it to be raised and lowered. This can be seen in the chandeliers depicted in Flemish Primitive paintings, especially in the central panel of the *Triptych of the Holy Sacrament* by Dieric Bouts in the Church of Saint-Pierre in Louvain, in the portrait of the Arnolfini-couple by Jan van Eyck in the National Gallery in London, and in this exhibition, in the painting by Petrus Christus, the *Virgin and Child in an Interior,* from Kansas City (cat. no. 14).

> *Physical data:* Brass, 30 ¹¹/₁₆ in. (78 cm.) without the rings. The lower part of the stem ends in the form of a lion's head, it seems to be a metal of another color and may have been restored.
> *History:* Belonged to the Saint John's Hospital in 1852 (*Inventory,* 1852, p. 373, no. 4).
> *Exhibitions:* Bruges, 1867, no. 69; Brussels, 1888, cl. 7, no. 848; Bruges, 1902, E, no. 11.

VERSCHELDE (Cat. Exhib. Bruges, 1867, no. 69) and WEALE (Cat. Exhib. Bruges, 1902, E, no. 11) date this chandelier from the end of the 15th century. The chandelier which is most close to this one is that at Machelen-lez-Deinze, in Flanders. A chandelier of the same type is preserved at the Victoria and Albert Museum, London, and at the Museum voor Oudheden der Bijloke in Ghent.

FRANCE(?), second half of the 15th Century

108. ASTROLABE

Ghent, Stedelijk Archief (on loan to the Museum voor Folklore)

This instrument is an astrolabe of the planispheric type which was used to tell time. It could also be used to observe the stars. In the Middle Ages it was the most precise and perfect instrument for telling time known before the invention of the cog-wheel clock.

An astrolabe may be seen in one of the paintings in this exhibition, *Saint Jerome in his Study* by Jan van Eyck (cat. no. 5).

> *Physical data:* Brass, diameter: 10 ⁵/₈ in. (27 cm.). The graduations and inscriptions are in 15th century Gothic numbers and letters. The alidade, or sighting arm, is missing; central pin and ring for suspension are modern (*Inventaire des Instruments Scientifiques Historiques conservés en Belgique,* Brussels, 1959, fol. 77).
> *History:* Origin unknown.
> *Exhibitions:* Brussels, 1957, no. A 12.

William D. Lemoine, research specialist at the Centre National d'Histoire des Sciences in Brussels, has provided the following description of this instrument:

275

"An analogous piece is known, the astrolabe preserved in the Museum of the History of Science in Oxford (cf. R.T. Gunther, *The Astrolabes of the World*, Oxford, 1932, no. 163, pp. 309-311). The astrolabe is a drawn projection of the sky and the earth. The instrument consists of two superimposed discs. The upper plate is called the rete; it is a projection of the celestial sphere where each important star is indicated by small pointers in the form of sparks. This rete is cut away to show, under it, the terrestrial planisphere or plate. This second plate shows the earth with circles on which astronomical measurements are taken: horizon, equator, meridians, and *almucantarats*. By turning the rete on the plate it is possible to reproduce the position of the sky in relation to the earth at a given moment. Thus, the position of the stars and sun, the amplitude of their trajectory, and other astronomical facts can be deduced. On the back of the instruments are shadow squares which are used to measure angles and a calendar with zodiacal concordances. The presence of a plate made for the latitude of 45° shows that it was an instrument made for use in France. The longitude of Regulus (*Cor Leonis*) indicated by the rete corresponds to a date between 1450 and 1500. Moreover, on the back of the astrolabe the zodiacal calendar indicates the entry of Aries as the 11 $^1/_4$ of March. The instrument being shown in this exhibition has all the characteristics of an astrolabe of the 15th century. In the beginning of the 14th century the Jewish astronomers in Spain had to emigrate to Southern France and brought with them the Hispano-Mooresque tradition. The Arabic names of the stars were thus transmitted to Northern European astronomers. Astronomers in the 15th century were very much favored by the Dukes of Burgundy. Several of these instruments are mentioned in the inventories of Philip the Good and Charles the Bold as well as in the royal inventories". For example, the Inventory of Charles the Bold made in 1467 mentions: *Item ung astrelabe de lecton doré* (DE LABORDE, Part 2, II, 1851, no. 3419).

276

DINANT or BRABANT, 15th Century

109-112. THE FOUR SYMBOLS OF THE EVANGELISTS
Reading desks of a large lectern

Baltimore, Md., The Walters Art Gallery. Inv. nos. 53.70-53.73

These four reading desks are in the form of the symbols of the Evangelists: the angel represents Saint Matthew; the lion, Saint Mark; the ox, Saint Luke; and the eagle, Saint John. These reading desks were originally supported by four cast brass arms projecting from a central shaft topped with a pelican, the symbol of Christ. The complete object was supported by a monumental base borne by lions. The entire lectern could be pivoted on its axis in order to make accessible to the reader the particular Book of Gospels to be used. This imposing lectern was once in the choir of the Cathedral of Messina, in Sicily, at the foot of the

steps leading to the altar: when at the top of these steps the reader was at the level of the reading desks.

The Cathedral of Messina was destroyed by the earthquake which demolished the city in 1908. Of the lectern itself, then damaged, the only parts still known are these four reading desks. The origin of this monumental piece of metalwork is unknown but judging from its style it may be placed among the products of the Netherlands, coming from a Dinant or Brabant workshop. It was certainly executed in the 15th century. Italy possesses other brass objects from the Netherlands; for example, in the Cathedral of Genoa there is a paschal candelabrum which also bears the symbols of the Evangelists, and there are two lecterns in Venice in the Church of San Stefano and in the Museo Civico.

The Messina lectern must have been one of the largest pieces of its kind. There formerly was a lectern at Champmol which, like the one in Messina, also bore the symbols of the Evangelists, but it was topped by a phoenix instead of a pelican.

FIG. 5.

Physical data: Brass, *Angel:* 18 x 16 x 12 1/4 in. (45.8 x 40.7 x 31.2 cm.); *Ox:* 19 1/2 x 14 x 14 3/8 in. (49.5 x 35.6 x 36.6 cm.); *Eagle:* 18 5/8 x 16 1/2 x 12 1/2 in. (47.4 x 41.9 x 31.8 cm.); *Lion:* 17 1/2 x 16 x 12 1/4 in. (44.5 x 40.7 x 31.2 cm.). Cast and chiseled. The eagle was lightly damaged.

History: An engraving of 1852 showing the lectern of the Cathedral of Messina (DIGBY WYATT, 1852, pl. XXXV; see illustration in this catalogue) clearly identifies the four reading desks now in Baltimore. A photograph taken before the 1908 earthquake (OMAN, 1937, p. 276, pl. 5) confirms this. In 1910, the four reading desks were acquired by Henry Walters of Baltimore from a Parisian art dealer. They were said to have come from the Cathedral of Reggio (Calabria) which might have acquired them after the earthquake (Ross, 1938, p. 290). The Walters Collection became The Walters Art Gallery in 1932.

Exhibitions: Baltimore, 1948, no. 9 (the lectern with the ox).

The 1852 engraving and the photograph taken before the 1908 earthquake permit the identification of the four reading desks in Baltimore with absolute certainty.

DIGBY WYATT (1852, p. 78) referred to the lectern in Messina as having been made in a local Sicilian workshop of the 15th century. OMAN (1930, p. 120,

278

note 6, and 1937, p. 274) was the first to recognize the lectern as having originated in the Netherlands. He called it Flemish and dated it from the end of the 15th century. Ross (1938, p. 290) viewed the Messina lectern as the model which might have inspired the paschal candelabrum in Genoa. Thus, he considers the lectern from Messina as earlier than the candelabrum in Genoa. SQUILBECK (1941, p. 354) points out the relationship between these two objects in metal and compares, especially, the two figures of the angels (Saint Matthew). However, he thinks the Genoa candlestick is an earlier work than the lectern from Messina. This conclusion would appear to be supported by the design of the base. SQUILBECK (ibidem) believes the Genoa candlestick might have been made in Dinant at the beginning of the 15th century. By analogy, it may be possible to consider the lectern from Messina, and consequently the four reading desks of Baltimore, as also having been produced in Dinant.

SOUTHERN NETHERLANDS, 15th Century

113. EWER

Léau, Church of Saint-Léonard

This ewer, also called a lavabo, is a liturgical object for the vestry of a church: it was used by the priest to wash his hands before and after mass. It has two spouts, one of which is used before and the other after mass. The church of Léau has preserved a group of three ewers, including this one, dating from the 15th century.

An almost identical ewer can be seen in the *Annunciation* called the *Merode Altarpiece,* in The Cloisters in New York, and in the *Annunciation* of the polyp-

tych of the *Adoration of the Lamb* by van Eyck in Ghent. They are shown there with a symbolic meaning, assimilating the Virgin's bedroom to a church.

> *Physical data:* Brass, height: 6 ¹¹/₁₆ in. (17 cm.) (without handle), diameter of the rim: 7 ¹/₁₆ in. (18 cm.).
> *History:* Belonged to the Church of Saint-Léonard in 1881 (Cat. Liège Exhib. 1881, Section IV, no. 213) and has probably always been there.
> *Exhibitions:* Liège, 1881, Section IV, no. 213; Léau, 1924, no no.

Numerous ewers have been preserved. Like this one, they generally have an oblate shape, the spouts terminate in the form of animals' heads and women's heads serve as swivel-pin-sockets in which the handle is set. The handle is pierced with a hole for a ring by which the ewer was suspended from a bracket fixed in the wall. In domestic use, this ewer was suspended above a basin; in church use, it was hung above a drain which led the used water directly to the consecrated ground.

At that time, sockets for the pail handles were generally in the form of a head for all kinds of religious and secular objects. The mouths of animals often served as the openings of water spouts; they were even found on the mouths of the first cannons made in the 15th century.

SOUTHERN NETHERLANDS, 15th Century

114. PAIL FOR HOLY WATER

Liège, Musée Diocésain. Manuscript cat., no. 356

This pail for holy water is of a traditional Gothic form, deep and bell-mouthed. The handle is attached to the pail by two swivel-pin-sockets in the form of heads of animals.

> *Physical data:* Brass, height: 5 ⁵/₁₆ in. (13.5 cm.) without handle and 11 in. (28 cm.) with handle; diameter of base: 4 in. (10.3 cm.).
> *History:* Origin unknown.
> *Exhibitions:* None known.

This pail can be dated in the 15th century by its triple molding and perforated base because pails of this type are seen in paintings by the Flemish Primitives. An example can be found in *The Death of the Virgin* by Petrus Christus in the National Gallery of Art in Washington. An almost identical pail belongs to the Church of Sainte-Gertrude in Louvain.

280

YPRES(?), 15th Century

115-116. TWO TANKARDS OF THE ALDERMEN OF THE "KEURE"

Ghent, Museum voor Oudheden der Bijloke. Cat. nos. 1399-1400

By "Keure" is meant certain official legal prescriptions freely accepted by communities in the 15th century.

These pewter tankards with lids were used to offer the wine of honor to distinguished guests. The city of Oudenaarde possesses the largest series still existing, twelve examples, dating from 1549. These tankards were also referred to in city accounts as *cimarres* or *cimaises*. They have a lid and one or two handles but no spout.

The two tankards from the Bijloke Museum belonged to the aldermen of the "Keure" in Ghent: they bear, on the body of the vessel, a shield with the coat of arms of the city. They are dated in the 15th century. Vessels of this kind are seen in paintings and miniatures of the time as in the painting by the Master of 1499 shown here as no. 43. However, this same form has been in use for such a long time that it is difficult to distinguish between objects of this kind made sometimes a century apart.

Physical data: Pewter, 21 $^7/_8$ x 8$^1/_2$ in. (55.5 x 21.5 cm.) and 22 $^{13}/_{16}$ x 8 $^{11}/_{16}$ in. (58 x 22 cm.). Both tankards have a shield decorated with a lion on their middle bulging section. They also both have two marks on the handle: one bears a shield with a chevron topped by a crown, and a lozenge decorated with a fleur-de-lis. The other has a shield bearing a chevron surmounted by a crown, and a shield with a Gothic "y". The second tankard bears in addition, a mark on the inside of the base in the form of a cross of Saint Andrew over which are the "briquets" and flames of Burgundy.

History: Origin unknown.

Exhibitions: Ghent, 1845, no. 10; Ghent, 1854, no. 17; Ghent, 1958, nos. 27-28.

281

These marks were identified by Boes (1935, p. 6, note 8) as being those of a pewter maker in Ypres. This same author dates the tankards in the 15th century.

Tankards of the city which were used for offerings of wine and at banquets were often noted in the accounts. There are various records of the purchase or repairing of these pieces (Van Duyse, 1897, p. 31).

SOUTHERN NETHERLANDS, 15th Century

117-120. FOUR SPOONS

Liège, Musée Diocésain. Manuscript cat., nos. 369-370

These four brass spoons have the characteristic shape of spoons of the 15th century, fairly round but slightly elongated towards the stem. This latter is polygonal, cylindrical or twisted, rather short and generally ending in a figurine.

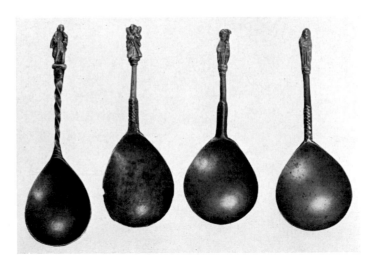

Here can be recognized a *Virgin and Child*, a *Saint Andrew* carrying an oblique cross and a *Saint James* with a pilgrim's staff.

Physical data: Brass, approximately 5 ¹/₈ in. and 5 ⁷/₈ in. (13 cm. and 15 cm.).
History: Origin unknown.
Exhibitions: None known.

In the 15th century, table cutlery consisted only of knives and spoons: forks were introduced later and were not in general use until the 17th century. The representation of tables prepared for a meal in miniatures, paintings and

282

tapestries prove it, as well as accounts of the Dukes of Burgundy. The spoons were made of wood, sometimes fixed onto a horn, rock-crystal or metal (brass, silver or even gold) stem. One of the most beautiful examples of spoons which has been preserved is that of the Museum of Fine Arts of Boston, exhibited here (cat. no. 131); it is made of silver decorated with enamel. The Inventory of Charles the Bold, in 1467, includes spoons in gold, silver, silver-gilt, crystal, sometimes with a gold stem, and some decorated with enamel (DE LABORDE, Part 2, II, 1851, nos. 2338, 2705, 2715, 2718, 2721, 2770, 2771, 3385, 3424, 3634, 3652, 3654).

BRUGES(?), 15th Century

121-122. TWO WAFFLE-IRONS

Bruges, Gruuthuse-Museum. Inv. XII, nos. 89-90

These two waffle-irons bear the coats of arms of the Dukes of Burgundy. One (Inv. 90) bears the coats of arms of the Dukes before 1430; the other (Inv. 89) those of the Dukes between 1430 and 1477. These coats of arms are

surrounded by a checker-board decoration. The second also has an illustration of the *Agnus Dei* surrounded by branches of holly and vines. Next to the coats of arms, the form of these particular waffle-irons and their ornamentation date them in the 15th century. Tradition says they came from the kitchens of the Dukes, but this tradition is probably merely based on the fact that the coats of arms of the Dukes appear on them.

283

Such waffle-irons were used to make a kind of thin cake still called *lukken* in Flanders. This term is also used in the Flemish colony of Detroit to designate a type of cake made for New Year's celebrations.

Physical data: Wrought iron, waffle-iron Inv. 89: length, 34 1/16 in. (86.5 cm.), plates: 4 3/4 x 7 7/8 in. (12 x 20 cm.); waffle-iron Inv. 90: length, 36 13/16 in. (93.5 cm.), plates: 4 15/16 x 8 1/4 in. (12.5 x 21 cm.). Coats of arms. Inscription *ihesus* in small Gothic letters, repeated four times around the *Agnus Dei* on Inv. 89.
History: Origin unknown.
Exhibitions: None known.

STALPAERT (1957, p. 25) has identified the coats of arms of the Dukes. This author believes that these two waffle-irons might be the oldest ones which are preserved in Flanders.

BRUGES(?), 15th Century

123. A PAIR OF ANDIRONS

Bruges, City Hall

These wrought iron andirons topped with brass lions, each holding a shield, were recently put in the aldermen's room in the City Hall, after the restoration of this room and the reconstruction of its large fireplace. Their origin is not known but they have been in Bruges for more than eighty years and it is reasonable to believe that they have always been there. They appear to date from the 15th century.

Physical data: Iron and brass, 38 9/16 x 16 15/16 x 31 1/2 in. (98 x 43 x 80 cm.); lions: 9 1/16 in. (23 cm.). The monogram **LD** (interlaced) and another mark, engraved on the shield of one of the lions, are not original.
History: Property of the Archaeological Society of Bruges in 1880 (REUSSENS, 1880-1882, pp. 188 and 193).
Exhibitions: Deurne-Brussels, 1957, no. 430.

284

DUCLOS (1910, pp. 402 and 451-452) pointed out that the Archaeological Museum possessed wrought iron andirons which were probably those of the aldermen's room in the City Hall for which Georges Coudruddere had been paid in 1401-1402. An account of that year in the city archives includes, in fact, a payment made to this ironworker for andirons weighing 101 pounds for the aldermen's room (GILLIODTS-VAN SEVEREN, III, 1875, p. 493). Unfortunately, DUCLOS did not say whether he had any particular reason for believing that the andirons of the Archaeological Museum came from the City Hall.

This type of andirons with trefoiled bases and hexagonal stems can be dated from the 15th century.

FLANDERS, 1499 and 16th Century

124-126. MASK, TWO FISTS, and PLACARD OF JUSTICE

Furnes, Museum of the City Hall

These mask and fists are expiatory symbols which condemned persons had to have made at their own expense to be exhibited at the town pillory with a placard giving the grounds for the sentence and the name of the guilty person. This type of sentence was peculiar to certain towns of Flanders, Zealand, and perhaps also Brabant in the 15th and 16th centuries, such as Furnes, Ypres, Dunkirk, Sluis, Middelburg, Veere, Ghent, and probably Malines. It appears to have been most commonly applied in the case of an

285

outrageous act against the court or a law enforcement official. The object exhibited in effigy was a head if the guilty person had sinned by word, a hand if he had struck a blow. Objects of this kind are now very rare and the city of Furnes is the only one which has preserved a whole group coming from its former law courts. There are two masks, two fists, and seven placards with inscriptions. From the placards it has been possible to interpret the meaning of these objects which can also be related to documents in the town archives.

The mask being exhibited may probably be related to the placard which says that a certain Pieter de Beert was sentenced in 1499 for having threatened to throw law enforcement officials out of the window. The fist which is cast in one piece represents the sentence of a man who struck a blow. The other fist, cast in two pieces, originally held a knife; it represents the sentence of a man who had stabbed someone. Both of these fists appear to be traceable to sentences pronounced in the 16th century, in 1551 and 1549 respectively.

> *Physical data:* Mask: bronze, 9 $^7/_8$ x 5 $^1/_8$ in. (25 x 13 cm.); lips and throat are pierced with holes for a ring which has disappeared. Fist: bronze, 4 $^3/_4$ in. (12 cm.). Fist: bronze, 5 $^7/_8$ in. (15 cm.); in two joined pieces with an opening for a dagger which has disappeared. Placard: bronze, 7$^1/_2$ x 16$^1/_2$ in. (19 x 42 cm.).
> Inscription in Flemish written in Gothic characters: *Pieter de Beert es gheco(n)de(m) pneert bij vo(n) nesse va(n) der wet slants van Veurenambocht te stellene dit hoofd o(m)me dat hij gheseijt heift eeneghe woorden inhoudende dreeghement va(n) der wet tvorseits sla(nt)s ter vei(n)stere uut te worpene 1499.*
> *History:* Noted for the first time in 1843 by V [AN] D [E] V[ELDE] (1843, pp. 186-192) who saw two heads, two fists, and seven placards bearing inscriptions, in a cupboard of the City Hall of Furnes. In 1872 these objects were in the archives of Furnes (DE BÉTHUNE, 1872, pp. 136-142).
> *Exhibitions:* None known.

The text of the placard may be translated as follows: "Pieter de Beert is condemned by sentence of the law of the country of Furnambacht to set up this head because he spoke some words threatening to throw the officials of the law of this country out of the window, 1499".

It seems evident that the objects of justice from Furnes have always belonged to the law courts of that city. CANNAERT (1835, pp. 66-70 and 127-128) discovered several examples of this kind of sentence in the archives of Ghent in 1396, 1481, and 1514, of Veere (Zealand) in 1550, and of Malines in 1561.

286

Metalwork

GOLDSMITH'S WORK

MASTER HENRI and THE GUFKENSES

From the middle of the 14th until the beginning of the 16th centuries, goldsmiths named Gufkens, or Gofkens, were active in Tongres. Their names appeared on various occasions in the accounts of the Church of Notre-Dame in that city. The possibility is not excluded that the goldsmith called Master Henri belonged to the Gufkens family. However, he may perhaps be identified as Henri Van Gelmen, a goldsmith cited in the accounts of the same church for 1420, or possibly even as Henri de Tongres the Younger, goldsmith in Hasselt, who died in 1448 and whose epitaph is preserved in the Church of Sainte-Dymphne in Geel. In any case, from 1400 to 1426 a certain Master Henri was paid on several occasions for works made for the Church of Notre-Dame. This church still possesses a head-reliquary of Saint Pinose in copper-gilt for which he was paid in 1426.

127. RELIQUARY-STATUETTE OF CHRIST BLESSING

Tongres, Collegiate Church of Notre-Dame

This silver reliquary-statuette of Christ Blessing or Salvator Mundi was ordered in 1400 along with several others by the church council from several Tongres goldsmiths, Master Henri and the Gufkenses. These statuettes accompanied the "large shrine of Notre-Dame", also in silver, which contained the most precious relic of the church, a belt of the Virgin. This shrine perished in a fire in 1677. The Church of Notre-Dame of Tongres, seat of a diocese from the 6th to the 11th century, was amply endowed with relics. It still possesses a series of fourteen silver reliquary-statuettes of which this one is among the oldest and most beautiful.

Physical data: Silver, 14 1/16 in. (35.8 cm.). Partially gilded. Base in gilded copper and in silver. The small leaves which decorate the cruciferous nimbus are embossed and chiseled. The nimbus is ornamented with a cameo and precious stones; it was bordered with pearls most of which are now missing. An amethyst surrounded by pearls ornaments the neck-opening of the robe. In His left hand, Christ holds a crystal orb, surmounted by a silver cross. On the back, a small door indicates that the statuette was used as a reliquary.
A stippled inscription in Gothic letters on the hem of the robe includes notably the words: *Salvator Mundi.*

History: An account book of 1400 mentions payments on April 5 and 29 and on May 22 for silver statuettes of the Saviour and the Virgin and for their gilding. The May 22 entry specifies that the goldsmiths Master Henri and the Gufkens Sons ("magistri Henrici et filiorum Gofkens") received the last payment (Archives de l'Eglise Notre-Dame, ed. PAQUAY,

287

1904, pp. 114-118 and 1911, pp.162-164). These two statuettes and others are noted in an inventory of 1453 as being placed at the large shrine of the Virgin: *Item feretrum magnum novum ad quod ponentur infrascripte ymagines argentee: primo ymago Salvatoris, ymago beate Marie Virginis (...)* (PAQUAY, 1904, p. 158). In 1677 a fire destroyed part of the treasure, including the large shrine, but the statuettes were saved since they appear in subsequent inventories (PAQUAY, 1904, p. 120). From 1677 to 1682, all the pieces saved from the fire were preserved in Liège; from 1689 to 1708 they were deposited in Maastricht to be protected from the invading French troops of Louis XIV; from 1794 to 1804 they were taken to Hamburg for safekeeping during the French Revolution; inventories were made at the time of these different journeys and a mention is always found of the *Christ Blessing* and the other reliquary-statuettes (PAQUAY, 1904, pp. 151-152, 154-156 and 161).

Exhibitions: Malines, 1864, no. 492 (1st ed.) and no. 528 (2nd ed.); Paris, 1924, no. 56.

There is no doubt that this *Christ Blessing* is the one for which Master Henri and the Gufkenses were paid. The documents are less explicit as to the relationship between this statuette and the large shrine. The 1435 text says: "Item, the large new shrine at which are placed the following silver images: first, the image of the Saviour, the image of the Virgin Mary(...)". It is possible that the statuettes were independent but that they were placed around the shrine at the time of its exposition and perhaps in processions. This would explain, moreover, how they could be saved from the fire in which the large shrine perished. DEVIGNE (1932, p. 108) pointed out that the characteristics of style of the *Christ Blessing* confirm the dating provided by the archives.

288

Goldsmith's Work

FRANCO-BURGUNDIAN, ca. 1400

128. NECKLACE

Cleveland, Ohio, The Cleveland Museum of Art. Inv. 47.507

This splendid necklace is composed of twelve medallions joined by a double chain enriched with pearls. The piece, as it is now assembled, is probably not in its original form. In the present arrangement, use was made of old medallions which date, at least some of them and particularly the central medallion, from the time of Philip the Bold at the end of the 14th century. These medallions match the descriptions of jewels, especially garment clasps, which filled the account books of the Dukes. Philip the Bold had a passion for jewels and he was lavish with them: he gave them on all sorts of occasions to his

Goldsmith's Work

family, friends, and servants and even to the King of France and to the Pope.

Those jewels, like the medallions of this necklace, were made of enameled gold enriched by precious cut stones and an abundance of pearls. The principal medallions (the five on the lower part of the necklace) are made-up of a gold circle at the center of which is a principal motif, a person or a flower, in enameled gold. Around this central motif, oak or other leaves in thin sheets of tooled gold alternate with pearls mounted on short stems and sometimes grouped in links of three. The very remarkable central medallion or pendant shows a young girl clad in an enameled white robe holding an unidentified gold object between her hands. She wears a thin green diadem in her golden hair. The six upper medallions are smaller. They are comprised of small enameled flowers, cut stones, or pendant pearls which can move in small gold cups. The medallion which serves as a clasp, almost as large as the central medallion, has an enameled central flower, enriched with pearls and precious stones, and surrounded by a wreath of leaves and pearls.

Physical data: Gold, enamel, precious and semi-precious stones, pearls, 28 1/2 in. (72.4 cm.). Diameter of central medallion: 1 3/4 in. (4.4 cm.).

History: G.J. Demotte art dealer, New York, 1928 (Cat. Detroit Exhib., 1928, no. 75); Joseph Brummer art dealer, New York *(Bulletin of The Cleveland Museum of Art, 1947,* p. 228); J.H. Wade Coll., The Cleveland Museum of Art (MILLIKEN, 1948, pp. 311-322). *Exhibitions:* Detroit, 1928, no. 75; Cleveland, 1947-48.

A dealer's tradition, which seems unfounded, claims this necklace was offered to the Virgin of Louvain by Margaret of Brabant, daughter of Duke Jean III and wife of Louis de Male, Count of Flanders.

The authorities are unanimous in considering that the parts of this necklace, if not its present form, belong to Franco-Burgundian art. WEIBEL, author of the Catalogue for the Detroit Exhibition in 1928 (no. 75), dated them in the 14th century. MILLIKEN (1948, pp. 316-318 and 321) placed them around 1400. MÜLLER and STEINGRÄBER (1954, p. 76, no. 26) dated it at the beginning of the 15th century. According to these last authors, the double chain in which the medallions are set is modern.

The figurine of the principal medallion is one of the rare still-existing examples of enamel in the round ("émail en ronde-bosse") (MILLIKEN, 1948, p. 321). It has a small green diadem, red lips, black eyes and gold hair and fingers. The style of the dress and especially the

290

Goldsmith's Work

use of white enamel suggest dating it ca. 1385-1400. It matches the description of certain clasps which are found in the accounts of the Dukes. For example in 1393, when Mary, daughter of Philip the Bold, married the young Duke of Savoy, the accounts note that Mary gave her husband a "golden clasp with a white lady" (DAVID, 1947, p. 49).

Medallions or clasps with figures on them are known. In the Kunsthistorisches Museum in Vienna is a later work, ca. 1450, also in enamel, showing two lovers; in the Cathedral of Essen is one which has the figure of a woman. The one in the former Figdor Collection in Vienna has the figure of a seated woman, as in the Cleveland necklace (KOHLHAUSSEN, 1931, pp. 164-165 and 167); she is carrying a thin golden stalk of the same type as the unidentified object which the "white lady" of Cleveland holds.

TOURNAI(?), first quarter of the 15th Century

129. BADGE OF THE CONFRATERNITY OF YOUNG GENTLEMEN called "QUIGNON DES DAMOISEAUX"

Tournai, Treasury of the Cathedral of Notre-Dame

This badge or "quignon", as this large silver medallion is called, is an emblem which was carried in processions at the head of the Confraternity of Young Gentlemen. This emblem shows the City of Tournai symbolized by a young girl, "La Pucelle de Tournai", seated within the middle of the surrounding walls of the city around which flows the Scheldt River. The young girl holds in her left hand a shield with the arms of the City of Tournai (as used prior to 1426). In her right hand she holds a shield with the arms of the Empire which is not original and could not have been added earlier than 1521. What was originally in that position is not known but there may have been a unicorn or some other symbol.

The piece must date from the first quarter of the 15th century but it has suffered very much and has been somewhat modified. Originally it must have been richly enameled; only a few traces of this remain.

The Brotherhood of the Young Gentlemen was instituted in 1280 by the Bishop of Tournai at the time of an epidemic of the bubonic plague. This

291

Goldsmith's Work

confraternity had sixty members who were among the leading citizens of the city. The magistrate of Tournai was chosen from its membership.

Physical data: Embossed silver, partially gilded and enameled, 5 1/2 x 6 1/8 in. (14 x 15.5 cm.). The conical roofs of three towers are missing as is the crown over the shield on the right and probably a pearl or precious stone in the young girl's crown. Only traces remain of the green enamel of the field and the blue enamel of the towers' roofs. On the back a plaque seems to have been added later. It bears the engraved date XV^cVIII (1508) and two stamped marks, possibly maker's marks, a lion and a scorpion.

History: This piece was made for the Confraternity of the Young Gentlemen and was their emblem. At the time of the French Revolution the piece was hidden, as were the reliquary and torch of the confraternity, by the pharmacist Desruez, who took care of them until his death, when he specified that they were to be returned to the Cathedral (Du Mortier, 1862, pp. 224-225).

Exhibitions: Malines, 1864, no. 773 (1st ed.) and no. 814 (2nd ed.); Brussels, 1880, no. A 466; Bruges, 1902, G, no. 41; Tournai, 1911, no. 1511; Mons, 1953, no. 208; Ghent, 1955, no. 500; Tournai, 1956, D, no. 2 (p. 212); Tournai, 1958, no. 80 (1st ed.) and no. 76 (2nd ed.).

DE LA GRANGE and CLOQUET (II, 1889, p. 304) have pointed out that the shield of Tournai shown in this piece bears the arms of the city as used before 1426. KOHLHAUSSEN (1931, p. 160, no. 3) compares this piece, in its technique, to such enameled pieces as the celebrated monkey goblet in the New York Metropolitan Museum, the small spoon with the sermon to the geese in the Boston Museum of Fine Arts (shown in this exhibition as no. 131), and the enamel of the emblems of the blow-pipe musicians of the city of Ghent.

The presence of the shield of Tournai, which is certainly before 1426, gives a date *ante quem* for this medallion. Moreover, it has the characteristics of a goldsmith's work of the beginning of the 15th century. The meadow in green enamel, perhaps originally scattered with flowers, brings to mind the decoration of certain clasps ordered at the end of the 14th century by Philip the Bold, Duke of Burgundy, which also included a figurine seated in a meadow. Because of later modifications, namely the arms of the Empire and the date 1508 on the plaque on the back, the work has sometimes been classified in a later period, generally in the sixteenth century.

SOUTHERN NETHERLANDS, 1430

130. COLLAR OF THE ORDER OF THE GOLDEN FLEECE

Le Roeulx, Collection of S.A.S. le Prince de Croy-Roeulx

Philip the Good founded the Order of the Golden Fleece January 10, 1430, on the occasion of his marriage to Isabella of Portugal. His purpose was to maintain the knightly ideal among the nobility. At its origin this Order included thirty-one "gentlemen of name and arms and without reproach". Its meetings were the occasion for extraordinary pomp and ceremony and the Order became

292

a kind of symbol of the wealth of its founder's reign. Its members wore a golden collar similar to the one on exhibition, composed of links showing the "Briquets" or fire steels of Burgundy and the flints from which the flames come, with a golden fleece hanging from the lower part of the collar. This ram represented the golden fleece won by Jason in the legend of the Argonauts. The Duke liked this legend and had it illustrated several times on tapestries. The ram also evoked the fleece which Gideon spread on the ground (Judges 6. 36-40). A magnificent tapestry telling the story of Gideon decorated the chapter room of the Order in The Hague in 1456. Meetings of the Order took place every year at first, and less frequently later on. Philip the Good called ten meetings: the first in Lille in 1431, then, in Bruges in 1432, Dijon in 1433, Brussels in 1435, Lille in 1436, Saint-Omer in 1440, Ghent in 1445, Mons in 1451, The Hague in 1456, and Saint-Omer in 1461.

Physical data: Gold and enamel, 46 $^7/_{16}$ in. (118 cm.). The ram: $^{14}/_{16}$ x 1 $^1/_{16}$ in. (2.1 x 2.7 cm.). The collar contains 28 double "briquets" and an equal number of flints from which spring the flames. The flints are enriched with black and white enamel.

History: The collar traditionally belonged to Antoine de Croÿ, Baron de Renty, adviser and first chamberlain to Philip the Good, who was named Knight of the Order at the time of its founding in 1430.

Exhibitions: Brussels, 1953, no. 109; Tournai, 1956, p. 173, no. 80 (1st ed.) and p. 179, no. 114 (2nd ed.); Le Roeulx, 1959, no. 220.

293

According to family tradition this collar dates from the founding of the Order and belonged to Antoine de Croÿ, Knight of the Golden Fleece since 1430. This tradition was reported in the Catalogue of the Exhibition "Brussels in the 15th century" (1953, no. 109). In the Tournai Exhibition in 1956 (p. 173, no. 80) the collar was listed as having probably been given by Charles V to his godfather Charles de Croÿ. The Catalogue of the Le Roeulx Exhibition in 1959 (no. 220) amends this information in specifying that the collar was given in 1530 by Charles V to Adrien de Croÿ, who had been a member of his escort when he went to Bologna to receive the crown from the hands of Pope Clement VIII. According to the catalogue, it was on that occasion that the emperor elevated Le Roeulx to a county, for the benefit of Adrien de Croÿ.

FLEMISH-BURGUNDIAN, second quarter of the 15th Century

131. SPOON with THE FOX PREACHING TO THE GEESE

Boston, Museum of Fine Arts. Inv. 51.2472

This little spoon is a remarkable example of historiated decoration in enamel on silver. It shows a fox preaching to geese while another fox seizes a member of the congregation, perhaps to add it to the lot of geese of which the heads appear out of the preacher's cowl. Akin to the drolleries and grotesques on the margins of medieval illuminated manuscripts, this representation of the fox preaching to a congregation of geese is a satirical commentary upon the life of the period. The inside of the bowl of the spoon is in dark blue enamel against which the figures stand out in white or clear blue while the setting of trees and raining stars is white and gold. The back of the spoon shows a forest on a black enamel background: trees and raining stars are in white, grey and gold. The subject matter is treated with humor and a great sense of composition. The artist managed, without apparent effort, to confine the scene within a difficult oval form. The most typical elements are the very special shape of the trees, the cutting-up of the earth in the foreground into wave-like patterns, and the rainfall of golden stars all over the background. The same elements are also seen in several other objects which form a group: they have not only the same typical details and the same technique but also the same inspiration and artistic vision. These objects are, notably, a small spoon which shows a monkey riding a stag in a forest (London, Victoria and Albert Museum) and the famous monkey cup (The Metropolitan Museum of Art, New York). Altogether there are some fifteen objects of this kind in the world.

These works are generally considered as having been made for the court of Philip the Good in the second quarter of the 15th century. They were probably

294

made in the Southern Netherlands, perhaps in a Flemish workshop.

Physical data: Silver, silver-gilt, and enamel, 6 $^7/_8$ in. (17.5 cm.). Reinforced along the edges and center line of the back by thicker metal, which encloses the storied enamel decoration. The bowl of the spoon is attached by a silver-gilt head to a twisted handle with niello in the grooves of the fluting and a long floriated finial in silver-gilt.

Inscriptions (save for the word *Pax...*) are almost illegible on the charter held by the fox and on the streamer above the fleeing goose. A small portion of the enamel is missing from the inside near the handle; some chips have come off the back of the spoon on the right side near the handle and in the upper part, on the left and right, in the foliage of the trees.

History: Princes of Anhalt-Dessau; Goldschmidt-Rothschild Coll., Frankfort on-Main, 1931; purchased through the H.E. Colburn Fund for the Museum of Fine Arts, Boston, 1951.

Exhibitions: None known.

KOHLHAUSSEN (1931, pp. 154-156 and 167-169) and BOSSERT (V, 1932, p. 389) compare this spoon to the monkey cup in The Metropolitan Museum in New York, formerly in the Rutschi Collection in Lucerne, showing monkeys stealing the goods of travelling merchants as they sleep. BOSSERT (V, 1932, p. 389) groups eight additional objects, also in enameled silver. They are comparable in technique, color and general subject. They are decorated on black or dark blue backgrounds with motifs in grisaille and white, touched up with gold.

It is certain that some of the objects in this group are earlier than 1464 or 1467: an inventory of Piero de'Medici for 1464 includes a "goblet with market of the monkeys, enameled in white" which might be the cup in New York or a similar one (KOHLHAUSSEN, 1931, p. 157); the Inventory of Charles the Bold ca. 1467 mentions "two salt cellars (...) and the lid enameled in light blue with figures in white enamel" (DE LABORDE, Part 2, II, 1851, no. 2657). The costume of the merchants on the monkey goblet would indicate a date of ca. 1430-1440 (KOHLHAUSSEN, 1931, p. 158). COLLON-GEVAERT (1951, pp. 340-341), like the just mentioned author, places the whole group of objects in the second quarter of the 15th century and believes they were works done for the Court of Burgundy because they are in black, grey and white, the colors which Philip the Good adopted after the assassination of his father, John the Fearless (1419).

BURGER (1930, p. 163), BOSSERT (V, 1932, p. 389) and COLLON-GEVAERT (1951, p. 342) all attributed this family of objects to a workshop in the

295

Southern Netherlands. BURGER (1930, p. 163) said this workshop must have been Flemish. BOSSERT (V, 1932, p. 389) placed it either in Bruges, Ghent, Lille, or Brussels. In support of that hypothesis, BOSSERT pointed out that two enameled jugs with lids, now in the Kunsthistorisches Museum in Vienna, appeared in the Ambraser Inventory in 1596 as *niederlenndische schmelzwerch*. COLLON-GEVAERT (1951, pp. 340-341) pointed out a beaker with white leaf-scrolls on a black background in the *Marriage of Cana* by Gerard David (Louvre, Paris) and observed that the subject of the New York cup was popular in the Netherlands. A pantomime of merchants being robbed by monkeys was presented at the wedding festivities of Charles the Bold (LEBEER, 1943, pp. 218-227). It could be added that the subject matter of the spoon in Boston was probably taken from Flemish literature, the famous *Van den Vos Reynaerde,* a poem written in the 13th century based on a very old theme which had inspired the French *Roman du Renard.*

KOHLHAUSSEN (1931, p. 155) also compared the spoon in Boston with 14th century works. The *Bulletin of the Museum of Fine Arts of Boston* (1957, p. 86), quoting SWARZENSKI, proposed the date ca. 1400, but this date seems too early because enamel on a black and on a dark blue background does not seem to appear before the time of Philip the Good.

BRABANT, middle of the 15th Century

132. MONSTRANCE

Léau, Church of Saint-Léonard

This Gothic monstrance is in the form of a crystal vessel with an architectural framework resembling a tower strengthened by three abutments with flying buttresses and pinnacles with many finials. It is one of the rare examples of this type to be found in Belgium. It is decorated with a great number of small statuettes: Saint Francis, kneeling, is placed at the center of the open tier under the main pinnacle; three bishop saints, among whom Saint Augustine may be recognized carrying a heart, occupy small niches in the buttresses, twelve half-length angels carry the Instruments of the Passion; six seraphs decorate the flaring base below the tower. The prominent place given to Saint Francis indicates that this monstrance was made for a Franciscan monastery. Scholars date it in the middle of the 15th century.

Physical data: Silver-gilt, cast, embossed, chiseled, 30 $^7/_8$ x 7 $^{11}/_{16}$ in. (78.5 x 19.6 cm.) (diameter of base). Large base with six convex lobes and perforated border; polygonal stem with knop; vertical cylinder of crystal in a silver-gilt architectural turret.

296

History: Belonged to the Recollect Friars of Tirlemont before 1823 ; acquired from them in 1823 by the Reverend Mr. Veulemens of Léau for the sum of 450 florins and restored, at that time, by the goldsmith D. Warnauts (Archives de l'Eglise de Léau, ed. Bets, 1888, p. 32, no. 1).

Exhibitions: Malines, 1864, no. 409 (1st ed.) and no. 442 (2nd ed.); Tirlemont, 1951, no no.

Piot (1860, p. 68) commented on this monstrance and its admirable decorative work. He suggested attributing it to the goldsmith Vander Moelen who is mentioned in the church accounts as having delivered a monstrance in 1466-1467 and another in 1486-1487. Piot however was not aware that this monstrance was not acquired by the church of Léau until 1823. Weale, who wrote the entries for the Catalogue of the Malines Exhibition in 1864 (no. 409) placed its execution around 1460 and, in the second edition of the catalogue (no. 442), about 1450. Reusens (II, 1875, p. 363) also dates it around 1450.

According to Weale (1867, no. 28) certain parts of this monstrance are more characteristic of the period before 1450; this may be due to the use of old casts. The imitation of architecture has been taken so far that the artist even shows the small gargoyles. The type of monstrance in the form of a turret with three buttresses was already being produced in the 14th century and examples can still be found dating from the beginning of the 16th century.

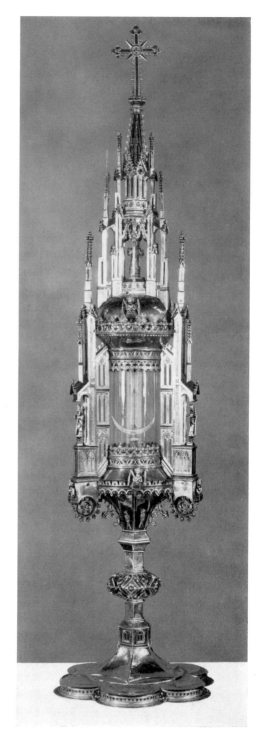

297

Goldsmith's Work

GERARD LOYET

Active in Lille, Brussels and Antwerp from 1466 to 1477

Gérard Loyet is mentioned on several occasions in the accounts of the Duke Charles the Bold. He is called "goldsmith to the duke" in 1466-1467 and he had the honorary title of "valet de chambre". He was a goldsmith and an engraver of coin dies. In 1466-67 he received the order for an object in gold which is identified with the precious reliquary preserved in the Cathedral of Saint-Paul in Liège. In 1477 he received payment for having previously made and delivered two statues and two silver busts of Charles the Bold, which were offered by the Duke to various churches: these last works have not been preserved. It is known that in 1470 he was commissioned by the Duke to engrave the coins of the new currency, after the designs of Jean Hennequart.

133. RELIQUARY OF CHARLES THE BOLD

Liège, Cathedral of Saint-Paul

This gold reliquary embellished by enamel shows Charles the Bold, Duke of Burgundy, kneeling and presenting a small crystal case containing a relic of the finger of Saint Lambert. Behind the Duke stands Saint George, who seems to be presenting him as well as paying homage himself by raising his helmet. The motto of the Duke *Je lay Emprins* ("I undertook it") is engraved on the base.

Charles the Bold gave this reliquary to the former Cathedral of Saint-Lambert in Liège in 1471. There is serious reason to believe that its maker was the goldsmith Gérard Loyet, and that the Duke ordered it in 1467, at the time he succeeded his father, Philip the Good. The kneeling figure appears to be a rather good likeness of Charles the Bold, judging from numerous portraits of him, especially the one by Roger van der Weyden in the Berlin Museum, as well as from contemporary descriptions of the Duke. Charles was slender and of athletic bearing. He had a firm chin, clear blue eyes, and black hair. He was violent and there was something savage in his nature which he could not control. Saint George was not the patron of the Duke, but of Burgundy, and Charles the Bold often had himself shown under his protection.

The Dukes of Burgundy had many gold pieces made, but they have almost all disappeared. This is one of the most precious pieces of this kind preserved in Belgium and along with the *Goldenes Rössl* in Altötting, Germany, one of the most important still existing anywhere.

298

Goldsmith's Work

Physical data: Gold and enamel, silver-gilt base, 20 $^7/_8$ x 20 $^7/_8$ x 13 $^3/_8$ in. (53 x 53 x 34 cm.). Hair of both figures and some parts of Saint George's armor in dull gold; flesh-tints enameled in natural colors, cushion and crest of helmet in blue enamel; dragon in green enamel; the rest in burnished gold.
There is no maker's or other mark.
On the base, inscriptions in Gothic letters, engraved on the sides: *Je lay Empri[ns]*; C and M joined by knotted cord; "briquets" of Burgundy and flames.
Rivet holes attest to the presence of lost accessories. They are on the top surface of the base, as well as on the sides, where there were probably coats of arms.
History: Described in a chronicle of 1455 to 1514 by Jean de Los as a reliquary with two figures, Saint George and the kneeling Duke, offered by Duke Charles to the Church of Saint-Lambert in 1471 in atonement for damages he had caused there (DE RAM, 1844, p. 66). The same fact was reported in 1641 by L. Melart, the historian of Huy, who described it as "an image of Saint George in fine gold at the foot of which is shown the Duke" (VAN DEN STEEN DE JEHAY, 1846, pp. 199-200). This reliquary, along with the other pieces in the treasury of the Cathedral of Saint-Lambert, were evacuated to Maastricht in 1792 to keep them from the French republican troops; they were returned in 1793; they were removed in 1794 to Hamburg and brought back in 1803 (THIMISTER, 1867, pp. 233-235). Meanwhile, the Cathedral of Saint-Lambert had been destroyed and the Church of Saint-Paul inherited its title and its treasures in 1803. The base was regilded in 1856 by C. Jacquet (THIMISTER, 1867, p. 366).
Exhibitions: Liège, 1881, no. 40; Brussels, 1888, no. 139; Bruges, 1902, no. 44; Liège, 1905, no. 33; London, 1927, no. 495; Liège, 1951, no. 148b; Dijon, 1951, no. 175; Amsterdam, 1951, no. 253; Brussels, 1951, no. 232.

There is no doubt that this is the reliquary given by Charles the Bold to the Cathedral of Saint-Lambert in 1471. It corresponds to contemporary descriptions and the Duke may be recognized, as well as his motto and the monogram CM (for Charles and Margaret, his wife).

HELBIG (1877, pp. 238-244) was the first to note the connection between this reliquary and a passage in the accounts of the Dukes, preserved in the archives of Lille and published by DE LABORDE (Part 2, I, 1849, p. 479, no. 1929). This passage appears in the accounts of the General Receipts from January 1, 1466 to December 31, 1467, as follows: *A Gérard Loyet, orfèvre de Mds, la somme de douze cens livres (...) sur ce qui lui pourroit estre deu à cause de certain ymage d'or, que MdS lui avoit ordonné faire, pour présenter de par lui à l'église Saint-Lambert de Liége XIIᶜl.* ("To Gérard Loyet, goldsmith of my Lord, the sum of twelve hundred pounds on account for what may be due him because of the gold image which my Lord had ordered from him to offer to the Church of Saint-Lambert in Liège, 1200 pounds"). It is generally admitted that the gold image to which this account refers is, in fact, the one in Liège. It was not given to the Cathedral of Saint-Lambert until 1471 because, after the reliquary had been ordered by the Duke for Liège, the city of Liège revolted against the authority of its archbishop Louis de Bourbon, and Charles the Bold had severely punished it by pillaging and the slaughter of many inhabitants. DEVIGNE (1932, pp. 109-110) observed that it was the only gift which Charles the Bold is known to have offered to the Cathedral of Liège.

It seems interesting to point out a comparison that has apparently not yet been made, between the donor kneeling on a cushion on the reliquary of Charles the Bold and a figure of the same type mentioned in the Inventory of Charles the Bold (ca. 1467-1469): *Item, ung personnage d'argent à une cote*

299

d'armes d'Angleterre, agenouillé dessus un coussin de bois paint en manière de drap d'or, une espée en son costé, une salade d'argent couronnée, à ung timbre dessus d'un liépart avec petis ganteletz(...) (DE LABORDE, Part. 2, II, 1851, p. 178, no. 3658). That is: "Item, a figure in silver wearing an English tunic, kneeling on a wooden cushion painted like goldcloth, a sword at his side, a silver sallet with a crown on it, an escutcheon of a leopard, with small gauntlets(...)".

On the other hand, Gérard Loyet was entrusted in 1477 with the making of two full length statues of the Duke, in a tunic and kneeling on a cushion, entirely in silver, to be offered to different churches (DE LABORDE, Part 2, I, 1849, pp. 507-508, no. 1974).

DURRIEU (1916, pp. 120-122) pointed out the similarity of composition between the two figures on the reliquary and those of an illumination done by Philippe de Mazerolles in a prayer-book of Philip the Bold. BURGER (1930, p. 149) noted the similarity between the Saint George on the reliquary and the one in the painting of Canon van der Paele by Jan van Eyck, in the Bruges Museum. It is certain that the pose of the Saint George on the reliquary was borrowed from the portrayal of the Saint by van Eyck.

BRABANT, 1493

134. CHALICE

Malines, Archiepiscopal Palace

This lovely silver-gilt chalice was offered to a church by a nun, Gertrude Beckers, in 1493, according to the inscription engraved under its foot. It is a perfect example of a 15th century Gothic chalice in its dimensions, proportion and shape: widely flared base with perforated edge and polylobed foot; polygonal stem with flattened, perforated and richly decorated knop, small, false cupa and a flaring cup of which the diameter is slightly less than half the height of the chalice. It is particularly outstanding on account of the engravings on the eight lobes of the base which are of the finest quality.

300

Goldsmith's Work

The engravings represent: Christ on the Cross, the Virgin and Child in Glory crowned with stars and standing on a crescent moon with the donatrix kneeling at her feet, Saint Francis of Assisi, Saint Catherine with sword and wheel, Saint Barbara with book and tower, Saint Gertrude with the book of her monastic rule, abbess' crozier and a mouse, Saint John the Evangelist blessing a chalice, and Saint Clare carrying a monstrance.

Physical data: Silver-gilt, cast, chiseled, and engraved. Height: 8¹¹/₁₆ in. (22 cm.); diameter of the cup 4¹⁵/₁₆ in. (12.5 cm.); diameter of the base: 7¹/₄ in. (18.5 cm.). Foot with eight convex lobes. Engraved inscription in Latin all around the inside of the foot in capital letters: GHERTRUDIS BECKERS ME FIERE FECIT ORATE PRO EA ANNO DOMINI 1493. These words are separated by crosses and small branches. Two engraved marks above the date in the inscription: a palm-tree and a globe topped with a cross.

History: The original inscription gives the date of the object: 1493; belonged to the Cellites Friars Monastery in Antwerp (WEALE, 1867, no. 44); Collection of Cardinal Sterckx, Malines, 1864 (Cat. Malines Exhib., 1864, 1st ed., no. 350); property of the Archdiocese of Malines, 1888 (Cat. Brussels Exhib., 1888, no. 155).

Exhibitions: Malines, 1864, no. 350 (1st ed.) and no. 375 (2nd ed.); Brussels, 1888, no. 155; Bruges, 1902, G, no. 46; Malines, 1911, no. 280; Antwerp, 1930, F, no. 71; Deurne-Brussels, 1955, no. 1.

The inscription under the base (see illustration) reads: "Gertrude Beckers had me made, pray for her, in the year of Our Lord 1493". The figure of the donatrix who according to this inscription was named Gertrude Beckers, is shown kneeling at the feet of the Virgin in the engraving on one of the lobes of the foot of the chalice. This figure appears to represent a nun. Among the six saints found on the other lobes of the foot are Saint Francis and Saint Clare; their presence suggest that Gertrude Beckers belonged to the Franciscan Order of St. Clare.

The engraved marks on this chalice have not been identified. There are two marks, both engraved, one in the form of a palm-tree and the other in the form of a globe topped by a cross: they are perhaps the ownership marks of a religious institution, rather than the indication of the maker of this chalice.

BRUSSELS, 15th Century

135. RELIQUARY-STATUETTE OF SAINT CATHERINE OF ALEXANDRIA

Louvain, Collegiate Church of Saint-Pierre

This Saint Catherine in silver is identified by her attributes, the broken wheel of her torture and the sword of her decapitation. She holds a small chain to which is attached a small ornamented turret containing a relic in a crystal tube. This silver-gilt turret is ornamented with pearls and pale rubies, "briquets" of Burgundy in silver, and two enameled shields with the coats of arms of the

302

Dukes Philip the Good and Charles the Bold as used between 1430 and 1477.

The turret with the relic may have been a gift from the Dukes. The statuette of Saint Catherine may have existed prior to the turret or more probably, was made for the displaying of the relic. It seems certain in any case, judging from a city mark which was recently discovered on the statuette, that it was made in Brussels.

The statuette is on a stand which is more recent and which obviously was made for another piece, because it bears the name of Saint Paul. Stands of the same type are found on several of the eight silver reliquary-statuettes owned by the Church of Saint-Pierre in Louvain and dating from the 15th to the beginning of the 17th century. This is the largest group of its kind preserved in Belgium after that in the Church of Notre-Dame in Tongres (cf. cat. no. 127).

Physical data: Statuette: chased silver, chiseled and partially gilded, 13 ³/₄ in. (35 cm.). Gilded hair. City mark in the form of a shield bearing a lion rampant. Some damage in the robe. Sword modern. Turret-reliquary: silver-gilt, chiseled, 4 ⁵/₁₆ in. (11 cm.), pearls, pale rubies, enameled shields. Small silver-gilt chain. The small octagonal support on which the turret stands is in partially gilded silver, and is chased. Base for statue: old but not belonging to the figure of Saint Catherine, copper-gilt, 5 ⁵/₁₆ in. (13.5 cm.), hexagonal, engraved inscription: PAUL.

History: The statuette appears always to have belonged to the Collegiate Church of Saint-Pierre. It was in the church treasury which, during the French invasion in 1794, was taken to Westphalia for safe-keeping and later returned (VAN EVEN, 1895, p. 316). A small reliquary of the 17th century was in the Saint's left hand as late as 1864 (Cat. Malines Exhib., 1864, 1st ed., no. 498). It has since disappeared and was replaced by a sword.

Exhibitions: Malines, 1864, no. 498 (1st ed.) and no. 534 (2nd ed.); Brussels, 1888, no. 85; Antwerp, 1930, no. F 29; Brussels, 1935, no. 1761; Louvain, 1945, no. 31; Antwerp, 1948, no. 626; Brussels, 1954, no. 357.

303

Duclos (1910, p. 560) places this reliquary in the 15th century: undoubtedly on the basis of the style and because at this time three members of the Adornes family, Pierre, Jacques and Anselme, made pilgrimages to the Holy Land. Gailliard (III, 1859, p. 105) gives this information, and numerous biographical details on the members of this family, their positions and titles; but no author has been able to give any specific information on the reliquary.

The Church of Jerusalem which owns the reliquary is mentioned in a bull of Pope Martin V dated May 12, 1427 (Duclos, 1910, pp. 559-60) by which Pierre and Jacques Adornes were authorized to add a campanile to their chapel of the Passion of Our Lord and of the Holy Sepulchre in Bruges and to celebrate mass there; according to Gailliard (III, 1859, p. 108) Anselme Adornes (1424-1483) finished the building of this church which had been started by his uncles.

The iconography of the Resurrection of Christ takes various forms in the 15th century. Christ is sometimes shown half length in the open tomb or placing a foot on the edge; at other times He is stepping over the edge, as here, or stands upright on the lid. Generally sleeping soldiers are placed around the tomb but here there are none. The presence of the two angels recalls a type of reliquary found in the Middle Ages, where the angels hold and present the reliquary. Here, however, they are integrated in the scene of the Resurrection and hold the lid of the tomb, as can be seen in another *Resurrection* on a tapestry from ca. 1400-1420 in the Louvre in Paris, which is probably Flemish.

SOUTHERN NETHERLANDS, 15th Century

137. MORSE OF A COPE

Tongres, Collegiate Church of Notre-Dame

This morse or buckle ornament for a cope, in silver-gilt, although somewhat restored, has a very finely embossed and chiseled central medallion. It shows the Virgin and Child under a canopy between two angelic thurifers. The Virgin holds a scepter in her right hand. The background is engraved with a diaper pattern decorated with fleurs-de-lis; it is also sprinkled with small six-petaled flowers similar to the larger flowers which form a wreath around the border of the morse. The central medallion is surrounded by a double border edged with torsades. The inside border, which forms a hollow molding, is decorated with a stalk adorned with small leaves and six-petaled flowers. The outside border includes a vine around which is wound a ribbon the decoration of which is almost entirely worn away. The structure and style of this piece seem to justify its dating in the 15th century.

306

Physical data: Silver-gilt, embossed and chiseled, 7 5/8 in. (19.5 cm.). Traces of gilding. Stippled letters, hardly legible, on the ribbon decorating the edge. The center of this morse seems to have undergone slight restorations, for example in the scepter of the Virgin.

History: The documents of the church archives which concern the purchase and restoration of morses are not sufficiently explicit to establish a relationship with the still existing objects, a number of which have long been owned by the church.

Exhibitions: Brussels, 1880, no. A 136; Liège, 1881, IV, no. 219; Brussels, 1888, no. 249.

The style of this piece indicates the 15th century. The church acquired a large number of morses in that period, particularly between 1453 and 1472. Some of them are the work of Gisbert Gufkens the Younger, a member of an old family of goldsmiths who had been at the service of the Collegiate Church of Notre-Dame for more than half a century (see no. 127); other morses had been offered by Martin Martens and still others were acquired in Maastricht (PAQUAY, 1904, p. 135 and 1911, p. 223, note 4). Unfortunately, these objects are not described in the archives.

This morse has, at least for a century, been associated with a cope given in 1698 to the Church of Notre-Dame in Tongres by the Provost Jean-René de Neufcourt, bearing his coat of arms. This may be the reason why the restoration of this morse was thought to have taken place at the end of the 17th century (THYS, 1866, p. 301; PAQUAY, 1911, p. 234).

307

Goldsmith's Work

JOOS PAUWELS THE YOUNGER

Active in Louvain beginning in 1474
Died in Louvain shortly before February 3, 1509

Joos Pauwels the Younger was the son of the goldsmith Wouter Pauwels, member of a Louvain family of goldsmiths. Joos' activity at Louvain after 1474 is documented; he died there shortly before February 3, 1509. He did much work for the magistrates of Louvain, for whom he was the official inspector of weights and measures as well as for the churches of that city. The Church of Saint-Pierre possesses a reliquary-statuette of Saint Stephen and the Church of Saint-Jacques has a reliquary-monstrance of Saint Hubert, both of which bear Joos' mark, with the initials JP. These works are evidence of a remarkable ability and outstanding talent.

138. CHRISMATORY

Brussels, Musées Royaux d'Art et d'Histoire. Inv. V, no. 2083.

Chrismatories are small boxes in precious metal made to hold the holy oils. They assume various forms, but are most often cylindrical and sometimes have two or three containers. This one, in silver, is in the most common form, a round turret supported by three seated lions. The conical roof serves as a cover and is attached by a hinge, and a fastening pin is fixed to the cover by a small chain.

This chrismatory bears the maker's mark of Joos Pauwels the Younger. Its execution can thus be placed either in the last quarter of the 15th century or in the early years of the 16th century.

Physical data: Silver, 5 7/8 in. (15 cm.). The lions, base molding, torsade, roped links of the chain, crenellations, and sphere at the top are gilded. The lions, torsade, and every other link in the chain are engraved. City mark of Louvain: the coat of arms of the city surrounded by a key. Maker's mark: JP in Gothic lettering joined (VAN MOLLE, 1957).

History: Abbé A. Mertens Coll., Louvain, in 1864 (Cat. Malines Exhib., 1864, no. 474), and also in 1880 (Cat. Brussels Exhib., 1880, no. A 231); bequest of Gustave Vermersch to the Musées Royaux d'Art et d'Histoire, 1911.

308

Goldsmith's Work

Exhibitions: Malines, 1864, no. 440 (1st ed.), no. 474 (2nd ed.) ; Brussels, 1880, no. A 231 ; Deurne - Brussels, 1955, no. 101.

The city mark of Louvain which was discovered on this piece by BARA (1941, p. 94), is the one used in the 15th century (CROOY, 1911, pp. 82-83). The maker's mark with the initials had been deciphered by BARA (1941, p. 94) as a Gothic M. VAN MOLLE (unpublished manuscript notes made in 1957) was able to decipher this mark as a Gothic J and P, which form the initials of Joos Pauwels the Younger.

309

ARMS and ARMOR

SOUTHERN NETHERLANDS(?), 14th and 15th Century

139-142. FOUR KIDNEY DAGGERS

Brussels, Musées Royaux d'Art et d'Histoire, Musée d'Armes et d'Armures
Inv. nos. 519, 3106, 3161 and 4069

The four daggers belong to types which were commonly used in the Southern Netherlands during the 14th and the 15th centuries. They were found in excavations and the places of their making are therefore uncertain. They have two more or less rounded projections forming the guard and from this feature receive their name of kidney daggers (*dagues à rognons*). The daggers have short stout blades, generally with two cutting edges. This type originated in the north of Europe in the 14th century. They were originally used in the right hand but in the 16th century they became left-hand weapons.

> *Physical data:* Iron, 12 ³/₄ in.; 15 in.; 15 ³/₈ in.; 9 ⁷/₈ in. (32.5 cm.; 38 cm.; 39 cm.; 25 cm.).
>
> *History:* no. 519, received from the Ministry of the Interior in 1877; no. 3106, acquired in 1920; no. 3161, acquired in 1921; no. 4069, legacy of Jules Vanden Peereboom, who died in 1917.
>
> *Exhibitions:* None known.

Nos. 519 and 3106 are thought to date from the 14th century; nos. 3161 and 4069 from the 15th century.

Although these daggers are reputed to have been used originally in the right hand, there is an early example of their use in the left hand in the *Calvary of the Tanners* from ca. 1400 in the Church of Saint-Sauveur in Bruges (see no. 1), where the Emperor Maximian (trampled under foot by Saint Catherine) brandishes in his left hand a dagger of this type.

Daggers can be seen in many works of art as an accessory to both civilian and military dress. In the first case it hangs on the front of a belt around the waist. In the second it is attached to the breast plate by a chain, or worn on the right side at the back. It was also worn on the left side as can be seen on the figure of Melchizedek's spear-bearer in one of the wings of the *Altarpiece of the Blessed Sacrament* by Dieric Bouts in the Church of Saint-Pierre in Louvain (this cat. no. 17) painted in 1464-1468. The figure of Haman dressed in a splendid long robe, in the

310

right foreground of the banquet scene in the tapestry *Esther and Ahasuerus*, ca. 1460-1480, from The Minneapolis Institute of Arts (this cat. no. 151), is an example of a dagger being worn at the back as part of a civilian costume.

SOUTHERN NETHERLANDS(?), 14th and 15th Century

143. TWO SWORDS

Brussels, Musées Royaux d'Art et d'Histoire, Musée d'Armes et d'Armures
Inv. nos. 4050 and 5101

These two swords are of types used in the Netherlands during the 14th and 15th centuries. The longer one is a tuck (or *estoc*), a sword with a long pointed blade, mainly used to force through the joints of plate armor. The second is a type of sword for mixed use with a sharp point as well as a cutting edge, that is to say, for use in cutting and thrusting. These are transitional forms between the broad-bladed slashing swords of the early Middle Ages and the slender-bladed thrusting swords of the Renaissance and later.

> *Physical data:* Iron, 42 $^{15}/_{16}$ and 37 $^3/_8$ in. (109 and 95 cm.).
> *History:* Unknown origin. They were probably excavated. Legacy of Jules Vanden Peereboom, who died in 1917.
> *Exhibitions:* None known.

It is difficult to date undecorated weapons of this type with any precision. Number 4050, the tuck or estoc, is closely related to the sword of Saint Catherine in the *Calvary of the Tanners* (this cat. no. 1) from ca. 1400 in the Church of Saint-Sauveur in Bruges. An equally simple model, but with a pommel of rock crystal, is found at the side of Melchizedek in the panel of *Abraham and Melchizedek* from the *Triptych of the Blessed Sacrament* by Dieric Bouts (this cat. no. 17). The other type of sword (no. 5101) is also shown in a painting in this exhibition, the *Martyrdom of Saint Ursula* by the Master of the Legend of Saint Ursula (cat. no. 39) from the end of the 15th century: it can be seen that in some cases, they had to be wielded with two hands and they were thus made with a long grip.

SOUTHERN NETHERLANDS (LIEGE?), middle of the 15th Century

144. BREAST PLATE

Brussels, Musées Royaux d'Art et d'Histoire, Musée d'Armes et d'Armures
Inv. no. 5442

This breast plate was discovered in Tongres, Belgium, in 1954 in a spot that was formerly the moat of the ancient city walls. The upper part of its braconnière

311

or taces is made up of three plates. The breast plate itself is wrought with five ribs radiating like a fan from the center of the waist: three similar ribs radiate downward over the taces. Its proportions and its ribbed design supply the elements for dating this piece of Gothic armor. It is possible to place it around the middle of the 15th century. With its combinations of utility and elegance, and obvious signs of use, it seems to bring us very close to the fighting man of the age of the Flemish Primitives.

Physical data: Iron, 18 1/2 x 14 15/16 in. (47 x 38 cm.). Mark of an armorer or place near the neck (reproduced in Squilbeck, 1954, p. 73).
History: Discovered in May, 1954 in a branch of the Geer River in Tongres (Squilbeck, 1954, p. 68).
Exhibitions: None known.

The mark, damaged by rust, is no longer very clear. It consists of a small sphere topped by a cross within a square which is placed with one corner at the

312

crossing of the arms of the cross and the opposite corner at the foot of the cross. A letter can be distinguished on each side of the long arm of the cross, perhaps an "L" and a "G". The complete mark is topped by a three-pointed crown. SQUILBECK (1954, p. 73) points out the analogy of these elements with the coat of arms of the city of Liège. This author does not believe, however, that any firm conclusions can be drawn from this although the presence of the cross suggests the *Perron* in Liège (monument to the early city rights). He compares the cuirass found in Tongres to others of the same type which still exist or which may be seen in manuscript miniatures and believes its execution can be placed in the second or third quarter of the 15th century (SQUILBECK, 1954, p. 72).

JACQUES VOYS(?), end of the 15th Century

145. JOUSTING HELMET

Brussels, Musées Royaux d'Art et d'Histoire, Musée d'Armes et d'Armures
Inv. no. 57

This magnificent jousting helmet bears two marks which may be those of Jacques Voys. He was a Brussels armorer who worked for Philip the Handsome at the end of the 15th century. This jousting helmet is a model which had long been abandoned for war because it was too rigid and uncomfortable to be worn for a long time or to allow free movement. For jousting, on the other hand, it guaranteed complete safety for the head.

Armor for jousting was different from armor for war. Jousting was courteous combat, man to man fighting, on horseback with lances. The jousters either galloped toward one another in an open field or along a barrier which separated them. The barrier was at the left of each jouster who, lance forward, tried to overturn his opponent.

Physical data: Iron, 17 5/16 in. (44 cm.). Two armorer's marks: a royal globe and a trefoil crown (SQUILBECK, 1953, p. 255). The mark in the form of a royal globe was stamped twice.

313

History: The piece probably belonged to the former Arsenal of Brussels from which various pieces which were not removed to Spain or Vienna eventually formed the nucleus of the Musée d'Armes et d'Armures in Brussels (SQUILBECK, 1953, p. 258).
Exhibitions: Brussels, 1953, no. 106.

The name of Jacques Voys and his qualification as Brussels armorer for Philip the Handsome are found in a 1594 inventory of armorers which is in Madrid. According to this document he should be the author of two armors, one in Madrid, the other in Vienna. They bear the same mark as the Brussels helmet, as do two other pieces of armor in the Wallace Collection, London, and the City Museum, Glagow (SQUILBECK, 1953, pp. 255-261).

The two marks on this helmet were reproduced by DE PRELLE DE LA NIEPPE (1903, p. 92).

SOUTHERN NETHERLANDS, 15th Century

146. HELMET known as a SALLET WITH MESAIL

Brussels, Musées Royaux d'Art et d'Histoire, Musée d'Armes et d'Armures
Inv. no. 3990

The name of this helmet, sallet or salade, is derived from the Italian *celata*. Helmets of this type were characterized by a projecting cover for the nape of the neck. Like all helmets, it had an inside leather lining which was attached within the bowl by rivets. These rivets were turned into an ornamental motif by making

314

them very large and sometimes decorated with grooves. The sallet could be made with either a vision slit in a fixed front or a movable visor called a "mesail".

It was the most widely known type of helmet in the 15th century. Two good examples can be seen in this exhibition: the helmet placed in front of the kneeling donor in the Reliquary of Charles the Bold (cat. no. 133) and the helmet worn by the centurion (cat. nos. 74-77) from the *Altarpiece of the Passion* in Geel.

> *Physical data:* Iron, height: 9 ⁷/₁₆ in. (24 cm.). Seven rivets are missing.
> *History:* Excavated in Belgium in the 19th century; acquired by Jules Vanden Peereboom (d. 1917), who left it by bequest to the Musée d'Armes et d'Armures.
> *Exhibitions:* None known.

The accounts of the Dukes mention numerous orders for sallets which, until 1447, were usually made in Milan. After that date they were often ordered in Valenciennes, but from an Italian who came from Milan to the Netherlands at the request of Philip the Good. From 1449 he bore the title of valet and armorer of the Duke (BEAULIEU and BAYLÉ, 1956, p. 169). The accounts also include payments made to embroiderers for covering these helmets with gold cloth. This was often done to both helmets and armor, perhaps to prevent the sun from making them too hot to wear.

SOUTHERN NETHERLANDS(?), 15th Century

147. TWO ROWEL SPURS

> *Brussels, Musées Royaux d'Art et d'Histoire, Musée d'Armes et d'Armures*
> Inv. nos. 4081 and 3108

These two spurs are not a pair, having different dimensions but both are types which were in current use in the Southern Netherlands during the 15th century.

> *Physical data:* Iron, 8 ¹³/₁₆ and 8 ¹/₁₆ in. (22.3 and 20.5 cm.).
> *History:* Legacy of Jules Vanden Peereboom, who died in 1917.
> *Exhibition:* None known.

The shanks of spurs in the 15th century were very long, in order to reach the horse's flank despite the cumbersome trappings, and with the least possible movement of the rider's leg.

The origin of these spurs is unknown; they were probably excavated. The present examples are simple iron spurs but more luxurious ones, in silver and even gold, were made. Spurs were an accessory which, with the sword, the helmet, the shield and gauntlets, made up the five pieces of great honor which were carried in front of princes in certain ceremonies.

TEXTILES

ARRAS, PIERRE FERE, 1402

148. THE STORY OF SAINT ELEUTHERE

Tournai, Cathedral of Notre-Dame

Pierre Feré was active in Arras between 1395 and 1429.

The tapestry exhibited is part of an Arras tapestry devoted to the *Story of Saint Eleuthère*. The Tournai Cathedral also possesses the corresponding tapestry of the *Story of Saint Piat*. Each of them was cut in two parts in the 18th century, making the four tapestries now to be seen in the Treasury of the Cathedral of Tournai. Saint Piat, martyred in the 3rd century, and Saint Eleuthère, bishop-martyr of the 5th-6th century, are credited with bringing Christianism to the region of Tournai.

The importance of these tapestries is very great as they are the only series definitely known to come from a workshop in Arras, a town which together with Paris had the monopoly of tapestry-weaving in Western Europe in the 14th century. This series is placed and dated by a votive inscription woven into the tapestry. This inscription has been lost but is known through a copy in a 17th century manuscript. It specifies that Canon Toussaint Prier ordered the series

316

from the workshop of Pierre Feré in Arras in 1402. Canon Prier was chaplain to Louis de Male and later to Philip the Bold; he died in 1437 and is buried in the Tournai Cathedral.

The portion on exhibition represents part of the legend of Saint Eleuthère. In the first scene, the Saint who had been made a bishop by the Pope, is shown tempted by the daughter of the tribune who declares her love for him and tries to hold him by his mantle. Then the Saint is seen resurrecting the tribune's daughter who has died of chagrin, on being spurned. Saint Eleuthère baptizes her and his mother acts as godmother. The last scene represents the sudden death of the daughter of the tribune and of others who were drawn back to pagan beliefs. The final scenes of the story are missing. The inscription in a French dialect of the top of the tapestry explains the whole subject matter.

Physical data: Wool, 6 ft. 9 7/8 in. x 20 ft. 4 1/8 in. (2.08 x 6.20 m.). Fine twisted wool called *fin fil d'Arras* (fine thread of Arras) (CRICK-KUNTZIGER, 1930, p. 184). Much worn and faded; some restorations. Inscriptions in Gothic letters in a French dialect: [*La fille tribun va*] *morir/ pour ce que ne pot obtenir/* [*le fol amour que*] *requérait/ au saint quand son mantiel tirait./ Co*[*m*]*ment J*[*esus*]*hcrist réclama/ le bon saint et ressuscita/ p*[*ar*] *chy la fille du tribun/ p*[*rése*]*nt son père et le commun./ Co*[*m*]*ment li bons sains baptisa/ la fille Tribun que leva/ de fons par t*[*rè*]*s grande mistère/ Blande qui du bon saint fu mère./ Tribuns volt sa fille retraire/ des crestiens et elle atraire/ a sa loy dont la mors soudaine/ en fu tost as paiens prochaine* (ed. SOIL, 1883, pp. 28-29).
History: A manuscript (Brussels, Bibliothèque Royale, ms. no. 13762) by Canon Dufief

317

Textiles

(17th century) tells that Toussaint Prier, canon of the Cathedral, gave the tapestries which were hung in the choir and that the following inscription could be seen on one of them: *Ces draps furent faicts et achevés/ En Arras par Pierrot Feré/ L'an mil quatre cent et deux/ En décembre, mois gracieux.* At the bottom: *Veuillez à Dieu tous Saincts prier/ Pour l'âme de toussaint Prier* (ed. SOIL, 1883, p. 26). In 1772 the tapestries were taken from the choir, cut up and misused in a number of ways; in 1873 they were restored and provided with a border belonging to a later tapestry, as was established by SOIL (1883, pp. 31-32). This border was removed at the time of a later restoration. Restored shortly before 1937 (Cat. Paris Exhib., 1937, no. 1269).

Exhibitions: Malines, 1864, nos. 603 (1st ed.) and 674 (2nd ed.); Paris, 1937, no. 1269; Tournai, 1949, no. 1, p. 80; Arras, 1951, no. 4; Dijon, 1951, no. 204; Brussels, 1951, no. 119; Amsterdam, 1951, no. 122; Tournai, 1958, no. 199.

A thorough study of this important set of tapestries and of its history has been made by SOIL (1883). The lost inscription known by Dufief's manuscript is translated as follows: "These cloths were made and finished/ At Arras by Pierrot Feré/In the year one thousand four hundred and two/ In December, month of grace" and the second inscription reads "pray to God all Saints/ For the soul of Toussaint Prier". The translation of the other inscription is: "The daughter of the tribune is going to die because she cannot obtain the mad love she expected from the Saint when she pulled at his coat. How Jesus Christ called the good Saint and resurrected by his hand the daughter of the tribune, her father and the people being present. How the good Saint baptized the daughter of the tribune, who was held at the baptismal font for this very great mystery by Blanda the mother of the good Saint. The tribune wants to take back his daughter from the Christians and attract her to his faith for which sudden death soon overcame her and the pagans."

A manuscript handbook for the use of the sacristans of the Cathedral, dating from the middle of the 15th century, mentions that the tapestries of Saint Piat and of Saint Eleuthère given by master Toussaint Prier must be hung op on feast days (VOISIN, 1863, p. 226). In 1619, in his history of Tournay, COUSIN (I, 1619, p. 95) said of the tapestries that they were "good and complete".

The original length of the two tapestries of Saint Piat and Saint Eleuthère is not known. Fourteen scenes can now be seen; originally there probably were eighteen. CRICK-KUNTZIGER (1930, pp. 183-184) praises the exceptional value and importance of the tapestries, and above all the technical perfection of the work. In every way these tapestries at Tournai are among the most important surviving from the 15th century.

TOURNAI(?), second quarter of the 15th Century

149. HUNTING PARTY WITH FALCONS

Minneapolis, Minn., The Minneapolis Institute of Arts. Inv. no. 15.34

This tapestry is a fragment of a large hanging representing a scene of ladies and gentlemen hunting with falcons. It seems to come from the same workshop

318

Textiles

and to belong to the same set as the four great hunting tapestries from Hardwicke Hall, formerly owned by the Duke of Devonshire and now in the Victoria and Albert Museum, London. A section which may be part of this set is in the Burrel Collection, Glasgow. The technique, the style and the fashion of the costumes have prompted most specialists to place this tapestry in the second quarter of the 15th century and to attribute it to a Tournai workshop.

Physical data: Wool, 11 ft. 2 ½ in. x 10 ft. 9 in. (3.41 x 3.27 m.).

History: Cathedral of Gerona, Spain; entered the collections of The Minneapolis Institute of Arts in 1916 as a gift of Mrs. Charles-Jairus Martin for the Charles-Jairus Martin Memorial Collection.

Exhibitions: Boston, 1940, no. 114; Hartford and Baltimore, 1951-52, no. 73.

In 1915-1916 when the tapestry of Minneapolis became known, it was immediately related to the series of four large tapestries from Hardwicke Hall, of which it seems to be another fragment (B[RECK], 1915, pp. 54-56, and KURTH, 1917, p. 66). Scholars all agree about this; therefore the identification and dating of the hanging from Hardwicke Hall involve those of the Minneapolis tapestry. The tapestries from Hardwicke Hall show scenes of a hunt in which appears an engaged or married couple. The young woman's name is probably Margaret judging from the letter M found on the trappings of her horse and the marguerites on her dress. According to THOMSON (1906, pp. 179-181) the tapestry may have been made on the occasion of the marriage of Margaret of

319

Anjou, daughter of René of Anjou, to Henri VI of England, in 1445. The same author considers them as made in a Tournai workshop. BRECK (1915, p. 54) attributed them to a workshop of Arras, KURTH (1917, p. 70) to a workshop of Tournai. This latter identification has been accepted by the authors of the Catalogues of the Boston Exhibition (1940) and of the Hartford and Baltimore Exhibition (1952, no. 73). However in the meantime KURTH (1946, p. 4) revised her opinion and attributed this set of tapestries to a workshop of Arras. Scholars agree about dating it in the second quarter of the 15th century and more precisely ca. 1440-1445.

PASQUIER GRENIER

Active in Tournai from 1449 to 1472 and probably until his death in 1493

Pasquier Grenier directed the principal tapestry workshop in Tournai in the second half of the 15th century. He was an important figure in the city, a member of the Noble Brotherhood of Damoiseaux (whose insignia is shown in this exhibition, cat. 129) and at one time an envoy sent by the city to the King of France. He was much occupied with the business of weaving and selling tapestries and is known to have received many commissions from Philip the Good to Tournai: in 1459 the *Story of Alexander;* in 1461 a *Passion of Our Lord* as well as *Peasants and Woodcutters;* in 1462 *Esther and Ahasuerus,* of which a part of a perhaps slightly later weaving is in this exhibition (cat. no. 151), and the *Story of the Swan Knight;* in 1466 *The Orange Trees* and *The Woodcutters;* in 1472, for Charles the Bold, a series devoted to the *Destruction of Troy,* bought by the City and the "Franc" of Bruges, of which an important fragment is in this exhibition (cat. no. 150). All these subjects include several tapestries and some were produced many times.

Pasquier Grenier died in 1493 and bequeathed all his tapestry cartoons to his sons. At least two of them, Jean and Antoine, each directed a workshop, of which some of the products were only copies after their father's cartoons.

TOURNAI, PASQUIER GRENIER, ca. 1471-1472

150. HECTOR AND ANDROMACHE, part of a set of tapestries of
THE STORY OF THE DESTRUCTION OF TROY

New York, N.Y., The Metropolitan Museum of Art. Inv. no. 39.74

This magnificent tapestry in an excellent state of preservation shows an episode in the story of the Destruction of Troy. Hector the most valiant of the

320

Textiles

Trojan leaders, is seen in the upper part putting on his armor in spite of the pleas of his wife Andromache who, in a dream, had a premonition of his death.

In the lower section Hector is on horseback, ready to leave for battle. His father, Priam, out of pity for Andromache, seeks to restrain him from going. These explanations can be read on the tapestry, in French and Latin verses.

Hector and Andromache is one quarter of one of eleven pieces which made up the *Story of the Destruction of Troy* and which were, when assembled, more than three hundred and ten feet in lenght by fifteen feet in height. From all this there remain only the section showing *Hector and Andromache* in The Metropolitan Museum of Art in New York, a very small fragment showing the *Tent of Achilles* in The Cloisters in New York, a larger fragment in the Montreal Museum of Fine Arts from which the inscriptions are missing and possibly still another fragment in the Higgins Collection in Worcester, Massachusetts.

The success of this set of tapestries was so great that all the sovereigns of that period apparently wanted to own a copy. Charles the Bold was probably the one who possessed the original set. It is the oldest one as it was given to him in 1472 by the City and the "Franc" of Bruges which paid eight hundred pounds *(huit cent livres de gros)* to the famous high loom weaver and merchant of Tournai, Pasquier Grenier. Louis XII possessed a copy in his castle at Blois in 1501. The King of Naples, Ferdinand, gave a set of tapestries of the same subject to the Spanish Ambassador, the Count of Tendilla, in 1487. The King of England, Henry VII, acquired a copy from Jean Grenier, Pasquier's son, in Tournai in 1487 or 1488. James IV of Scotland is also supposed to have had one. Of all these versions only a few scattered fragments remain.

The artist who made the cartoons (the drawings used by the weaver) is not known. Some authorities have suggested attributing them to Jean Le Tavernier of Oudenaarde, painter and miniaturist to the Dukes. Several authorities believe a series of eight drawings now in the Louvre in Paris to be the sketches *(petits patrons)* for these hangings.

Physical data: Wool and silk, 15 ft. 7^1/$_2$ in. x 8 ft. 9^1/$_2$ in. (4.69 x 2.64 m.). Cut along the left side. Small restorations in the inscriptions (RORIMER, 1939, p. 226, note 1). Inscriptions in Gothic letters, in verse, in French and Latin, giving the subject matter of the scene, translated and commented on notably by RORIMER (1939, p. 226). Identity of names of the figures on background and on clothing.

History: The accounts of the City of Bruges for Sept. 2, 1471 - Sept. 1, 1472, fol. 121, no. 6, show the following entry: *Item, betaelt by ordonnancie van der camere Pasquier Grenier de somme van C lb grooten up ende in minderinghen van den IIII^c lb. gr. daerin dat dese stede jeghen hem verbonden staet als over haar deel ende avenant van den VIII^c lb. gr. ter causen van zekere scoone ende groote tapytserien inhoudende de historie van der destructie van Troyen, dewelke by deser stede ende by die van de Vryen ghegheven hebben gheweist onzen harde gheduchten heere ende prince te ziere neerenster bede ende begheerte, dus hier de voors. C lb.* (ed. GILLIODTS-VAN SEVEREN, VI, 1876, p. 66; corrected by A. Schouteet, 1960).
The city accounts for 1472-73, 1473-74, 1474-75, and 1475-76 include other payments made to Pasquier Grenier. These entries complete and confirm that of 1471-72. Accounts for 1473-74 mention the final payment by the "Franc" of Bruges of the amount they still owed (ed. PINCHART, 1883, p. 60).
The tapestry showing *Hector and Andromache* first appeared in 1877: sale Roybet Coll., Paris, March 24, 1877, Hôtel Drouot, no. 21; sale Jean Dollfus Coll., Paris, April 1-2,

321

1812, Galerie Georges Petit, no. 189; Clarence H. Mackay Coll.; acquired by The Metropolitan Museum of Art in 1939 through the Fletcher Fund.
Exhibitions: Philadelphia, 1915, no. 3; New York, 1931, no. 535.

RORIMER (1939, p. 226) compares *Hector and Andromache* to other fragments and drawings and demonstrates that it was the right quarter of a tapestry, probably the fifth of a set of eleven. GOMEZ-MORENO (1919, p. 271) compares it to the fragments in the tribunal of Issoire in France which had been in the Castle of Aulhac in France, were taken from there by the revolutionaries and sent to the tribunal of Issoire (JUBINAL, 1838, p. 9). In 1955 The Cloisters in New York acquired a small fragment of the hangings from Issoire. This gave FORSYTH (1955, pp. 76-84) the opportunity to prove what RORIMER (1939, pp. 224-227) had suggested, that *Hector and Andromache* had formerly belonged to the tapestries in Aulhac. The latter are generally considered the oldest and best known examples of the subject. GOMEZ-MORENO (1919, p. 282) judges it older than the hangings of another series in the Cathedral of Zamora. He was able to date this latter work to about 1487 from a manuscript document which appears to indicate that the tapestries in Zamora were given to the Count of Tendilla by the King of Naples, Ferdinand, after 1486. THOMSON (1906, pp. 172-173) proved that Henry VII acquired his copy of the *Story of Troy* from Jean Grenier of Tournai in 1487 or 1488. RORIMER (1939, p. 224) and FORSYTH (1955, p. 82) report a tradition according to which the tapestries of Aulhac came from Charles the Bold. JUBINAL made no reference to this but said (1838, p. 9) that the Aulhac tapestries once belonged to the Besse family.

KURTH (1917, p. 96) was the first to suggest a relationship between the Tournai tapestries of the *Story of Troy* and the tapestries of the same subject given by the City of Bruges to Duke Charles the Bold. The translation of the accounts cited earlier is: "Item, paid by order of the Chamber to Pasquier Grenier the sum of one hundred *livres de gros* (pounds) on, and to be deducted from, four hundred *livres de gros* which this city owes him as his part and according to the agreement, of the eight hundred *livres de gros* for certain large and beautiful tapestries showing the story of the destruction of Troy which, by this city and members of the Franc (of Bruges), were given to our much feared lord and prince upon his instant prayer and desire, thus the aforementioned 100 pounds". HUNTER (1925, p. 78), MARILLIER (1925, p. 36), MIGEON (1929, p. 235), RORIMER (1939, pp. 224-227) and FORSYTH (1955, pp. 76-84) believe the tapestries made for Charles the Bold to be the original. These authors were slightly mistaken in placing the execution of this tapestry between 1472 and 1474, as the document says the tapestry had already been given and it only mentions the payment. GOMEZ-MORENO (1919, p. 281) dates the original series ca. 1465 and thinks it might have been ordered by Louis XI or by the Dukes of Burgundy. An inventory made in 1536 of the Burgundian inheritance belonging to Charles V (MICHELANT, 1872, p. 245), mentions a set of tapestries called *l'Histoire de Troie la Grande*, comprising eleven pieces, each measuring six ells and a half; this may have been the one exhibited in Brussels in 1501 on the occasion of a gathering of the Chapter of the Order of the Golden Fleece.

322

Textiles

SCHUMANN (1898, pp. 6-7) published eight colored drawings on paper representing nine scenes from the story of the destruction of Troy; they resemble the fragments still preserved closely enough to be considered as sketches (*petits patrons*) for the hangings. They belong to the Louvre in Paris. They are fairly large (12 $^3/_{16}$ x 22 $^7/_{16}$ in.; 31 x 57 cm.), are drawn on ragpaper, the watermark of which is the coat of arms of the Kings of France with three fleur-de-lis and a crown. On the basis of this watermark, SCHUMANN (1898, pp. 6-7) dates the drawings between 1460 and 1480. Based on another interpretation of the watermark, GUIFFREY (1899, p. 206) dates them between 1480 and 1500. RORIMER (1939, p. 227) considers they may date as far back as 1455. Most specialists consider them to be sketches for tapestries: SCHUMANN (1898, pp. 6-7) who thinks they were done in a North French workshop, MÜNTZ (1898, pp. 263-264), who thinks they came from Paris; also SIMOND (1898, p. 84) and MARILLIER (1925, pp. 36-37). GUIFFREY (1899, p. 206) believes them to be designs for a later weaving of this series of tapestries such as the one in Zamora (owned by the Count of Tendilla, ca. 1487) and in the Victoria and Albert Museum in London (owned by Henry VII, ca. 1488). HUNTER (1925, pp. 74-75) and MIGEON (1929, p. 236) consider these sketches to be of poorer quality than the tapestries, and therefore to be copies of them. RORIMER (1939, p. 227) relates a payment made by Philip the Good to Jean Le Tavernier in 1455 for three sketchbooks with designs of the history of Troy. FORSYTH (1955, p. 80) believes this payment may refer to the drawings in the Louvre. The accounts of the Dukes (DE LABORDE, Part 2, II, 1851, pp. 217-218, account no. 4021) mention for April 4, 1454, a payment of 121 *écus* 44 *gros* to Le Tavernier for different works among them: "*Item en trois parques de pappier, trois histoires de Troie: pour ce un écu*". This very small payment may correspond to the price paid for illuminating a page or half a page. Therefore it seems unlikely that this payment is for the eight large drawings in the Louvre.

TOURNAI, PASQUIER GRENIER(?), ca. 1460-80

151. ESTHER AND AHASUERUS

Minneapolis, Minn., The Minneapolis Institute of Arts. Inv. no. 167.21

This tapestry is a fragment cut from part of a hanging representing the *History of Esther and Ahasuerus* and of which several copies once existed.

From the accounts of the Dukes of Burgundy it can be learnt that Philip the Good paid Pasquier Grenier, in 1461-1462 for a tapestry in six parts representing this subject: it is possible that this document concerns the original or a replica, of which Minneapolis possesses a fragment.

The Minneapolis tapestry shows in its lower part a Latin text briefly indicating the subjects of the scenes, an episode of the history of Esther and

324

Ahasuerus which is told in the Book of Esther. During the captivity of the Jews in Babylon the King Ahasuerus having signed a decree for the extermination of the Jews, his young Jewish wife Esther braved the interdiction against entering the throne room without being summoned there, in order to beg grace for her people. She risked death but Ahasuerus inclined his golden scepter towards her in a sign of pardon and accepted her suggestion to attend a banquet which she had prepared, and in the course of which she obtained the revocation of the edict. At the top left she can be seen, in penitent's garments, in prayer and receiving instructions from Mordecai. Next she can be seen in royal garments in front of her husband Ahasuerus: she rests her hand on the shoulder of a lady in waiting and her train is carried by another. All these details are specified in the Biblical text of the Complements of the Book of Esther (15. 4-8).

The style of the costumes permits the dating of this tapestry ca. 1460-1480 at the time of the *Justice of the Emperor Otto* painted by Dieric Bouts (Brussels, Musées Royaux des Beaux-Arts).

> *Physical data:* Wool, 11 ft. 1 ¹/₂ in. x 10 ft. 8 in. (3.43 x 3.30 m.). Cut along the length of the right and left borders. Good state of conservation. Inscriptions in Gothic letters, in Latin, near the lower border. The identity of the principal figures is given by inscriptions on their garments. At the bottom, an unidentified mark in the form of a fleuron *(Bulletin of the Minneapolis Institute of Arts, 1934, p. 48).*
>
> *History:* Sale A. Tollin, May 20-21, 1897, no. 205; Coll. Bourgeois, Cologne; Coll. Georges Hoentschel, 1908; Coll. J. Pierpont Morgan; Gift of Mrs. Charles Jairus Martin to the Charles Jairus Martin Memorial Collection of The Minneapolis Institute of Arts, in 1916.
>
> *Exhibitions:* Hartford, 1951-52, no. 75; Baltimore, 1952, no. 75; Minneapolis, 1955; New York, 1958; Raleigh, 1959, no. 98.

A tapestry of this subject was bought by Philip the Good from Pasquier Grenier in Tournai. The item in the accounts of the Dukes which mentions this purchase in 1461-1462 specifies that the payment concerns a wool and silk set of tapestries in six parts which the Duke had bought earlier and had offered to the Cardinal of Arras. This document was published by DE LABORDE (Part 2, I, 1849, no. 1871).

The connection between the tapestry bought by the Duke and the still-existing fragments of the same subject, is uncertain. On the whole, authors have established a correlation between all the examples, of which the principal ones are the fragment at Minneapolis, two fragments in the Musée Lorrain of Nancy, and a complete series in three pieces belonging to the Cathedral of Saragossa, Spain. The Saragossa series is woven in wool and silk and bears a Latin inscription (Cat. Bruges Exhib., 1907, nos. 1-3). It seems probable that the hanging acquired by Philip the Good was given by him to the Cardinal of Arras and that it, therefore, could not be identified with the tapestry which, according to a tradition accepted by KURTH (1917, pp. 91-92) and mentioned with great reserve by MIGEON (1929, pp. 229-230), were taken with the belongings of Charles the Bold after his death in the battle of Nancy in 1477, and from which might have come the two fragments in the Musée Lorrain at Nancy. According to KURTH (1917, pp. 91-92) the Dukes might have possessed, however, a tapestry of this

325

subject, which possibly decorated a room on the occasion of the marriage of Charles the Bold. KURTH (1917, pp. 91-92) thinks he recognizes the Tournai dialect in the inscriptions on the two Nancy fragments. SCHMITZ (1921, p. 196) attributes them to the workshop of Pasquier Grenier, as does KURTH. The example of the Cathedral of Saragossa may come from the same workshop, according to KURTH (1917, pp. 91-92), whereas MIGEON (1929, pp. 229-230) thinks it may be from another workshop and date from the end of the 15th century.

The fragment of The Minneapolis Institute of Arts belongs, according to SCHMITZ (1921, p. 196) to the workshop of Pasquier Grenier. *The Minneapolis Institute of Arts Bulletin* (1934, p. 48) places it ca. 1475, and as produced in

326

Textiles

Tournai or Brussels. It thus reflects a doubt which might have its origin in the opinion of Göbel (I, Part 1, 1923, pp. 275-276) who considered the group of tapestries of the History of Esther and of the History of Troy as coming from a Brussels workshop. Göbel based his opinion on a signature which he thought he was able to read on one of the tapestries in this group. Rorimer (1939, p. 227, note 2) pointed out that this reading was incorrect. The catalogues of the exhibitions at Hartford and Baltimore in 1951-52 identify this tapestry as a work from Tournai; the catalogue of the exhibition at Raleigh, 1959, as being Flemish-Burgundian.

TOURNAI, between 1476 and 1488

152. THE YOUTH OF HERCULES

Brussels, Musées Royaux d'Art et d'Histoire. Inv. no. 3176. Tapestry Cat. no. 7

This large fragment of tapestry is part of a hanging representing the Story of Hercules which was woven, some time between 1476 and 1488, for the Cardinal Archbishop of Lyon, Charles of Bourbon, a cousin of Charles the Bold. It was very probably done in a workshop in Tournai. Three fragments are still known to exist of this set of tapestries which perhaps originally included nine pieces. These three fragments are in the Musées Royaux d'Art et d'Histoire in Brussels, the Musée d'Archéologie in Tournai, and the Musée de la Manufacture des Gobelins in Paris.

The scenes shown are episodes from the childhood and youth of Hercules: the bath of the new-born hero; the first exploit that made him famous; the strangling of two snakes; the request to the King to hold a joust; the announcement of this; an episode of the joust.

It has been shown that the artist who did the cartoons for this hanging of the Story of Hercules faithfully followed the text of the *Recueil des Histoires de Troie,* written by Raoul Lefèvre for Philip the Good in 1464: Hercules, reputed ancestor of the Dukes of Burgundy, is naturally given a prominent place.

Physical data: Wool and silk, 12 ft. 8 $^3/_8$ in. x 16 ft. 8 $^{13}/_{16}$ in. (3.87 x 5.10 m.), five to six threads per centimeter (Crick-Kuntziger, III, 1931, p. 66).
Names of the persons inscribed on their clothing: Alcmena, Cheso, Eristeus, Hercules. Wear, especially in the silk parts.
History: Sale of the de Somzée Coll., Brussels, May, 1901, no. 524; acquired at that sale by the Musées Royaux d'Art et d'Histoire in Brussels.
Exhibitions: Tournai, 1956, no. 3; Tournai, 1958, no. 8.

Crick-Kuntziger (1931, pp. 66-67) demonstrated that the piece in the Brussels Museum and the one in the Musée d'Archéologie in Tournai belonged to the same tapestry as shown by the subject, style, technique, and inscriptions.

327

BACRI (1934, pp. 204-208) shortly later proved that the piece in the Musée des Gobelins in Paris belonged with the Brussels and Tournai tapestries. DESONAY (cited by CRICK-KUNTZIGER, 1931, pp. 68-74) showed that the artist who did the cartoons for the pieces in Brussels and Tournai had faithfully followed the text of the *Recueil des Histoires de Troie* written by Raoul Lefèvre in 1464, of which one manuscript copy bears the coat of arms of Charles the Bold as Count of Charolais (Brussels, Bibliothèque Royale, no. 9263). BACRI (1934, p. 206) proved the same for the section in Paris. He identified the coats of arms, which appear in incomplete form on the Paris tapestry and complete on the one in Brussels, as those of the Cardinal-Archbishop Charles of Bourbon after 1476, when he was made cardinal, and before his death in 1488.

The *Youth of Hercules* in Brussels was said to be of French origin in the catalogue of the de Somzée sale in 1901. DESTRÉE (1904, p. 55) classified it the same way. GÖBEL (1923, pp. 276 and 409), who mistakenly believed there were good reasons for considering it as coming from Jan van Roome's workshop in Brussels was nevertheless hesitant to make this attribution. KURTH (1917, p. 96), HUNTER (1925, p. 82), MIGEON (1929, p. 231), CRICK-KUNTZIGER (1931, p. 76), and BACRI (1934, p. 211), all said the tapestry came from Tournai.

KURTH (1917, p. 96) dated the hanging of the Story of Hercules ca. 1470. SCHMITZ (1921, p. 200) placed it somewhere in the last years of

328

Charles the Bold, who died in 1477. Crick-Kuntziger (1931, p. 70) first dated it in the third quarter of the 15th century, but since the identification of the coat of arms of Charles of Bourbon, she dates it around 1483 (Crick-Kuntziger, 1956, p. 177). Bacri (1934, p. 211) places it ca. 1483-1485 judging from the type of clothing, armor, and head-dress.

No replica or second weaving of this set of tapestries is known.

TOURNAI OR BRUGES, 1480-1483

153. PENELOPE
Fragment of a tapestry in the series of THE FAMOUS WOMEN

Boston, Mass., Museum of Fine Arts. Inv. 26.54

This small but very lovely fragment of tapestry shows Penelope at her unending work of tapestry-weaving while waiting for the return of her husband Ulysses from the Trojan War. This fragment was cut from a set of tapestries known through old descriptions and which had for its subject *The Famous Women*.

This series bears the coat of arms of Cardinal Ferry de Clugny who was adviser to the Dukes of Burgundy, Philip the Good and Charles the Bold, and then to Mary of Burgundy; he became Bishop of Tournai, and was made a cardinal in 1480. This indicates that the tapestry must have been ordered between 1480 and the death of the prelate in 1483. It also has his motto: *Espoir qu'en vous* ("My hope rests in you"), which he adopted in honor of Mary, Duchess of Burgundy.

Crick-Kuntziger recently proposed attributing this tapestry to a Bruges worshop. This attribution carries great importance from the fact of the close kinship between the set of tapestries of *The Famous Women* and that of *The Lady with the Unicorn* in the Musée de Cluny in Paris, one of the masterpieces of tapestry design and weaving. Until very recently it was believed that *The Lady with the Unicorn* was done in France, but no specialist had been able to determine the workshop or even in what province of France it could have been located. Rather vaguely founded hypotheses have proposed the banks of the Loire, the center of France, or even an itinerant workshop. The tapestry series of *The Famous Women* is an important link in the resolving of this question.

Physical data: Wool, 5 ft. 1 in. x 3 ft. 4 ¹/₂ in. (1.55 x 1.03 m.). Restorations to the neck and chin of Penelope. Pieces added to fill the gaps in the upper corners (T[ownsend], 1929, p. 6). Inscription in Latin in capital letters: penelope : co[n]ivnx : se[m]per : vlixis : ero : (Penelope will be the wife of Ulysses forever).

History: It is possible to trace this series of tapestries from owner to owner from its origin until the present time. It was already noted in works by historians and students of

330

Textiles

heraldry of the 17th and 18th centuries (T[ownsend], 1929, p. 3) and notably by Palliot (1661, pp. 176 and 574); it was described in detail in an anonymous manuscript of the 18th century edited and commented on by Varax (1926, pp. I-III and 1-29). It was then in the Castle of Thenissey (Côte-d'Or, France) and included ten pieces; Penelope was part of the third piece in the series. Its owners seem to have been, successively: Cardinal Ferry de Clugny; Guillaume de Clugny, nephew of the Cardinal; the Clugny-Montholon family; the Montholon-de Chaugy family; the Le Belin-de Chaugy family; bequeathed in 1702 to a relative in the Guiet family; Comtesse de Chamillard-Guiet; sold in 1750 to the Marquis de Clugny, Lord of Thenissey. In 1791, the Castle of Thenissey burned and only eight fragments of the tapestry survived; in 1793 in the Villefranche-Clugny family (de Varax, 1926, pp. II-III). Acquired from the Marquis de Villefranche in 1926 by the Museum of Fine Arts, Boston, through the Marie-Antoinette Evans Fund.

Exhibitions: Hartford-Baltimore, 1951-52, no. 77.

Six of the eight fragments acquired by the Museum in Boston belonged to the third tapestry of the set, the one showing Penelope. Its original composition is known from the description given by the anonymous author of an 18th century manuscript published by de Varax (1926, pp. 6-9). A lion was seen in the piece, wearing a shield with the coat of arms of Ferry de Clugny and the Cardinal's hat (this fragment also belongs to the Museum in Boston).

The tapestry could only have been ordered between 1480 and 1483 and, more exactly, between May 15, 1480, when Ferry de Clugny was named cardinal and March 12, 1482, date on which he left for Italy, where he died in 1483. If the motto really was a homage to Mary of Burgundy the tapestry must have been ordered before her death on March 27, 1482.

The supposition by the anonymous author of the 18th century manuscript that Mary of Burgundy gave this hanging to Ferry de Clugny at the time of the baptism of her daughter, Margaret of Austria, born in January, 1480 (de Varax, 1926, pp. 24-25) seems to have little foundation (Crick-Kuntziger, 1954, p. 13).

Authors of the 18th century considered the tapestry of *The Famous Women* a work done in the former Southern Netherlands; this is also the opinion of later writers (de Varax, 1926, pp. I-II and 25-26) who added the suggestion that it might possibly have been of English origin. Townsend (1929, p. 10) suggested it had been done in a workshop in Tournai and compares the fragment of Penelope to the tapestry of *The Lady with the Unicorn* in the Musée de Cluny in Paris. Crick-Kuntziger (1954, pp. 1-17) points out that Ferry de Clugny has provisionally transferred his diocese from Tournai to Bruges, that he did not return to Tournai after 1480, and that, as a result, there is little likelihood that he ordered this tapestry in Tournai. This author believes this hanging may have been done in a Bruges workshop. This hypothesis involves the attribution of *The Lady with the Unicorn* and of the *Story of Perseus* (Private collection, France). There is such a close kinship among these three tapestries that it is reasonable to attribute them to the same artist. The series of *The Famous Women* would be the first in date (Crick-Kuntziger, 1954, p. 12). Ackermann (1926, p. 153) thought she could distinguish some letters on the different fragments and tried to identify them as monograms. On that basis she proposed attributing the hanging of *The Famous Women* to the workshop of van Buyck who was an Antwerp master in 1482. This rather tenuous hypothesis has not been followed by other specialists.

331

FRANCO-FLEMISH, ca. 1500

154-155. NEPTUNE AND JUPITER

Detroit, Mich., The Detroit Institute of Arts. Acc. nos. 58.414 and 58.415

The two heroic figures placed against a background scattered with flowers were parts of a set of tapestries which has not been identified. They represent *Neptune,* King of the Sea, and *Jupiter,* King of the Gods of Olympus. The former is holding a trident and two fishes; the latter is wearing a crown, holding a scepter and is accompanied by an eagle.

These two fragments of tapestry are related to the tapestry of *The Life of the Nobility* in the Musée de Cluny in Paris, those of the *"Preux"* and the *"Preuses"* in Angers (Musée des Tapisseries) and Paris (Musée des Arts décoratifs), and others, all of which show figures posed before a dark blue background filled with flowers. These all belong to the large category of *Millefleurs tapestries.*

The origin of these tapestries is unknown. They date from the end of the 15th and the beginning of the 16th century. Several of them decorated castles along the banks of the River Loire, and this fact has prompted some authorities to believe that an important tapestry center existed in this region or that itinerant workshops were located there. Other scholars believe that these tapestries came from workshops in the Southern Netherlands, perhaps from Tournai.

Physical data: Wool and silk, **8 ft.** 1 in. x 3 ft. ⁵/₈ in. (2.42 x 0.93 m.) and 8 ft. 1 in. x 3 ft. 3 ³/₈ in. (2.24 x 1 m.). Inscriptions in capital letters on the clothing: NEPTVNVS RE[X] and IVPITER followed by many letters which cannot be interpreted with certainty.

332

Textiles

History: Said to come from the collection of the Princes de Ligne in Belgium; French and Company, New York; acquired by The Detroit Institute of Arts, 1958, *Jupiter* as the gift of Mrs. Edsel B. Ford and Mr. and Mrs. K.T. Keller and *Neptune* as the gift of Mr. and Mrs. Douglas F. Roby.
Exhibitions: None known.

These two figures could possibly have been made for use on narrow walls as between windows as suggested by WEIBEL (1960, p. 96), or they may have been cut from larger tapestries similar to that of *Penthesilea* in the Musée des Tapisseries in Angers or that of *Hercules* in the Musée des Arts décoratifs in Paris. *Hercules* and *Neptune* have many common characteristics such as the form of the arm, the right hand, and the two feet (position and shoes). Comparisons can also be made with the tapestry of *The Life of the Nobility* in the Musée de Cluny in Paris which also has a floral background.

VERLET (Cat. Brussels Exhib., 1947, p. 9) stated that these "Mille-fleurs" hangings were "astonishing masterpieces" which appeared in France at a time when tapestry-weaving was in decline there but was experiencing an extraordinary splendor in Brussels. The authorities who consider them as coming from the Loire valley have not been able to identify the exact place where these tapestries were made. WEIBEL (1960, pp. 96-97) places the origin of *Neptune* and *Jupiter* in Tournai or the north of France, between 1500 and 1525.

ACKERMAN (1932, p. 11) suggested that the author of the cartoon for these tapestries was a painter from Tournai named Bonaventure Thieffries active in 1505. She bases this conclusion on the deciphering of the ill-formed letters which follow Jupiter's name on the border of his robe. This theory seems unfounded.

333

334

Textiles

SOUTHERN NETHERLANDS, 1437-1460

156. CHASUBLE OF JEAN CHEVROT

Vellereille-lez-Brayeux, Petit Séminaire de Bonne Espérance

The gold and silk embroidery of the orphreys on this chasuble was done for the Bishop of Tournai, Jean Chevrot, whose coat of arms can be seen twice. This allows dating these orphreys during the years of his episcopate, that is, between 1437 and 1460, and tends to place their execution in a Tournai workshop.

The red velvet of the chasuble is modern. The transfer of the orphreys from the ancient vestment onto the new one caused the disappearance of part of them: one scene at the top of the cross on the back, two others toward top and bottom of the front band. The two small bands at the neck have undoubtedly been made from one of the scenes cut off.

The scenes represent events in the life of Christ: the Flight into Egypt, the Adoration of the Magi, the Presentation in the Temple, the Virgin finding Christ in the Temple, the Baptism of Christ, the Entry into Jerusalem, and then a group eating around a table, not easily identifiable as the Last Supper.

Jean Chevrot was one of the principal counsellors of Philip the Good. He can be seen in the foreground toward the left in the celebrated miniature of dedication in the *Chroniques de Hainaut*, a miniature which is sometimes attributed to Roger van der Weyden and which is reproduced in this catalogue (p. 40). This manuscript is in the Bibliothèque Royale, Brussels (ms. 9242). Jean Chevrot also was a great patron of the arts commissioning paintings and illuminated manuscripts.

These orphreys have not yet been studied or published.

Physical data: Embroidery in gold and silk thread. Modern red velvet. Dimensions of the cross: 42 $^1/_2$ x 29 $^1/_8$ in. (108 x 75 cm.). The orphreys are no longer complete. Some scenes have disappeared and some have been cut up for a border at the neck. Escutcheons with the arms of Jean Chevrot on the base of the cross and the straight band on the front.

History: Origin unknown. Given to the Petit Séminaire at the beginning of the 19th century. It is probably this chasuble which figures in the Inventory of the Petit Séminaire of August 12, 1841 as *ornements rouges: une chasuble très vieille mais précieuse* ("red vestments: a very old but precious chasuble").

Exhibitions: Tournai, 1949, no. 6; Brussels 1952-53, no. 473; Mons, 1953, no. 435; Tournai, 1956, section Embroidery, no. 1; Tournai,1958, no. 163.

The presence of the coat of arms of Bishop Jean Chevrot allows the dating of these orphreys and the presumption of their attribution to a Tournai workshop. There are no difficulties identifying the scenes except in the case of that represented at the foot of the cross. Five figures can be seen in it, each with a nimbus, among whom Christ can be recognized with a cruciferous halo. The attitude of Christ is that which is seen in the *Marriage at Cana* but in that case it is difficult to understand all the guests being nimbed. As this scene follows *The Entry into Jerusalem* it may be suggested that it relates a rarely represented scene: the meal in the house of Zacchaeus, but this is only a hypothesis. It is

335

Textiles

probably better to identify it as a simplified representation of the Last Supper. In the bands which were cut and placed at the neck-opening can be seen, on the left, a kneeling figure followed by a standing figure: it may be one of the Magi from a *Nativity,* or a donor. On the right is a standing figure and behind him a Franciscan monk. It is noteworthy that in the scene of the *Presentation in the Temple* Simeon is assisted by a monk who might be the donor.

SOUTHERN NETHERLANDS, BRUGES(?), end of the 15th Century

157. DALMATIC called "OF MARY OF BURGUNDY"

Bruges, Church of Notre-Dame

This dalmatic is part of a collection of church vestments which, according to a tradition devoid of foundation, were embroidered by Mary of Burgundy. The motto *En vous me fye* ("In you my trust") is embroidered twice on this dalmatic. The white silk which forms the vestment is not original.

The style of the orphreys seems to belong to the end of the 15th century. They represent on the long bands at the front, the Saints Agnes, Barbara and Gudule, and three prophets; on the back, the Saints Catherine(?), Agnes and Dorothy, and three prophets; on the small arm-bands, Saint Peter twice, and two other Saints; on the small transverse bands, angels are carrying a cloth of honor in front of which a motif has been masked by the addition of an embroidered lozenge-shaped motif.

> *Physical data:* Background, white silk, not original: 44 $^7/_8$ x 44 $^1/_8$ in. (114 x 112 cm.). Orphreys of gold and silk thread: width: 4 $^5/_{16}$ in. (11 cm.). Traces of wear. Somewhat restored. Inscriptions *En vous me fye* in Gothic letters on the scroll embroidered on the shoulder: they may have been fitted between the orphrey bands.
>
> *History:* Seems always to have belonged to the Church of Notre-Dame. Duclos (1910, p. 480) points out that the documents from the archives concerning the gifts of Maximilian of Austria and his son Charles V in memory of Mary of Burgundy (d. 1482), and to which certain authors have referred, have been published by Gailliard. These may throw light on the origin of the vestments called "of Mary of Burgundy".
>
> *Exhibitions:* Malines, 1864, nos. 665 (1st ed.) and 714 (2nd ed.); Bruges, 1867, no. 291; Bruges, 1907, no. 25; Brussels, 1951, no. 147; Dijon, 1951, no. 228; Amsterdam, 1951, no. 146; Ghent, 1955, no. 497; Malines, 1958, no. 392.

The set of vestments called "of Mary of Burgundy" comprises a dalmatica, a tunic, a corporale, the cross of a chasuble and some other unmounted pieces of orphrey. A thorough study of them has not yet been made.

The corporale is ornamented with coats of arms framed by branches of thistle and the motto *En vous me fye.* These coats of arms are those of Mary of

336

Textiles

Burgundy and her husband Maximilian of Austria, according to WEALE (1862, p. 94). The motto is that of Margaret of Austria according to DUCLOS (1910, p. 480). The coats of arms are also to be seen on an escutcheon at the top of the cross of the chasuble as well as the motto which is repeated on the shoulders of the dalmatic and the tunic. VERSCHELDE (Cat. Bruges Exhib., 1867, no. 291) places these vestments in relation to the documents which testify that Maximilian of Austria made a gift of precious cloth, pearls and jewels to the Church of Notre-Dame in May 1517 and that Charles V, a little later, gave 566 *livres* (pounds). DUCLOS (1910, p. 480) supposes that the vestments were not finished before 1560. According to the catalogues of the latest exhibitions of Brussels - Dijon - Amsterdam (1951) and Malines (1958) the vestments date from ca. 1480: this date is more in harmony with their style.

337

SOUTHERN NETHERLANDS(?), ca. 1500

158. CHASUBLE

Blankenberge, Church of Saint-Roch

Of this chasuble, only the embroidered orphreys are old: the velvet on which they are placed is modern; so is the braid which is used as a border.

The cross on the back of the chasuble bears a representation of Christ on the Cross; above His head, the figures of God the Father and the Holy Ghost. Angels catch in chalices the blood which pours from the wounds of Christ. Below, in a separate section, is seen the Centurion, identifiable by the inscription which he holds, written on a scroll: *Ecce filius dei erat iste* ("He truly was the Son of

338

Textiles

God"). On the straight band at the front are represented Saint Andrew and a prophet. Between them, the fragment representing the Education of the Virgin, probably dates from the 17th century. With the exception of this addition, the embroidery seems to date from about 1500. It may be an English work which has long been in Flanders.

Physical data: Silk embroidery mounted on a modern velvet background. Dimensions of the cross: 42 $^9/_{16}$ x 24 $^3/_8$ in. (108 x 62 cm.) ; straight band: 33 $^1/_2$ x 9 $^1/_{16}$ in. (85 x 23 cm.). The central motif of the straight band is a later addition.

History: Supposed to have come from the Church of Saint-Antoine in Blankenberge and to have been transferred to the Church of Saint-Roch about 1925 (VERSYP, 1956, p. 3).

Exhibitions: None known.

VERSYP (1956, pp. 3-4) dates this work at the end of the 15th century and points out its kinship with a chasuble previously in the Collection of Count Walstein in Cambridge. Therefore the embroidery on this chasuble might be considered as being English. Its style has little ressemblance to that of Flemish embroidery.

SOUTHERN NETHERLANDS(?), beginning of the 16th Century

159. COPE from NONNEN-MIELEN

Antwerp, Oudheidkundige Musea, Vleeshuis

This cope belongs to a group of church vestments which can be found at various places in Belgium and in particular in the province of Limburg. They are considered as imports from England by comparing them with unquestionably English embroidery. These works date back to the 15th and 16th centuries.

The cope is made of red velvet embroidered with gold thread. Some motifs seem to represent thistles, others pomegranates. In the middle of the cope a *Virgin in Glory* can be seen. This kind of embroidery is typically English; the orphrey bands which border the front of the cope, and represent apostles and prophets in architectural niches, are also typically English. Only the hood, which represents the Death of the Virgin, is different in style and seems Flemish.

It must logically be presumed that the cope was imported from England and that a hood, made in the Southern Netherlands was adapted to it. Recently a specialist has presented a new thesis: according to him the embroidery now referred to as English could have been imitated in workshops of the Southern Netherlands.

Physical data: Velvet embroidered in gold thread, 57 $^1/_8$ x 128 in. (145 x 325 cm.). Embroidered hood and orphrey.

History: Benedictine Convent of Nonnen-Mielen near Saint-Trond; Convent of the Bernardine Sisters of Coolen in Kerniel; Bernardine Sisters in Bornem; acquired by Mr. Van Snick of Saint-Nicolas, Belgium, in 1906, and sold almost immediately to the Oudheidkundige Musea, Vleeshuis, in Antwerp, January 1906 (DOUILLEZ, III, 1956, pp. 12-13).

Exhibitions: Ghent, 1956, no. 662.

DUVERGER (1955, pp. 18-27) who dates this cope at the beginning of the 16th century, thinks that contrary to the opinion generally expressed it is not to to be excluded that the so-called English embroideries of church vestments preserved in Belgium could be the work of a Netherlandish workshop. This would be the case for the cope from Nonnen-Mielen, a typical example to support this thesis. He observes that the Flemish character of the embroidery on the hood is striking, whereas the English character of the rest of the cope is undeniable. Yet he does not find traces of reworking in the cope and thinks that the hood has always been part of it. He expresses the view that this allows him to suppose that certain Flemish workshops might have imitated English models, and that this may explain the great number of orphreys of an English type in Belgium. This author also observes that there are no archival documents mentioning the importation of church vestments from England to Belgium.

Against this theory, however, it can be said that if Flemish workshops have imitated the English style, it does not explain the discrepancies in style existing in the same piece as is the case for the cope from Nonnen-Mielen.

340

Textiles

ENGLISH(?), beginning of the 16th Century

160. COPE called "OF MAXIMILIAN OF AUSTRIA"

Léau, Church of Saint-Léonard

This large cope in green velvet covered with the heraldic motif of two-headed eagles, is a work which seems to date from the beginning of the 16th century.

The orphreys on the border represent three prophets alternating with three saints in niches which have an architectural decoration unusual to Flemish productions. Saint John the Evangelist and probably Saint James the Major can be recognized. The hood represents the Virgin and Child enthroned.

The presence of the imperial eagle gave rise to the legend that the cope was a gift of Maximilian of Austria, the husband of Mary of Burgundy. Comparison with authenticated work from English workshops has led several specialists to suppose that the cope was imported from England. As such it is a witness to the diversity of artistic exchange of which the Netherlands was the center.

Physical data: Orphreys embroidered with silk and gold thread; green velvet embroidered with gold thread, 57 $^1/_8$ x 55 $^1/_8$ in. (145 x 140 cm.).

History: Origin unknown: it seems to have belonged for many years to the Church of Saint-Léonard.

Exhibitions: Brussels, 1888, no. 3154; Léau, 1924; Antwerp, 1930, no. D 1147; Antwerp, 1948, no. 758; Brussels, 1954, no. 87.

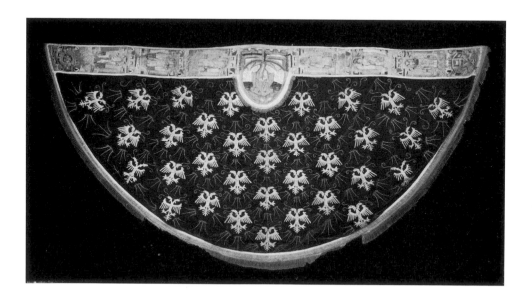

Textiles

JANSEN and VAN HERCK (1949, p. 93, no. 344) point out the close relationship of the orphreys of this cope with those of Gierle (near Turnhout), and think they were made in the same workshop. These authors suggest, but not without reservations, recognizing in it the product of an English workshop at the beginning of the 16th century, the main evidence for this being the technique of the embroidery, particularly the orphreys. DUVERGER (1955, pp. 18-27) proposed attributing to Flemish workshops embroideries of this type preserved in Belgian collections: they would then be an imitation of English embroidery made in the Netherlands. The cope from Nonnen-Mielen exhibited here (cat. no. 159) is related to the cope of Maximilian, but its hood is of Flemish character.

342

Textiles

BRABANT, 15th Century

161. CRADLE FOR THE CHRIST CHILD ("REPOS DE JESUS")

New York, Ruth and Leopold Blumka Collection

These miniature cradles reproduced in small size the types of larger cradles actually used for babies in the Netherlands in the 15th century, of which the most famous example (close in date though of a different type) is the so-called Cradle of Charles V in the Musées Royaux d'Art et d'Histoire in Brussels, which bears the arms of the Duchy of Burgundy and may well have been used for Philip the Handsome (b. 1478), his sister, Margaret of Austria (b. 1480), and Philip's son, Charles V (b. 1500).

Small "cradles of Jesus", originally containing a figurine of the Christ Child, are objects of devotion which were exhibited on the occasion of certain religious celebrations, especially at Christmas time, in convents or private homes. They were made of wood, silver, or ivory.

Cradles of Jesus had their greatest popularity in the 15th and first half of the 16th centuries. These objects were often referred to in public records of notaries or archives of convents. They were sometimes given to nuns at the time they took their vows.

The example in the Blumka Collection is richly carved and painted; the bedding is an historiated embroidery. The figure of the Christ Child has disappeared.

This cradle was probably executed in a 15th century Brabant workshop. It comes from the *Grand Béguinage* (Beguine Convent) of Louvain. It is in the shape of a small bed; the outer sides of the head and foot boards are decorated with carvings in bas-relief showing *The Nativity* and *The Adoration of the Magi*. On the inside, parchments are glued to the panels. The one at the head of the bed shows three angels singing and the one at the foot an angel holding a scroll. On top of the bed posts are four angels playing musical instruments; two, old-fashioned guitars *(guiterne)*, one a psaltery, and one a viol *(vièle)*. The polychromatic scheme of the cradle is white (which predominates), blue, red, and gold. A *Tree of Jesse*, the iconography of which is rather unusual, is embroidered on the red silk coverlet: only the head of Jesse is shown and the tree comes from his mouth. The pillow is embroidered with an *Agnus Dei* surrounded by the symbols of the Evangelists. These embroideries in gold thread are decorated with pearls, translucent enamel work, and pendant silver lamellas cut-out in the form of holly and violet leaves.

343

Physical data: Oak, 12 ¹/₂ x 11 x 7 ³/₁₆ in. (35 x 28 x 18 cm.). Carved and polychromed; painted parchment; twisted rods in gilded copper and gilded silver bells; gold embroidered silk bedding decorated with pearls and silver pendants. Vestiges of an inscription, not legible, on the gilded border under the *Nativity*. The statuettes on top of the central finial at the head and foot of the bed have disappeared. Posts and arcades along the sides damaged. Almost all the crockets decorating the extrados of the arcades are missing; the small consoles in front of these arcades may have held statuettes. A case for a relic is inside the bed.

History: Belonged to the Grand Béguinage of Louvain which sold it to Jules Frésart in Liège, 1882 (VAN EVEN, 1895, p. 541); acquired by Albert Figdor, Vienna, shortly before 1894 (DESTRÉE, 1894, pp. 122 and 129, ill. 32; VAN EVEN, 1895, p. 541); sale of Albert Figdor Coll., Berlin (Cassirer), September 20-30, 1930, no. 161; Bondy Coll., Vienna; Blumka Coll., New York, 1947. The wax figurine of the Christ Child in swaddling clothes and a linen cap still existed in 1894 and was reproduced by DESTRÉE (1894, fig. 32). It subsequently disappeared.

Exhibitions: None known.

This "Repos de Jésus" was attributed to a Louvain workshop by DESTRÉE (1894, p. 122), VAN EVEN (1895, p. 541), and NIFFLE-ANCIAUX (1896, pp. 48-49). The author of the descriptive catalogue of the Albert Figdor Sale (Berlin, 1930, no. 161) and BERLINER (1955, pp. 226-227) credited it to a Brabantine workshop. DESTRÉE (1894, p. 122) dated it at the beginning of the 15th century.

344

Furniture

The Figdor sale catalogue (Berlin, 1930, no. 161) and BERLINER (1955, pp. 226-227) placed it at the middle of that century. MAERE (1943, pp. 81-84) dated it at the end of the 15th century and VAN EVEN (1895, p. 541) at the beginning of the 16th century.

The cradle most like this one is in the Mayer van den Bergh Museum in Antwerp (cat. 407). It is also in carved wood, polychromed, and decorated with paintings. Another one, in silver, in the Musée de la Société Archéologique in Namur, is also decorated with bells.

BRUGES(?), 15th Century

162. PRAYER-STOOL

Bruges, Gruuthuse-Museum

This small piece of furniture is a prayer-stool such as can be seen in numerous paintings of the Flemish Primitives and in particular in the painting by the Master of the View of Sainte-Gudule belonging to the Musée Diocésain of Liège, in this exhibition (cat. no. 27), and in the *Annunciation* by Gerard David from The Detroit Institute of Arts (cat. no. 46).

It shows the style characteristics of 15th century Flemish furniture.

Physical data: Oak, 25 $^3/_{16}$ x 11 $^7/_{16}$ in. (64 x 29 cm.). Carved inscriptions on both sides: *Maria* and *Jhesus,* in Gothic letters.

History: Nothing is known.

Exhibitions: Several small prayer-stools belonging to museums of Bruges have been lent to exhibitions. Their certain identification therein is not possible.

According to LEMAIRE (1942, p. 34) it is only around 1400 that furniture began to be fashioned in Gothic style, and it is in Flanders and Brabant, before France and Germany, that this change first took place.

This prayer-stool is a piece of domestic furniture and not for use in a church. In churches in the 15th century the congregation knelt on the ground: benches and chairs were not introduced until the 17th century.

345

163. WOODEN LECTERN

Louvain, Church of Sainte-Gertrude

This folding lectern of wood is one of the rare stands of this type which are still preserved. It is a delicate example of furniture, probably made at the end of the 15th century in Brabant, where the art of furniture - making seems to have been ahead of that in neighboring regions.

The front crossbar of the stand bears a coat of arms decorated with a chalice, thus indicating it was intended for church use.

Physical data: Oak, 61 x 29 ^{15}/$_{16}$ in. (155 x 76 cm.). Traces of gilding. Some parts have been restored.

History: Broken during the last war, 1940. Restored.

Exhibitions: Brussels, 1954, no. 219.

The carving of the legs in the shape of lozenges, spirals and broken lines appears throughout the 15th century. These characteristics are found in paintings dated around 1430, for example, in the *Marriage of the Virgin* by the Master of Flémalle in the Prado. In the present exhibition an example may be seen in the Roger van der Weyden's *Saint Luke Painting the Virgin* in the Museum of Fine Arts in Boston (this cat. no. 7), ca. 1450, and another in *The Nativity* by the Master of the Saint Ursula Legend in The Detroit Institute of Arts (this cat. no. 41), between 1493 and 1499. This type of decoration becomes more usual at the end of the 15th century.

The varied shapes of the carvings on the legs of this lectern may be compared with the colonnettes which are represented on Flemish tapestries in the 15th and early 16th century, separating the many scenes and incidents included in one tapestry.

346

Furniture

164. DOOR of the CLOSURE OF THE CHAPEL OF THE WHEELWRIGHTS

Bruges, Cathedral of Saint-Sauveur

In response to numerous requests for the granting of chapels for the use of the various "métiers", trades and professions, as well as the confraternities of the 15th century, the church vestries had many chapels built, mainly between the supports of the buttresses of the main church. They were generally granted on the

condition that the beneficiaries contributed to their construction and outfitting.

This door is from the closure for the chapel of Sainte-Catherine granted to the "métier" of the Bruges Wheelwrights in 1516.

It is decorated with the canting arms of the Wheelwrights, the wheel, which is also the principal decorative motif of the lock. It bears the date 1517.

The wheel is the iconographic symbol of Saint Catherine who, for this reason, was chosen by the wheelmakers as their patron saint. The relief carvings also represent tools used by the wheelwrights and two workmen making wheels; beside one of the two men is a tankard.

Physical data: Oak, 78 x 35 $^5/_{16}$ in. (198 x 90.5 cm.). Dated 1517 on the panelling of the outside of the door. Original lock and pilasters in brass.

History: Documents in the archives prove that the chapel of Sainte-Catherine was granted to the Wheelwrights by an agreement dated July 28, 1516, on the condition that they provide at their expense an openwork enclosure with brass pilasters as well as a stained-glass window; the church council promised to furnish the stones and metal framework of the window (VERSCHELDE, 1863, p. 248).

Exhibitions: None known.

Through historical documents it is known that the crown of chapels which surround the ambulatory of the Bruges Cathedral was undertaken by the architect Jan van de Poele in 1480. The work began with the chapel of Sainte-Catherine. Ambroise Roelants succeeded Jan van de Poele in 1516. Everything was finished in 1556 (ENGLISH, 1959, pp. 13-14). After the masonry was done, Saint Catherine's chapel was granted to the wheelwrights by an act of July 28, 1516. The date 1517 on the door thus agrees with the archival documents.

347

Furniture

Enclosure of the chapel of Sainte-Catherine in the Bruges Cathedral

Furniture

GLASS and STAINED-GLASS

CHRETIEN VAN DE VOORDE

Active in Bruges from 1386 to 1404

Chrétien van de Voorde was a master glassmaker whose name appears several times in the city accounts or in those of the Dukes of Burgundy for works done in Bruges. In 1385-86, 1397-98, and 1403-04, he made stained-glass windows for the Bruges City Hall. In 1387-88 he was commissioned to repair the stained-glass windows of the ducal castle and in 1394-95 the large stained-glass window of the chapel of the ducal residence in Bruges.

349

Bruges, Gruuthuse-Museum. Inv. III, nos. 1403, 1404, 1410, 1411

These four fragments of stained-glass in the flame shapes found in the tracery of the upper section of late Gothic windows, come from the façade of the Bruges City Hall, according to a seemingly well founded tradition. They probably decorated the large windows of the aldermen's room. They could be the work of Chrétien van de Voorde of Bruges, dating from between 1385 and 1404.

These fragments show angels in yellow, red or white on a colored diaper background. Three of the angels bear a phylactery indicating their high rank in the angelic hierarchy: a Seraph with six wings, a Cherub and an Angelic Power, each with four wings. These three angels are feathered but they wear white neckerchiefs. The fourth angel has only one pair of wings and wears a white robe; he has a halo. The four angels have curly hair held by a ribbon enriched with a carbuncle.

Very few examples of Flemish stained-glass have been preserved. The fragments shown in this exhibition demonstrate the artistic and technical ability of Flemish glassmakers at the end of the 14th and the beginning of the 15th centuries.

Physical data: Polychromed stained-glass window fragments; some details in grisaille and silver-stain. Inv. 1403: 24 x 13 $^3/_8$ in. (61 x 34 cm.) ; Inv. 1404: 25 $^3/_4$ x 13 $^9/_{16}$ in. (65.5 x 34.5 cm.) ; Inv. 1410: 25 $^3/_{16}$ x 16 $^1/_8$ in. (64 x 41 cm.) ; Inv. 1411: 25 x 13 $^3/_{16}$ in. (63.5 x 33.5 cm.).
Good state of preservation, but there is a piece missing from the stained-glass window of the angel in the white robe.
Streamers with inscriptions in Gothic letters: *che ru bin, che ra phin, po tes ta tes.* These syllables are separated by small cross-shaped ornaments. Two of the scrolls bear a small winged dragon.
History: Traditionally said to have come from the City Hall (Cat. Bruges Exhib., 1905, Addenda, II, no. 1, p. 115).
Exhibitions: Bruges, 1905, Addenda, II, no. 1.

In his repertory of stained-glass in Belgium, HELBIG (1943) does not mention these four fragments of stained-glass windows. DEVLIEGHER (1954, p. 197, note 1) dates them ca. 1400.

The construction of the Bruges City Hall dates back to the last quarter of the 14th century. In the city accounts it is possible to follow the progress of the building, decoration and interior installation. Payments made to the glassmaker Chrétien van de Voorde for delivering several stained-glass windows are mentioned three times, namely for the aldermen's room. In 1385-1386 there is a mention of a window representing Saint John for which Chrétien was paid *trois livres de gros* (three pounds). In 1397-1398 he was paid for sixteen panels of new stained-glass windows measuring one hundred and sixteen feet, destined for the aldermen's room and for the adjoining Church of Saint-Basile; also for thirty-five feet of stained-glass. Finally in 1403-1404 he delivered two stained-glass windows,

350

one representing the Miracles of Our Lady, the other, the Story of King David for the price of *cinq livres dix sous de gros* (five pounds ten pence) each (GILLIODTS-VAN SEVEREN, III, 1875, pp. 488 and 492). During that period the city accounts do not mention any other glassmaker. The four angels may well have been included in one of the commissions just cited.

It is known that later on more stained-glass windows were made for the City Hall. Jan de Rynghel made some in 1409-1410. DUCLOS (1910, p. 393) mentions in that respect an account in the Bruges archives of that year, fol. 74 v°. Nevertheless it is normal to believe that the windows on the principal façade of the City Hall, which are those of the aldermen's room, were fitted with stained-glass panels at the time the interior of the room was completed, before 1409-1410.

According to RÉAU (II, 1, 1956, p. 35) angels are represented with feathers at the end of the Middle Ages. This author states that numerous examples of feathered angels can be found starting with those on Sluter's *Well of Moses* at Champmol (1395-1405).

There is an obvious relationship of style between the angel in a white robe (ill. p. 351) and the angel on the corbel of *Zacharias and the Angel* dating from 1377 from the façade of the Bruges City Hall, exhibited here (cat. no. 68).

351

169. DRINKING GLASS

Liège, Musée Diocésain. Manuscript Cat. 1937, no. 405

Drinking glasses of this kind are shown in 15th century Flemish paintings and manuscript miniatures. Beakers and tumblers of a greenish or brownish hue were made in the Netherlands. They were blown in molds which created their characteristic twisted or embossed sides. Fine examples are represented in the panel of *The Jewish Passover Meal* (this exhibition, cat. no. 17 and ill. p. 105). Similar glasses were sometimes used to hold relics to be placed in the masonry of an altar at the time of its dedication. It is probable that this glass is from a 15th century Liège workshop.

Physical data: Glass, 2 ³/₄ x 3 ¹/₈ in. (7 x 8 cm.). Blown in a hollow mold. Slightly flaring form; crossing whirled ribs; smooth rim; greenish hue.
History: Found in Polleur (province of Liège), in the masonry of the high altar of the church; deposited in the Musée Diocésain in 1906 (*Leodium,* V, 1906, p. 42).
Exhibitions: Liège, 1958, no. 221.

The date of the dedication of the high altar of the church in Polleur is unknown, but it appears to have been in the 15th or 16th century and so supplies an approximate date for this glass.

The Principality of Liège and the County of Hainault manufactured similar drinking glasses in the 15th and 16th centuries. This has been confirmed by documents found in several archives. Recent excavations carried out on the site of former glassworks have proved that this type of glass was also made in Brabant (CHAMBON, 1955, p. 67). The hue of these glasses comes from the metal oxides contained in the sand (BERRYER, 1958, p. 106). They are sometimes called *woudglas* or *verres-fougère.*

HISTORICAL DOCUMENTS

Off all the means used in the Middle Ages to give a document legal validity, the *seal* impressed in wax, lead, or even gold, was the most common. Today such seals are not only still one of the principal marks of the authenticity of a medieval legal instrument, but also they are of great value to the historian, since usually we know from the document to which they were attached both their exact date and place of origin, and hence the pictures and inscriptions on the seals afford a unique source of dated and localized information on a variety of subjects, styles of dress, armor, and architecture, the development of heraldry and of the insignia, titles, and legal status of the owner.

A seal is classified by the type of picture on it. A crowned figure enthroned in majesty could only be used by a king or emperor, just as a mounted knight was proper for a lesser lay noble. Often it is hard to know whether a robed standing human figure represents a woman or a churchman, for the distinguishing marks of the owner's status frequently have become effaced over the centuries.

The validity of a document was dependent in large part on its seal, and therefore elaborate and ingenious means of attaching the seal to parchment were devised to prevent loss or breakage of the seal, not to mention its possible removal and reuse by forgers. A seal placed directly on the parchment would easily be detached, but if a cord or parchment strip were imbedded in the soft sealing wax as the impression was being made, the seal could be suspended from the parchment in a protective case. One advantage of this system was that the back of the wax could also be sealed with a second seal, called the *counter-seal,* thus giving added proof of authenticity and further discouragement to forgers. The simplest method of suspending a seal was to make a horizontal cut partway across the bottom of the parchment, which produced a single narrow, semi-detached strip of parchment around which the seal could be molded. The most satisfactory means, however, was to pass a loop of parchment or cord through two holes at the bottom of the sheet and then to embed the free ends of the cord in the hot sealing wax. Hemp, flax, or colored silk made durable cords which could be braided, twisted, or woven. Before the seal and its cord were fastened on, the parchment was reinforced at the joints where the cord passed through it by making a horizontal fold across the bottom to double the thickness of the sheet.

Bruges, like many medieval cities, not only had a seal for its own business, called the commune's great seal or *common seal,* but also possessed a lesser seal for authenticating the acts of persons who had no seal of their own. Like the modern public notary, the city charged a fee for the use of this seal, which from its most common use was known as the *seal for lawsuits* or for contracts (sigillum ad causas, ad contractus).

Seals were attached to various kinds of acts: the *ordinance,* a general legislative act for an entire kingdom or domain; the *privilege,* an act conceding exclusive rights, advantages, or prerogatives to one or more persons; and the *charter,* which is a general term for any public act drawn up with all the

353

formalities necessary for its authenticity. The texts of many medieval documents are preserved today not in the original charters but in copies made in record books called *cartularies,* because copies of charters were collected together in them.

HENRI HEUBENS, 1394

170. PLAN OF THE CASTLE OF COURTRAI

Brussels, Archives Générales du Royaume,
Charters van Vlaanderen, 2de reeks

This is the oldest known plan of a medieval castle constructed in Belgium. It was made by Henri Heubens, a master mason of Sluis near Bruges, at the command of Philip the Bold. The Duke wished to have a new castle on the banks of the Lys, on the site of the old fortress of Courtrai which had been demolished in 1382.

The plan drawn up by Heubens is that of a square stronghold, surrounded by water with an enclosure defended by ten round towers. The plan was presented to Philip the Bold in 1394. Three years later the construction was finished and in February 1398 Philip the Bold made his first stay. It is known that his grandson, Philip the Good, stayed there on twenty-four occasions.

> *Physical data:* Parchment made of the skin of the entire animal, 29 $^1/_2$ x 37 $^3/_8$ in. (75 x 95 cm.). The plan has annotations in the handwriting of the end of the 14th century which gives, in feet, the dimensions for the construction. At the back is written: *pourtraicture du nouvel chastel de Courtray* ("plan of the new castle of Courtrai").
> *History:* Ordered before April 27, 1394, date at which it was submitted by Henri Heubens to the master masons of Saint-Omer (LAVALLEYE, 1930, p. 159).
> *Exhibitions:* None known.

According to the original documents which he had found at the Archives Générales du Royaume, LAVALLEYE (1930, pp. 157-168) traced the complete history of the construction of the new castle of Courtrai, the plan of which is one of the few of its kind still preserved. After the demolition of the old fortress of Courtrai in 1382, Philip the Bold decided to construct a new castle. In 1394 he appointed commissioners and a receiver to direct, supervise and pay for the work. April 27, 1394, the master mason Henri Heubens of Sluis presented a project to the master masons of Saint-Omer who brought it to Boulogne in order to show it to Philip the Bold and hear his decision. At the end of May 1394 the plan was sent back to Henri Heubens. In July of that same year the work was commenced; in 1396 the masonry was finished; in 1397 the construction was completed. Thirty years later a chapel was constructed in the castle; the altar was put in place in 1429 and the stained-glass windows in 1433. The castle was demolished in 1684.

354

MATHIEU DE LAYENS(?), second half of the 15th Century

171. PROJECT FOR THE WEST FRONT OF SAINT-PIERRE IN LOUVAIN

Louvain, Vanderkelen-Mertens Museum

Architectural designs dating back to the 15th century are relatively rare. This one here relates to the west front of the Church of Saint-Pierre in Louvain. It was discovered and identified at the Vanderkelen-Mertens Museum scarcely two years ago by Frans Van Molle and Raymond Lemaire. There already existed another architectural drawing and a stone model on large scale which was made in the third decade of the 16th century; they were projects for a gigantic west front with three towers which was never finished. With the drawing which has recently been discovered, they form a unique ensemble of great importance.

The monumental façade of Saint-Pierre seems to have been conceived by Mathieu de Layens, who was architect for the city of Louvain. He directed the construction of Saint-Pierre as well as of the city-hall of Louvain (see illustration p. 48). He died in 1483.

> *Physical data:* Parchment, pen drawing, 70 $^7/_8$ x 24 in. (180 x 61 cm.). This design, which was in a very bad condition, has been cleaned at the Institut Royal du Patrimoine Artistique to make possible its exhibition at Detroit.
> *History:* Found in 1958 in the attic of the Vanderkelen-Mertens Museum. Its previous history is unknown.
> *Exhibitions:* None known.

In 1458, after the Romanesque west front of the Church of Saint-Pierre burned down, Mathieu de Layens was charged with making a project for the construction of a large tower *(la grande tour)*. In 1481-82 a design of the west front with three towers for which the foundations were already started, was exhibited in the church (MAERE, 1936, pp. 52-53 and 82). Thus the conception of the west front goes back to the period in which Mathieu de Layens directed the construction of the new church, that is to say from 1445 to 1483 (VAN EVEN, 1858, pp. 17-18; IDEM, 1895, pp. 334-335). As this architect is already mentioned in 1458 as the author of the first project for the large tower, he probably also conceived the project for the three towers. It was only in the 16th century, after an interruption in the work, that a part of the west front was erected which was similar to the conception of Josse Metsys (MAERE, 1936, p. 55).

With the help of the sculptor Jan Beyaert, Metsys made, from 1525 to 1530, a stone model for a west front with three towers which is still preserved in the Church of Saint-Pierre. He also completed, well before his death in 1530, a project for this monumental tower which might be the design known for a long time and preserved at the Vanderkelen-Mertens Museum (MAERE, 1936, pp. 54-57 and 84-88). The project recently discovered diverges appreciably from the stone model and the design attributed to Josse Metsys. It must antedate Metsys' work, as he was the last to elaborate plans for the tower. The drawing exhibited here may then be considered as corresponding to the conception of Mathieu de Layens, the only architect who is known to have drawn up a plan for this west front, before the activity of Josse Metsys.

355

Central section of the map

172. MAP TRACING THE COURSE OF THE REIE AT BRUGES FROM THE POOR-TERSLOGE OR LODGE OF THE BOURGEOIS (AT JAN VAN EYCK SQUARE) TO THE GATE OF DAMME, AND SHOWING THE CONNECTION BETWEEN THE CITY AND THE SEA. Undated [ca. 1450]

Bruges, Stadsarchief

This map contains a great number of very interesting details, such as the construction of different bridges over the Reie, as well as the northern gates of the city (the Speipoort, the Saint-Nicolas and Saint-Léonard gates, all of which have since been torn down and replaced by the Damme gate), also the water-powered mill and the man-powered loading hoist, the system of locks near the city of Sluis, the types of ships, and many other features of commerce in and around medieval Bruges (see p. 34).

Exhibitions: Bruges, 1924-25, no. 232.

356

Matrices of the great seal and counter-seal of the City of Bruges (cat. 173).

357

173. MATRICES OF THE GREAT SEAL (1304) AND COUNTER-SEAL (1318) OF THE CITY OF BRUGES

Bruges, Stadsarchief

The great seal of the City of Bruges, also called the common seal, seal of obligations or *sigillum ad contractus* was engraved in 1304 by Jan Inghelbrecht, called Jan de zeghelmakere. The seal cost enough (25 *livres*, 9 *escalins*) to indicate that artists were well paid.

Circular in form, the matrix is 3 $^5/_8$ in. (98 mm.) in diameter. The face depicts the coat of arms of the city: a crowned lion rampant collared with a cross to the right, fessey with eight pieces surrounded by a frame of twelve lobes; above the shield a crowned lion striding to the right; at the sides two crowned lions rampant, with their backs against the shield. The shield is held at the upper corners by two hands. Inscription in Gothic majuscules: + SIGILLUM SCABINOR[UM] ET BURGENSIUM VILLE DE BRUGIS AD CON-TRACTUS.

This seal gives a good idea of the ability of the engraver. It would be difficult to find a more pleasing example of sphragistics.

The counter-seal of the great seal also reproduces the coat of arms of the city. It was engraved by the same Jan Inghelbrecht in 1318. Inscription: + CONTRA S[IGILLUM] VILLE DE BRUGIS AD CONTRACTUS. This counter-seal is also very handsome.

The great and the small seals are connected by a chain. All are in solid silver. These two seals remained in use throughout the fifteenth century.

Exhibitions: Bruges, 1950, no. 453.
Bibliography: GILLIODTS-VAN SEVEREN, *Introduction,* 1878, p. 181; DUCLOS, 1910, p. 125.

174. MATRIX OF THE SEAL FOR LAWSUITS OF THE CITY OF BRUGES, ca. 1430

Bruges, Stadsarchief

In addition to the great seal or *sigillum ad contractus*, cities generally used another seal, commonly called the seal for lawsuits or *sigillum ad causas*.

About 1430 the city of Bruges had a new seal made for lawsuits, the matrix of which is in the City Archives.

Circular in form, the matrix is 3 $^1/_{16}$ in. (78 mm.) in diameter. The field depicts the coat of arms of the city: a lion rampant, crowned and collared with a cross fessey with eight pieces. The shield is carried at the upper corners by an angel half crouching, with wings outspread, held from below

358

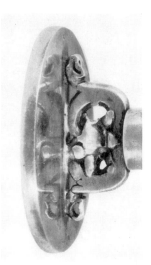

by a recumbent man, and flanked by two lions rampant with their backs against the shield. Inscription in Gothic minuscules: + SIGILLUM SCABINORUM ET BURGENSIUM · VILLE · BURGENSIS · AD · CAUSAS ·. The matrix is of silver, attached to a wooden handle.

Bibliography: GILLIODTS-VAN SEVEREN, *Introduction,* 1878, p. 181; DUCLOS, 1910, p. 125.

175. PRIVILEGE BEARING THE SEAL OF COUNT LOUIS DE MALE, 1373

Bruges, Stadsarchief, Politieke Charters, no. 624

June 23, 1373, Ghent. - In Flemish. Louis de Male, Count of Flanders, authorizes the City of Bruges to continue the collection of the *droits d'assises* for a period of three years, beginning July 1, provided an annual payment of 3.200 *livres parisis.*

Original on parchment, h. 9 $^9/_{16}$ in. (243 mm.), fold 1 $^3/_4$ in. (45 mm.), l. 15 $^{13}/_{16}$ in. (402 mm.), bearing the great equestrian seal of the count, counter-sealed, in yellow wax, suspended from the parchment on a doubled strip of parchment. Inscription, slightly damaged: SIGILLUM L[UDOVICI] CO[MITIS] FLANDRIE NIVERNEN[SIS] ET REGISTETEN[SIS].

Bibliography: GILLIODTS-VAN SEVEREN, II, 1873, pp. 233-234.

359

176. PRIVILEGE BEARING THE SEAL OF PHILIP THE BOLD, DUKE OF
BURGUNDY, 1387

Bruges, Stadsarchief, Politieke Charters, no. 687

February 28, 1387, Bruges. - In French. Letters of safe conduct of Philip the
Bold, Duke of Burgundy and Count of Flanders, for the merchants and other
people, who wished to go to the next festival in Bruges: every safeguard was
promised to these travellers for fifteen days before, during the festival and for
fifteen days after it. The festival, or fair, of Bruges began May 1 and ended
eighteen days later.

Original on parchment, h. 5 ³/₈ in. (136 mm.), l. 13 ¹/₈ in. (334 mm.),
bearing the great equestrian seal of Duke Philip, counter-sealed, in red wax,
suspended on a single strip of parchment. Inscription: S[IGILLUM] PHI[LIPPI]
FILII REG[IS] ET PARIS FRA[N]CIE DUCIS BURGO[N]DIE CO[M]ITIS FLA[N]DRIE
ARTESII ET BURGO[N]DIE PALATINI D[OMI]NI DE SALINIS CO[M]ITIS
REGITESTEN[SIS] ET D[OMI]NI DE MALINES.

Bibliography: GILLIODTS-VAN SEVEREN, III, 1875, p. 104.

360

177. PRIVILEGE BEARING THE SEAL OF JOHN THE FEARLESS, DUKE OF BURGUNDY, 1411

Bruges, Stadsarchief, Politieke Charters, no. 914

September 1411, Roye. - In French. Letters patent of John the Fearless, Duke of Burgundy, Count of Flanders, etc., which grant the request of the people of Bruges, confirming and renewing, for as much as is necessary, freedom from the *tonlieux* or *travers* (a toll paid by merchants) throughout all of Flanders in favor of the Brugeois.

Original on parchment, h. 9 $^1/_{16}$ in. (230 mm.), fold 2 $^3/_{16}$ in. (55 mm.), l. 14 $^3/_8$ in. (365 mm.), bearing the great equestrian seal of Duke John, countersealed, in bronze wax, suspended by lacings of green and red silk. Inscription: JOH[ANN]IS DUCIS BURGU[N]DIE COMITIS FLANDRIE ARTHESIE ET BURGU[N]-DIE PALATINIS DO[MI]N[U]S DE SALINIS ET DE MACHLINIA.

Bibliography: GILLIODTS-VAN SEVEREN, IV, 1876, pp. 87-88.

178. PRIVILEGE BEARING THE SEAL OF DUKE PHILIP THE GOOD, 1419

Bruges, Stadsarchief, Politieke Charters, no. 940

September 22, 1419, Bruges. - In French. Letters of Duke Philip the Good, Count of Flanders, dated the day of his Joyous Entry at Bruges, by which he gives notice of the solemn oath that he has just made in this city, in these terms: *C'est assavoir que nous comme droiturier seigneur et conte de Flandres et de ce que y appartient, à noz bonnes gens de nostredicte ville de Bruges, serons bon et loyal seigneur, et leurs privilèges, franchises, lois, bonnes coustumes et usages, aussi bien vielz comme nouveaulx bien et loyaulment tenrons et ferons tenir, et tout faire que un bon loyal seigneur et conte de Flandres doit faire à ses bonnes gens et subges. Ainsi nous ait Dieux et tous ses sains.*

Philip swears that he will and should respect the recent and the traditional privileges, freedoms, laws and customs of his subjects. Moreover, he renews and confirms all the privileges, customs and liberties of the city of Bruges.

Original on parchment, h. 9 $^3/_{16}$ in. (233 mm.), fold 3 $^1/_{16}$ in. (78 mm.), l. 16 $^1/_{16}$ in. (408 mm.), with the small heraldic seal of Duke Philip, in green wax, suspended by lacings of green and red silk. Inscription: S[IGILLUM] PHILIPPI PRIMOGENITI DUCIS BURGUNDIE COMITIS KARIALENSIS.

Bibliography: GILLIODTS-VAN SEVEREN, IV, 1876, p. 352.

361

179. ORDINANCE BEARING THE SEAL OF DUKE PHILIP THE GOOD, 1434

Bruges, Stadsarchief, Politieke Charters, no. 987

June 20, 1434, Ghent. - In French. This ordinance of Philip the Good, Duke of Burgundy and Count of Flanders, fills a lacuna of the last ordinance about money and concerns the punishments of persons who would not observe currency regulations.

Original on parchment, h. $7^3/_4$ in. (197 mm.), l. $1^5/_{16}$ in. (33 mm.), with the great equestrian seal of Duke Philip, counter-sealed, in red wax, suspended on a strip of parchment. Inscription (slightly damaged): S[IGILLUM] PH[ILIPPI] DEI GRA[TIA BURGUNDIE LOTHARINGIE BRABAN]TIE ET LIMBUR-GIE DUCIS FLANDRIE ARTHESIE BURGUNDIE PALATINI HANNONIE/ HOLLAN-DIE ZELLANDIE ET NAMURCI [COMITIS] SACRI IMPERII MARCHIONIS ET D[OMI]NI FRISIE DE SALINIS ET MECHLINIA.

Bibliography : GILLIODTS-VAN SEVEREN, V, 1876, p. 18.

180. PRIVILEGE BEARING THE SEAL OF DUKE PHILIP THE GOOD, 1452

Bruges, Stadsarchief, Politieke Charters, no. 1060

March 28, 1452, Brussels. - In French. Letters of Duke Philip the Good, Count of Flanders, by which he authorizes the extension of the fair at Bruges.

In view of the considerations presented by the city of Bruges, the Duke decides: *que doresenavant la franchise dudit tonlieu commancera quinze jours après lesdis Pasques charnelz, qui sera le Dimenche que on chante Jubilate en nostre Mère Sainte Eglise, et durera quinze jours après continuelment ensuivans, dont les neuf jours, assavoir le Jeudi, Vendredi et Samedi de la première sepmainne et les six jours de la seconde, seront jours de monstre tous francs de tonlieu; et après lesdis XV jours francs de tonlieu seront autres XV jours non francs de tonlieu, sauf que les marchans pourront sauvement retourner ainsi qu'il est de coustume... .*

Philip grants exemption from the *tonlieu,* or tax affecting merchants, for certain of the fifteen days following the second Sunday after Easter. After this period there will be another fifteen days during which merchants will be taxed, though they may depart without being taxed.

Original on parchment, h. $13^1/_4$ in. (336 mm.), fold $4^1/_8$ in. (105 mm.), l. $20^1/_{16}$ in. (510 mm.), bearing the small heraldic seal of Duke Philip, in green wax, suspended by lacings of green and crimson silk. Inscription: S[IGILLUM] PHILIPPI DEI GRA[TIA] BURGONDIE LOTHA[RINGIE] BRABAN[CIE] ET LIM-BUR[GIE] DUCIS CO[MES] FLA[N]D[RIE] ART[ESIE] BUR[GUNDIE] ET NA[MURCI] ETC.

Bibliography : GILLIODTS-VAN SEVEREN, V, 1876, pp. 358-359.

362

181. PRIVILEGE BEARING THE SEAL OF DUKE CHARLES THE BOLD, 1468

Bruges, Stadsarchief, Politieke Charters, no. 1101

April 9, 1468, Bruges. - In French. Letters patent of Charles the Bold, Duke of Burgundy and Count of Flanders, on the occasion of his visit to Bruges. As a result of the death of his father, Duke Philip the Good, Charles the Bold succeeded to the County of Flanders.

Et meismement au jour de la date de ces présentes, comme prince et seigneur héritier d'iceulx pais et conté de Flandres en nostre ville de Bruges, en laquelle les bourgeois, manans et habitans et toute la communaulté d'icelle en nous démonstrant vraye et plénière obéyssance et faisant le serement envers nous tel comme bons et loyaulx subgez doivent faire à leur droicturier seigneur, nous aient trèsgrandement notablement et joyeusement receu à leur seigneur et prince.

Savoir faisons que à ce meismes jourduy, nous au lieu ou noz prédécesseurs contes de Flandres, auxquelz Dieu face vraye mercy, ont acoustumé de faire leur serement à leur première entrée et réception en icelle nostre ville de Bruges, avons promis et juré ce que s'ensuit. C'est assavoir: que nous comme droicturier seigneur et conte de Flandres et de ce que y appartient, à noz bonnes gens de nostredicte ville de Bruges serons bon et loyal seigneur, et leurs prévilèges, franchises, loix, bonnes coustumes et usaiges, aussi bien vielz comme nouveaulx, bien et loyaulment tenrons et ferons tenir. Et tout ce ferons que ung bon loyal seigneur et conte de Flandres doit faire à ses bonnes gens et subgez. Ainsi nous ait Dieux et tous ses Sains.

According to this text the Duke was joyously received by the people of Bruges who demonstrated their obeisance as subjects loyal to their natural prince. At the same time Charles, like his ancestors, promised to respect and have respected the old and the new privileges, freedoms, etc., of the people of Bruges, and to do all that a good lord should do for his subjects. In this might he have the blessing of God and the Saints.

Furthermore, to the humble supplication of the people of Bruges, considering their complete and perfect obeisance, and hoping moreover that they would comport themselves as loyal subjects of their prince, he confirms by these letters all their privileges, freedoms, laws and customs.

Original on parchment, h. 9 $^7/_8$ in. (237 mm.), fold 4 $^1/_8$ in. (105 mm.), l. 18 $^{13}/_{16}$ in. (475 mm.), bearing the great equestrian seal of Duke Charles, counter-sealed, in green wax, on lacings of green and red silk. Inscription: S[IGILLUM] KAROLI DEI GRATIA BURGUNDIE LOTHARINGIE BRABANCIE LIMBURGIE ET LUXEMBURGIE DUCIS FLANDRIE ARTHESII BURGUNDIE PALATINI HANNONIE / HOLLANDIE ZEELANDIE ET NAMURCI COMITIS SACRI IMPERII MARCHIONIS D[OMI]NI FRISIE DE SALINIS ET DE MECHLINIA.

Bibliography: Gilliodts-Van Severen, V, 1876, p. 471.

182. PRIVILEGE BEARING THE SEAL OF MARY, DUCHESS OF BURGUNDY, 1477

Bruges, Stadsarchief, Politieke Charters, no. 1154

April 17, 1477, Bruges. - In Flemish. Mary, Duchess of Burgundy, Countess of Flanders, proclaims that she has accorded grace and pardon to the insurgent Bruges citizens. ...*hebben vergheven, quite ghescolden ende gheaboliert, ende by onser specialer ende zonderlinghe gracie, macht ende moghenthede vergheven, quitteschelden ende abolieren by dese onse lettren alle mesdaden, offenciën, mesgrypen ande abusen, die zy ende elck zonderlinghe jeghen ons, onse hoocheide ende heerlichede ter cause van tghuent dat voorseit es ende diesser ancleven mach hebben ghedaen, gheperpetreert ende gheorboirt....* (By special dispensation, the Duchess of Burgundy forgives, acquits, and abolishes all misdeeds, offenses, errors and abuses).

Original on parchment, h. 14 in. (355 mm.), fold 4 $^1/_{16}$ in. (103 mm.), l. 18 $^5/_8$ in. (474 mm.), bearing the great equestrian seal of Mary of Burgundy, counter-sealed, in green wax, suspended by lacings of green and red silk. Inscription: S[IGILLUM] MARIE DEI GRA[TIA] BURGUNDIE LOTHARINGIE BRABANTIE LIMBURGIE LUCEMBURGIE ET GHELDRE DUCISSE FLANDRIE ARTHESIE BURGUNDIE PALATINE HANONIE / HOLLANDIE ZELLANDIE NAMURCI ET ZUTPHANIE COMITISSE SACRI IMPERII MARCHION[ISSE] DOMINE FRISIE SALINARUM AC MACHLINIE 1476.

Bibliography: GILLIODTS-VAN SEVEREN, VI, 1876, p. 145.

364

183. PRIVILEGE BEARING THE SEAL OF MAXIMILIAN, ARCHDUKE OF AUSTRIA, 1487

Bruges, Stadsarchief, Politieke Charters, no. 1225

August 21, 1487, Brussels. - In German. Letters of Maximilian, King of the Romans, Archduke of Austria, in his capacity as regent and guardian of his son, Archduke Philip the Handsome, Duke of Burgundy and Count of Flanders, approving traffic in merchandise between Germany and Flanders, the right of staple (a town was appointed by royal authority to have exclusive rights of trade in a certain commodity) of the city of Bruges and the privileges of the Hanseatic merchants (a guild of merchants representing a number of towns in Northern Germany and adjacent countries, for the promotion and protection of commerce) who reside there.

Original on parchment, h. 17⁵/₈ in. (448 mm.), fold 5 in. (127 mm.), l. 25 ¹/₈ in. (639 mm.), bearing the great royal seal of Maximilian, counter-sealed, in red wax, suspended by a doubled strip of parchment. Inscription: S[IGILLUM] MAXIMILIANI ET PHILIPPI DEI GRACIA AUSTRIE ARCHIDUCU[M] BURGU[N]DIE LOTHARI[N]GIE BRABANCIE STIRIE KARI[N]TIE KARNIOLE LI[M]BURG[IE] LUCE[M]B[UR]G[IE] GELDR[IE] DUCU[M] FLA[N]DRIE / TIROL[IS] ARTHESII BURG[UNDIE] PALANTIN[E] HANO[N]IE HOLA[N]DIE ZELA[N]D[IE] NAMURCI ZUTPHA[N]IE COMITU[M] SACRI I[M]PERII MARCHIONU[M] FRISIE SALI[N]A-RU[M] ET MACH[LINI]E D[OMI]NOR[UM].

Bibliography: GILLIODTS-VAN SEVEREN, VI, 1876, pp. 282-295.

365

184. PRIVILEGE BEARING THE SEAL OF PHILIP THE HANDSOME, ARCHDUKE OF AUSTRIA, 1498

Bruges, Stadsarchief, Politieke Charters, no. 1277

December 3, 1498, Brussels. - In French. *Lettres de provision* of the Archduke Philip of Austria, Duke of Burgundy and Count of Flanders, to attract foreign merchants, to renew industry and commerce in the city of Bruges, and to regulate the fairs of Antwerp and of Bergen-op-Zoom.

Original on parchment, h. 14 $^{13}/_{16}$ in. (377 mm.), fold 4 $^{1}/_{2}$ in. (115 mm.), l. 21 $^{7}/_{8}$ in. (556 mm.), bearing the great equestrian seal of the Archduke Philip, counter-sealed in red wax, suspended by a doubled strip of parchment. Inscription: S[IGILLUM] PHI[LIPPI] DEI GRA[TIA] ARCHIDUCIS AUSTRIE DUCIS BURGU[N]-DIE LOTH[ARINGIE] BRA[BANCIE] STIRIE CARINTIE CAR[N]IOLE LIMB[URGIE] LUXE[M]B[URGIE] ET GELD[RIE] COMITIS HABSB[UR]GENSIS FLA[N]D[RIE] TIROLIS / ARTESI[E] BURG[UNDIE] PALATINI HANO[N]IE ALSACIE B[UR]GO-[V]IE HOLL[ANDIE] ZELL[ANDIE] FERETIS KIB[UR]GI NAM[UR]CI ET ZUT-PH[ANIE] D[OMI]NI FRIZIE PORTUSNAONIS SALIN[ARUM] ET MECHL[IN]IE.

Bibliography: GILLIODTS-VAN SEVEREN, VI, 1876, pp. 433-436.

185. INSURANCE POLICY, 1445

Bruges, Stadsarchief, Politieke Charters, no. 1035

January 11, 1445, Seville. - Flemish translation from Latin. Insurance policy underwritten by two merchants who obligate themselves to pay within six months one hundred and two hundred doubloons, respectively, that they have agreed to pay for insurance of merchandise that Jan Wendel has loaded in the ship of Ramond Vigher. It is understood that this obligation will cease to be effective twenty-four hours after the ship and its cargo have arrived at Sluis, the outport of Bruges.

Document on paper, h. 6 $^{5}/_{8}$ in. (169 mm.), l. 8 $^{11}/_{16}$ in. (220 mm.), signed at the bottom by the notary: *de Hoofsche*.

Bibliography: GILLIODTS-VAN SEVEREN, V, 1876, p. 276.

366

186. BUSINESS ACCOUNT BOOK IN TOOLED LEATHER BINDING, ca. 1503

Bruges, Stadsarchief

Commercial record in Flemish. Begun in 1503, as indicated by an annotation in the first folio: "REGYSTERE BEGHINNENDE DEN EERSTEN DACH VAN JULLET XVᶜ III". The register is bound in brown leather. The front cover is embossed with a panel imitating damask in very high relief. The ornamentation is completed by a frame stamped with lilies and roses. TENES BON COMPTE is inscribed within a frame on the closing flap in large minuscules between two rows of trefoiled arches. The frame itself is surrounded with embossed lilies and roses; h. 16 ¹/₂ in. (42 cm.), l. 11 ⁷/₁₆ in. (29 cm.).

Exhibitions: Bruges, 1927, no. 50.

187. VISIT OF THE MUNICIPAL ADMINISTRATION OF BRUGES TO THE WORK-SHOP OF JAN VAN EYCK, 1432

Bruges, Stadsarchief, Stadsrekening, 1431-1432

On July 17, 1432, the municipal administration of Bruges paid a visit to the workshop of Jan van Eyck. This event is recorded on folio 78 of the accounts of the city, between September 2, 1431 and September 2, 1432. On this occasion the magistrate gave a bonus of three *livres parisis* to the pupils of the celebrated painter.

This entry is positive proof that Jan van Eyck had several assistants in his employ. The fact that the municipal authorities went to van Eyck's home as a group, magnificently illustrates the esteem in which they held the master and his work.

In itself, this record book is a good example of communal accounting during the first half of the fifteenth century; it is at the same time, a rich source of diverse information from the point of view of local history.

Bibliography: GILLIODTS-VAN SEVEREN, V, 1878, p. 15.

Historical Documents

Bruges, Stadsarchief, Poorterboek, 1454-1478, folio 72 v°

Until the end of the Old Regime, the population of Bruges was divided into two distinct categories: the *poorters*, or bourgeois, and the ordinary citizens. The bourgeois profited from a great many prerogatives, of which others were deprived. The bourgeois alone participated in the government of the city; they alone were eligible for administrative positions; and it was necessary to be a bourgeois to become a member of the guilds or métiers. Bourgeois status was obtained by birth or by purchase. Foreigners could acquire the status of bourgeois by marrying a bourgeois, or through payment of a certain sum and the perform-ance of certain formalities. Occasionally, the municipal authorities gratuitously granted the status of bourgeois, or they lowered the cost of it. Persons who rendered singular service to the city, or proposed to establish new industries there, were so honored. Abolition or reduction of the initiation fee was sometimes granted when high dignitaries intervened. The names of persons who acquired the status of bourgeois of the city of Bruges, whether by purchase or by grant, were recorded in the registers kept for this purpose called the *Poorterboeken*.

The registration of Hans Memlinc as a new bourgeois of Bruges is recorded at the bottom of folio 72 verso, of the *Poorterboek* of the years 1454-1478. In this text: *Jan van Mimnelinghe, Harmans zuene, ghebooren Zaleghenstadt, poortere XXX in Laumaent (1465) omneXXIIII s. gr.* In translation: "Jan Memlinc, son of Herman, born at Seligenstadt, became a bourgeois of the city of Bruges, January 30, 1465 and he has paid on this occasion the sum of 24 *escalins de gros*. This important text was discovered only in 1938. Since then the hypo-theses that Memlinc might have been born at Bruges, at Damme, at Mömlingen near Aschaffenburg in Germany, at Medenblik near Alkmaar in Holland, or in the city of Mainz have been abandoned. This text also reveals the name of his father, the approximate date of his settling at Bruges and the manner by which he there obtained the status of bourgeois.

Bibliography: PARMENTIER, II, 1938, pp. 630-631.

368

Historical Documents

189. DECLARATION OF THE MATERNAL INHERITANCE OF THE CHILDREN OF
HANS MEMLINC, 1487

*Bruges, Stadsarchief, Register van de Brugse Weeskamer,
St-Nikolaaszestendeel, 1467-1490,* fol. 199 v°-200

Upon the death of the father, or of the mother, leaving minors, the custom
of Bruges prescribed that an inventory of the parents' wealth be compiled, in
order to determine the share to be inherited by the children. Thereafter the
municipality was responsible for supervising the good management of the inheritance until the children attained their majority.

The declaration of the inheritance of minors was made by the Court of Wards
where it was recorded in registers for that purpose. Special registers existed for
each of the six quarters of the city. Since Hans Memlinc lived in the sector of
Saint-Nicolas, the estate of his wife is found recorded in the register for that
quarter.

Hans Memlinc was married to Anne de Valkenare, who died shortly before
September 11, 1486. Three children were born of this marriage: Jan, Cornelis
and Nikolaas. Their guardians, Louis de Valkenare and Didier van den Gheere,
made a declaration of the maternal inheritance of their wards, September 10,
1487, one year after the death of Anne de Valkenare. The acts of the Court of
Wards always provide many important biographical data. Thanks to these
documents, we have information about the family and social status of the famous
painter.

Bibliography: WEALE, 1901, pp. 51-53.

190. REGISTER OF THE CORPORATION OF BREWERS OF GHENT, 15th Century

Ghent, Stadsarchief, series 160/6

The most precious possession of the archives of the ancient Corporation of
Brewers of Ghent is the register containing the by-laws of the corporation and
the names of its members from 1313 to 1787. Begun in 1453, it was kept up to
date until the end of the Old Regime; its present binding dates from 1653.

A Flemish calendar occupies the first six folios. At the beginning of the text
itself, on folio 7 verso, and folio 8, are two illuminated pages which undoubtedly
date from the year in which the register was begun, 1453. These pages are
concerned with a single subject: the invocation of Saint Arnold by the brewers of
Ghent.

The first illustration is of Saint Arnold of Soissons, a native of Tiegem in
Flanders, whom the brewers have chosen as their patron saint. The artist depicts
the Saint in episcopal vestments, a white alb, a red dalmatic and a blue chasuble,
with crozier and mitre, seated on a curule chair and reading from a book lying on
a portable lectern which stands before him, bearing the coat of arms of the brewers

369

of Ghent on its elbow joint: party, the dexter half gules, the sinister half fessey gold and synobill, a silver oar (used in stirring mash) overlies the whole. This coat of arms also decorates the blue edge of Saint Arnold's alb. The artist has placed Saint Arnold inside a low crenellated wall, revealing the countryside beyond. The hanging on the wall is goffered gold and the floor is paved with a black and green labyrinthine pattern. A little dog crouches in a corner. At the highest point of the sky, in a glory of cherubim, is the Virgin crowned by the Holy Trinity.

The picture is framed by a foliated border, which is enlivened on the lower part, by two censing angels: on the side of the inner margin, by a bird and three small figures; on the side of the outer margin, by a peacock which is spreading its tail and holding the coat of arms of the brewers. This armorial is repeated in the middle of the lower and outer borders. The outer border also includes three times two oars crossed like a saltire, and joined by a pennon intertwined with a sprig of hop. The motto of the corporation decorates the pennon: *et moet wel* ("it must be done"). The miniature lacks subtlety, the best part of it is the head of Saint Arnold, strikingly realistic and lifelike.

The second miniature represents at the bottom the Confraternity of the Brewers of Ghent, kneeling and imploring the Saint who appears on the opposite page. From the hands of the first figure slips a phylactery bearing the following Flemish verse: *O vader Sente Arnaud helich sant/ Gheeft ons allen bruwers die hant/ Dat wy so leven in desen dale/ Dat wij onganghen den helschen wale/ Ende met hu moghen commen daer boven/ Daer dinghelen eenpaerlic Gode loven.* ("Oh Saint Arnold, holy saint/ aid all of us brewers/ so that we can live in this world/ and that we can escape Hell/ and that with your aid we can go to Heaven/ where the Angels praise God in one voice").

The first figure is dressed in black clothing, with a three-pointed green hat; since he is tonsured, it is presumed he is the chaplain of the corporation. The chaplain is seated to the right of the dean who is identifiable by the wide band of red cloth with a border of silver braid which hangs from his shoulder to the bottom of his robe. The dean is followed by other dignitaries of the corporation, who like him, wear three-pointed green hats and blue mantles, to the back of which is attached the coat of arms of the confraternity, surrounded by a silver braid. In the foreground, but slightly behind and to the side, is the messenger of the corporation with an ornament on the left sleeve of his blue jerkin.

On the upper part of the miniature appears a double shield of Flanders, with crest and mantlings, the shield of Ghent, and that of the brewers of Ghent, held by little monsters with human torsos and the lower parts of an animal. Each of these borders is foliated; on the dexter side appears a peacock, a person holding an oar, an owl and a bird, while on the sinister side the escutcheon of the brewers appears twice and their emblem three times: two oars crossed like a saltire, connected by a banderole and a sprig of hop, with the motto: *et moet wel*. The name of the painter of this two-page miniature is unknown, but its origin in Ghent is incontestable.

Exhibitions: Ghent, 1956, no. 32.
Bibliography: CASIER and BERGMANS, II, 1921, pp. 47-50.

370

191. REGISTER OF THE CORPORATION OF TANNERS OF GHENT, 1478

Ghent, Stadsarchief, series 192/1

The register of the Corporation of Tanners of Ghent, containing the statutes of the profession and the list of its members, was begun in 1478 and was kept up to date until 1697. The first page shown here is a remarkable example of illumination as it was done in Ghent, very valuable since its date most probably corresponds exactly to the year in which the manuscript was begun. It is, furthermore, an interesting document on corporate organization.

The foreground of the miniature shows the dean (*deken*) and the four members of the board of directors of the corporation, dressed in ceremonial attire, adorned with insignia of their office: the large piece of cloth hanging from the shoulder of the dean; the coat of arms of the corporation attached to the hem of the members' robes. Behind them is the messenger, recognizable by the insignia on his chest. The six kneeling figures are praying before Saint Giles. He is wearing a hermit's cap and is seated before his house; he reads from a book opened upon his knees, and strokes the hoof of an animal, a doe at which a hunter aimed an arrow which, according to the legend, spared the animal but wounded the Saint. In the background, in a hilly landscape, the scene of the hunt is depicted: the archer who is turning away after shooting the arrow, and the royal entourage: episodes from the life of Saint Giles.

The page is framed with a scroll of flowers and foliage; on the outer margin, the coat of arms of Ghent: sable a lion silver; in the lower margin that of the Corporation of Tanners: sable a lion silver accompanied by a hatchet and a tanner's scraping knife with two gold handles; in chief, party: in the first gold a lion sable, in the second, sable a lion silver, the two lions facing each other. The ends of this inner margin are decorated with pictures of tanners at work: on the dexter side, a seated man with a hatchet removes the bark of an oak sapling which rests on a block; on the sinister side another man, standing, scrapes the skin of an animal.

Exhibitions: Ghent, 1956, no. 42.
Bibliography: CASIER and BERGMANS, II, 1921, pp. 56-57.

192. CARTULARY OF THE "PIJNDERS" OR PORTERS OF GHENT
14th-16th Centuries

Ghent, Stadsarchief, series 186/1

This register of the Corporation of "Pijnders" or Porters, contains a document curious for more than one reason. The document concerns the schedule of rates for the transport of grain to the different breweries of the city. It is found recorded following an annotation of 1494; it thus dates from the end of the 15th century.

Besides the name of each establishment and the indication of the street, sketches representing the shop signs of the breweries are found interspersed throughout the text. These sketches give information about the appearance of several different forms of barges and flat boats called *cogghe,* some curious designs of Flemish lanterns, some round mirrors, a valise, a baking dish, a litter, a pewter jug, and various angels. One shop sign in the form of a little barrel known as a *laghelkin,* another is that of a *paenderkin* or little basket. The *keerscorf* was a basket for candles. *Schomminkel* meant a little monkey. Several objects resemble those which we have today such as hats, grills, rakes, skimmers, bellows, augers, and others.

The purpose of reproducing the shop signs in this book was probably to facilitate the work of the illiterate "Pijnders".

At the top of the record a "Pijnder" is depicted with a sack upon his head and holding in his left hand the escutcheon of the métier. Inscription: *Loen verzoet den arbeit* ("Wages sweeten work") was the device of the profession.

Bibliography: VAN DER HAEGHEN, 1886, pp. 125-133.

193. CARTULARY OF THE WENEMAER HOSPICE IN GHENT, 15th-16th Centuries

Ghent, Stadsarchief

The Wenemaer Hospice was founded in Ghent in the 14th century by Guillaume Wenemaer and his wife Marguerite Brunen. After the death of Wenemaer, who was killed at the head of his troops near Deinze in 1325, his widow assumed the management of the hospice; later she bequeathed her fortune to it. Reconstructed in the 16th century, the hospice was ceded in 1866 by the Commission of Hospices to the City of Ghent. The cartulary of the Wenemaer Hospice contains the founding act and other documents, as well as the genealogical tables of the ancestors of its founders. The cartulary contains, moreover, two large full-page portraits of the founders.

On the left page is shown Guillaume Wenemaer, *Willelmus Wenemaer fundator.* Inside an oratory, the vaults of which are supported by columns of green marble with blue bases and capitals, Guillaume Wenemaer is kneeling, his hands joined, before the altar on which is a candlestick, an open book, a small chalice, etc. The inscription at the top of the rose-colored antependium reads: O BEATE GUILLAM. He is dressed in a black cloak lined with yellow, open in such a way that the cuirass which he wears is revealed. His hair is long, and his large pointed nose is full of character. Before him, upon the floor, his coats of arms, synobill nine billets silver; it is also seen affixed to the wall of the chapel,

372

Historical Documents

at the top of the miniature. A pennon, the end of which extends beyond the picture, bears a verse: *De genealogie ghestruuct hier vooren staende/ Es de afcompste mer Willems zijde angaende* (The genealogy written here above is the line of descent on the side of Messire Willem).

Saint Guillaume de Mallavalle, known as William of Aquitaine, Wenemaer's patron saint, stands behind him. He wears the black habit of the Order of the Guillelmites, of which he was the founder; under his ample costume may be seen the helmet, gauntlets and sollerets which recall his high birth and his rank of feudal lord of the Kingdom of France. In his left hand he carries an open book; in his right hand he holds a staff with an azure and gules pennon, on which a quartered shield can be seen: in the first and fourth, azure three fleur-de-lis gold, in the second and third, gules a carbuncle gold; this pennon is characteristic of Saint Guillaume, of whom legend has made a Duke of Aquitaine.

At the right, is Marguerite Brunen, *Margareta sBrunen uxor Willelmi fundatrix*. She is also shown kneeling, her hands clasped in prayer, in the oratory. Especially prominent are geminate windows in which two figures appear, a man and a woman, and a great bay window where a kneeling woman (a nun?) can be seen. She is dressed in a long mauve robe with a white collar, sleeves bordered in green and is wearing a widow's bonnet; on the floor before her, a shield with her coat of arms: sable with a woman's bust in natural colors. A phylactery, like the one which Wenemaer has, extends into the margin of the miniature, and bears an inscription continuing the one in the preceding miniature: *De genealogie volghende van hier achterwaert/ tGheslachte van siner vrauwe zijde verclaert* (The following genealogy describes the family of his wife).

Behind Marguerite Brunen is her patron, Saint Marguerite of Antioche, rising from the spine of the dragon who has devoured her. In the mouth of the dragon is still to be seen the hem of her blue cloak. Under this cloak, she wears a loose yellow robe, drawn together at the waist by a girdle. Her long blond hair falls upon her shoulders; in her right hand she holds an open book; in her left, a cross. On the wall of the oratory is a small placard containing a text written in two columns; an analogous placard is hung on a pillar of the oratory in the other miniature where Wenemaer appears.

The two miniatures are framed with two gilded fillets separated by a fillet of alternating red and blue ornaments. Without being of high quality, these miniatures evoke, nevertheless, a certain interest by their realistic execution and their obvious Ghent origin. They were probably executed at the beginning of the 16th century.

Exhibitions: Ghent, 1956, no. 65.
Bibliography: CASIER and BERGMANS, II, 1921, pp. 94-95.

194. CHARTER BEARING THE SEALS OF SIX CARDINALS, 1464

Ghent, Stadsarchief, Sint-Jorisgild, no. 1

August 14, 1464, Ancona. - In Latin. Letters by which Cardinals Bessarion, Guillermus, Alanus, Ricardus, Gerardus, and Ludovicus proclaimed, at the request of Petrus Zoeturs, that they granted indulgences to persons who would come to pray or to give alms for the benefit of the chaplaincy of the altar of Saint George, founded in the Church of Saint-Nicolas in Ghent.

Original on parchment, h. 9 $^7/_8$ in. (250 mm.), fold 2 $^{15}/_{16}$ in. (75 mm.), l. 19 $^{11}/_{16}$ in. (500 mm.), bearing the seals of six cardinals suspended on cords of hemp. Of these six seals only one is intact, three are damaged and two are lost. The text of the charter is surrounded by illuminations.

195. CHARTER BEARING THE SEAL OF MARY, DUCHESS OF BURGUNDY, 1477

Ghent, Stadsarchief, Charters, no. 706

February 11, 1477, Ghent. - In Flemish. Letters by which the Duchess Mary of Burgundy, Countess of Flanders, granted various privileges to the *Vier Leden* (Four Members) of Flanders.

Original on parchment, h. 19 $^1/_4$ in. (490 mm.), fold 3 $^7/_{16}$ in. (88 mm.), l. 27 $^9/_{16}$ in. (700 mm.), bearing the great equestrian seal of the Duchess Mary, in green wax, counter-sealed, on lacings of green and red silk. Inscription: S[IGILLUM] MARIE DEI GRA[TIA] BURGUNDIE LOTHARINGIE BRABA[N]CIE LIMBURGIE LUCEMBURGIE ET GHELDRE DUCISSE FLANDRIE ARTHESIE BURGUNDIE PALATINE HANONIE / HOLLANDIE ZELLANDIE NAMURCI ET ZUTPHANIE COMITISSE SACRI IMPERII MARCHIO[N]II DOMINE FRISIE SALI-NARUM AC MACHLINIE 1476.

Bibliography: Van Duyse and De Busscher, 1867, pp. 244-245.

ILLUMINATED MANUSCRIPTS

PARIS, ATELIER OF THE BOUCICAUT MASTER, ca. 1415

196. BOOK OF HOURS FOR THE USE OF PARIS

Baltimore, Md., The Walters Art Gallery. Ms. W. 260

This manuscript is a characteristic product of the Paris atelier presided over by the anonymous personality whom PANOFSKY has termed "the most brilliant genius of pre-Eyckian painting." Doubtless a man of Franco-Flemish background, his significance was first realized by DURRIEU. Efforts, so far unsuccessful, have been made to identify him with Jacques Coene, a painter from Bruges who is recorded to have had a great reputation in Paris in the early years of the 15th century. Lacking evidence as to his real name, the artist is generally known by his most monumental work, a large and elaborately illuminated Book of Hours executed for Jean II le Meingre de Boucicaut, Marshal of France (Jacquemart-André Museum, Paris), dating sometime between the last years of the 14th century and 1415 when the Marshal was taken prisoner at Agincourt. Not only works that may be considered from his own hand but the prolific productions of his extensive atelier reveal his innovations in the rendering of space, of interior and exterior lighting, of aerial perspective, of landscape and genre details. He seems to have introduced into the repertoire of marginal decoration the Italian acanthus, which experienced a vogue in French and later in Dutch, German and Flemish book illumination. These features, as well as his compositional and iconographic inventions, were perpetuated through model-sketches not only in his own atelier, but spread abroad to have a lasting impact upon French, Flemish and Dutch illumination throughout the 15th century. In any event, his innovations seem to have played an important part in paving the way for the great Flemish panel painters culminating in Jan van Eyck.

This Book of Hours seems not to be by the Boucicaut Master's own hand, but it is an exceptionally delicate product of his atelier, using the motives and compositions which he devised. It is less insistent upon effects of illumination than would be the Master himself, and the delicate modelling does not show the surface brushwork by which he was accustomed to develop the plasticity of his forms. PANOFSKY has suggested that the manuscript may not have received the final customary "going-over" in these respects.

Every page of the book has an illuminated border of vines and flowers, peopled by drolleries and figures of music-making angels, executed in a flat, linear sketchy style, quite different from that of the chief illuminations. Numerous small miniatures at the front and back part of the volume are executed in the

375

376

same style as the drolleries. Among the miniatures, which show the characteristic work of the atelier, is *The Death of the Virgin* (illustrated here).

Physical description: Written in Latin, with some rubrics in French, on vellum; 298 leaves, 7 ⁵/₈ x 5 ⁵/₈ in. (19.4 x 14.3 cm.); 13 large and 28 small miniatures; illuminated borders throughout. Bound in old velvet.

History and Bibliography: De Ricci, I, 1935, p. 786, no. 185; Cat. Baltimore Exhib., 1949, no. 86; Panofsky, 1951, p. 83, fig. 16; Panofsky, 1953, notes 59(2), 125(2), 173(1), 278(1), fig. 73 on pl. 33; Cat. Los Angeles Exhib., 1953-54, no. 53.

SCHOOL OF GHENT, ca. 1420-25

197. BOOK OF HOURS

Baltimore, Md., The Walters Art Gallery. Ms. W. 166

This Book of Hours, as indicated by its armorials, was executed for Elizabeth van Munte and her husband Daniel Rym, members of two prominent Ghent families. The characteristics of its style, the figures delicately drawn and expressive of gesture, though vacuous in facial expression, a clear and luminous coloring, a willingness to violate the frames of the pictures, abundance of delightful and original drolleries, a combination of various ornamental repertories in the borders: dragon-headed grotesques, spikey ivy leaves, as well as a thinner, more sketchy gold ivy vine, heavy, winding acanthus, and a surprising use of overly large and realistically studied flowers - all these elements characterize several other manuscripts which must be grouped with this, notably the *Hours of John the Fearless* of Burgundy (ms. nouv. acq. lat. 3055 in the Bibliothèque Nationale, Paris). Other manuscripts related closely in figure-style, although not always showing the same border features, are another Horae in The Walters Art Gallery (W. 170) and two manuscripts in The Pierpont Morgan Library (M. 48 and M. 439). Although two of these have many English saints in their calendars, they all give every evidence of having been done in Flanders, W. 170 having not only prayers in Flemish but 16th century entries of Ghent ownership, and an early 16th century calf binding signed by Joris de Gavere in Ghent. Much other circumstantial evidence points to Ghent as the place of origin of this group, and is accepted by Panofsky (1953, pp. 119-121) and Leroquais (1939, pp. 53-54). Delaissé, however, considers that one of the artists of the *Hours of John the Fearless* was the anonymous Master of Gilbert de Metz, who was later to head a prolific atelier. The developed style of this artist and his assistants is considerably hardier and less piquant than in this earlier group of manuscripts, but there unquestionably must be a connection of some sort. Delaissé points out that the Master of Gilbert de Metz seems to have worked in several places before eventually settling in Lille. However, the fact that several of his earlier acknowledged productions

377

also have Ghent connections seems to strenghten the likelihood that the atelier represented by W. 166 was in fact centered in that city.

The illustrations include one of *Daniel in the Lion's Den,* with Habbakuk brought by an angel, and Daniel Rym in prayer (illustrated here). Through the pages are abundant and amusing drolleries, some based upon proverbs, and one showing Elizabeth van Munte kneeling before St. Elizabeth of Hungary. These are by the same hand as the miniatures.

378

Physical description: Written in Latin and Flemish on vellum; 186 leaves, 6 ¹/₄ x4 ⁵/₈ in. (15.8 x 14.7 cm.); 13 full-page miniatures; 1 historiated initial; many marginal drolleries. Bound in modern rose calf over boards, inlaid with panels from 14th century French or Lower-Rhenish binding, having nothing to do with this manuscript.

History and Bibliography: Executed for Elizabeth van Munte and Daniel Rym of Ghent. DE RICCI, I, 1935, p. 787, no. 190; LEROQUAIS, 1939, pp. 53-54 (erroneously confused with W. 170); BYVANCK, 1940, p. 32, figs. 1-2 (also confused with W.170); Cat. Baltimore Exhib., 1949, no. 125; DE TOLNAY, 1949, pp. 49-54; Cat. Los Angeles Exhib., 1953-54, no. 74; PANOFSKY, 1953, pp. 119-121, notes 114(6), 118(8), 119(2, 6, 8), 120(5), 121(1, 2, 6), figs. 186-189; DIRINGER, 1958, p. 440, pl. VII - 29; *Allen Memorial Art Museum Bulletin,* 1960, p. 108, no. 26, fig. 9.

BRUGES, PUBLISHING OFFICE OF DAVID AUBERT, STYLES OF VRELANT, LIEDET, MAZEROLLES, AND OTHERS, ca. 1450-60

198. JACOBUS DE VORAGINE, LA LÉGENDE DORÉE, Vol. I

New York, N.Y., The Pierpont Morgan Library. Ms. M. 672

The writing of this work is in the style of David Aubert, noted author, scribe and publisher, who produced many manuscript books for the best miniaturists and illuminators of Flanders. Written probably while Aubert was in Bruges (a native of Hesdin, he worked also in Oudenaarde and Brussels), the book was richly decorated with a vast number of miniatures which have been attributed on the basis of style to such celebrated artists as Loyset Liédet (one miniature, vol. I, fol. 88, is in fact signed *Loysit,* a very rare occurence), the Master of Wavrin, Philippe de Mazerolles, and Guillaume Vrelant.

The miniature on the first page of this volume representing the translator of Jacobus de Voragine's Latin text into French, Jean de Vignay (fl. 1326-1341), an accurate portrayal of 15th century costumes and furnishings, is the work of Loyset Liédet (illustrated here).

Loyset Liédet was living in Hesdin in 1460, was first known to be active in Bruges in 1468, and apparently died in Bruges in 1478. The Master of Wavrin, active in the third quarter of the 15th century, is chiefly noted for the lively pen-and-ink style with which he illustrated a number of secular works, written on paper, for Jean Bâtard de Wavrin (1394-1474), counsellor of Philip the Good. Philippe de Mazerolles was a most productive miniaturist. He was working in Paris 1454, then he worked in Flanders about 1465 for Charles the Bold before he became Duke of Burgundy; and in 1467, on being made court painter, he settled in Bruges, where he died in 1479. Guillaume Vrelant was born in Utrecht, and was active in Bruges from 1454 until his death there about 1481 (WINKLER, 1925; DELAISSÉ, 1959).

379

Physical description: Written in French on vellum; originally in two volumes of 268 and 293 leaves, now bound in four volumes; vol. I, 124 leaves, 15 x 10 ⁵/₈ in. (38 x 27 cm.). In the four volumes, 143 miniatures by several hands; also illuminated initials. Bound in modern dark-red morocco over boards.

History and Bibliography: Made for Jean d'Auxy (fl. 1422-1470), counsellor of Philip the Good, knight of the Order of the Golden Fleece (his arms are on first pages of vol. I and vol. III) ; Charles de Chabannes, seigneur de la Palisse (1540-1552) ; Henriette de la Guiche (1598-1682) or in 1651 given by Louis de Valois, duc d'Angoulême, to the monastery of the Minims of La Guiche, near Charolles (Saône-et-Loire), where it remained till the French Revolution; Moreau sale (Mâcon, 1835), purchased by the City of Mâcon, where original volume III is preserved in the Municipal Library, ms. no. 3; J. Barrois Coll., no. 69; sold in 1849 to the Earl of Ashburnham (*Catalogue of the Manuscripts at Ashburnham Place,* London, 1853, part II; Barrois, no. 69; Delisle, 1883, pp. VI-VIII; Lex, 1886, p. 132) ; his sale (London, 1901, no. 616) to Quaritch, London; Lebœuf de Montgermont Coll. (Cat. 1914, VII, no. 467) ; purchased by J. Pierpont Morgan about 1920. Leroquais, 1929, pp. 163-165; Cat. New York Exhib., 1933-34, no. 104 (M. 673, that is, vol. II only) ; Cat. Brooklyn Exhib., 1936, no. 80; De Ricci, II, 1937, p. 1480, nos. 672-675.

Illuminated Manuscripts

BRUGES, PUBLISHING OFFICE OF DAVID AUBERT, STYLES OF VRELANT, LIEDET, AND MAZEROLLES, ca. 1450-60

199. JACOBUS DE VORAGINE, LA LÉGENDE DORÉE, Vol. IV

New York, N.Y., The Pierpont Morgan Library. Ms. M. 675

In another volume of this work, as now bound, appear the styles of the same artists as found in volume I: Guillaume Vrelant, Loyset Liédet, and Philippe de Mazerolles.

To Philippe de Mazerolles is attributed *The Martyrdom of Saint Prothus and his Companions* (fol. 74 v°); to Guillaume Vrelant, the *Story of Saint Jerome and the Lion* (fol. 118; illustrated here).

Physical description: Written in French on vellum; originally in two volumes, now bound as four; vol. IV, 155 leaves, 15 x 10 ⅝ in. (38 x 27 cm.). In the four volumes, 143 miniatures; also illuminated initials.

History and Bibliography: same as for the last-mentioned manuscript, M. 672.

Illuminated Manuscripts

TOURNAI, WORKSHOP OF THE MASTER OF GUILLEBERT DE METZ, second quarter of the 15th Century

200. BOOK OF HOURS

New York, N.Y., The Pierpont Morgan Library. Ms. M. 357

The existence of a Calendar for Tournai preceding the main text of this Book of Hours has led to its being attributed to that city. In the decoration of the volume are recognized the hands of two artists, one of whom is called the Master of Guillebert de Metz, since he partially decorated and illustrated a manuscript copied by a scribe of that name. This miniaturist is best localized in Southern Flanders, although it has been suggested that he worked in Ghent and in Lille. His style parallels the work of the first generation of the Flemish Primitive painters in the 15th century (WINKLER, 1925, p. 29), though somewhat crude and far from realistic.

The miniatures in this book include one of *Christ in the Garden of Gethsemane* (fol. 152; illustrated here), with characteristic borders.

Physical description: Written in Latin on vellum; 335 leaves, 7 ³/₄ x 5 ¹/₂ in. (19.7 x 14 cm.); 1 large and 29 small miniatures; many illuminated initials and borders. Bound in contemporary stamped calf over boards by IA. POULLE (apparently not elsewhere recorded).

History and Bibliography: Owned by Hieronymus Van Winghe, canon of Tournai (d. 1637); E.H. Lawrence Coll., his sale, London, 1892, no. 287; sold to Quaritch, London; Lucien Delamarre; Sotheby sale (London, 6 May 1909, no. 12) to Quaritch, London; purchased by J. Pierpont Morgan, 1909. DE RICCI, II, 1937, p. 1433, no. 357.

FLANDERS (TOURNAI?), middle of the 15th Century

201. BOOK OF HOURS FOR ROME USE

New York, N.Y., The Pierpont Morgan Library Ms. M. 421

Possibly produced in Tournai and certainly for use in that city, as indicated by a Calendar for Tournai preceding the Hours of the Virgin.

383

The miniatures and illuminated initials and borders of this book present a great diversity of styles, recalling, on the one hand, the work of French artists (many of whom came from Flanders, and some of whom removed to Flanders with the Dukes of Burgundy) and, on the other hand, some of the Flemish book decorators who occasionally show an Italian influence. Yet most of these characteristics disappeared with the great blossoming of Flemish book illumination under Philip the Good (1419-1467) to the surprise of DELAISSÉ (1959, p. 166).

The most attractive of the miniatures is that of *Saint George Slaying the Dragon* (fol. 28 vº; illustrated here).

Physical description: Written in Latin on vellum; 76 leaves, 6¼ x 4½ in. (16 x 11.5 cm.); 2 full-page miniatures, 6 smaller miniatures, illuminated initials and borders. Bound in modern brown morocco.

History and Bibliography: Purchased through A. Imbert by J. Pierpont Morgan, 1910. DE RICCI, II, 1937, p. 1445, no. 421; [DELAISSÉ], Cat. Brussels - Amsterdam - Paris Exhib., 1959, no. 219.

HESDIN, ATELIER OF LOYSET LIÉDET, 1455-60

202. JEAN MANSEL, LA FLEUR DES HISTOIRES, Vol. II

Baltimore, Md., The Walters Art Gallery. Ms. W. 305

Loyset Liédet, a native of Hesdin, seems to have had his apprenticeship under the great painter and miniaturist, Simon Marmion. The latter was one of the chief illustrators in the atelier at Valenciennes presided over by Jean Mansel, an editor and translator, as well as the author of *La Fleur des Histoires*. Liédet, on returning for a period to his native Hesdin, was active in the decoration of texts of exactly the same kind as those produced in Valenciennes by the office of Jean Mansel. Later - sometime after 1460 - he moved to Bruges where he worked in collaboration with the scribe and editor David Aubert upon books for the library of Philip the Good, and soon headed an enormous atelier which was one of the most prolific in Flanders.

This example of his production at Hesdin, while he still reflected the influence of Simon Marmion, and before his style became too dry, resembles in its best miniatures the *Histoires Romaines* (Paris, Arsenal, ms. 5087-5088), which we know was completed by him at Hesdin for Philip the Good in 1454 and paid for in 1460. In our manuscript the first miniature is painted in an entirely different style from that of Liédet, but yet in a manner which likewise seems to reveal a connection with Simon Marmion - the large scale of the figures and the treatment of architecture and landscape recalling that master's panel

384

Proleme

Omme en nostre premier
volume nous auons traittie
des histoires rommance de-
vuis le commencement et
fondation de rome iusques
au temps de lempereur constantin le grand
et que nous auons iller dit & declauret co
ment il fut le premier des empereurs qui
donna a sainte eglise et aux membres dicelle
a tenir rentes et possessions car par auat les
mestres ne dunost q des offrandes des homes
gene Et coment icellu noble empereur
transporta et establit en la cite de constanti
noble le siege imperial pour le temps en
suiuant en delaussant la cite de rome et la
seignourie dicelle au pax silnestre pour lui
et pour ses successeurs pares sen tablement
& a tousiours Et coment il constitua celle
cite de constantinoble chief de tout orient
et en fist ainsi come une nouuelle rome
en la memore de la vielle rome quil eut

delaussu come dit est Et coment il donna au
pax silnestre son palais ou lieu du palais il
fist faire et edefier leglise du lateran et voult
& ordonna pour tout le teps aduenir q celle eglise
du lateran fust la premiaple et le chief de
toutes les eglises du monde en quelle ma
umce ou kenon quelles fussent Et mesme
ment que cellu qui seroit euesque de celle
eglise du lateran fust euesque des euesques
Cestadure le chief et le souueraim des autres
euesques & de toute vprente Maintenant
donques pour parsuur les histoires de ro
siconne romme sauons en fin desdictes histo
res en nre premier volume Nous entsu
urons icelles histoires en cestu second vo
lume et le plus amplement que nous
porrons iusques an tempe que lempire
de rome deuola aux rois de france Est
assauoir au roi charles le grant et a ses
successeurs pres, lui Et lors parlerons
nous von ou neant desdictes histoires
romance pour ce que pou en auons ten

385

Illuminated Manuscripts

paintings (such as the *Saint Bertin Altarpiece*) rather than his miniatures. The anonymous artist may be the same as the one who a decade or so later was established at Bruges and, because of several manuscripts executed for the English King, has been called "The Master of Edward IV".

DELAISSÉ discovered that the original owner of our manuscript, whose arms have been clipped out, but leaving a "take-off", was Philip the Good. The arms of a later owner (a member of the de Plaines family?) have been painted in the borders of several pages.

The miniatures include one of *The Princes of the World Proceeding to the Court of the Emperor in Constantinople*, by Liédet (illustrated here).

> *Physical description:* Written in French on vellum; 310 leaves, 18 x 13 ¹/₂ in. (46 x 34 cm.); 2 large and 2 small miniatures. Bound in 16th century stamped brown leather over boards.
>
> *History and Bibliography:* Library of Philip the Good, Duke of Burgundy; family of de Plaines(?); acquired by Henry Walters, 1904. DELISLE, 1903-4, pp. 269-275 and pl.; DE RICCI, I, 1935, p. 850, no. 525; Cat. Los Angeles Exhib., 1953-54, no. 64; [DELAISSÉ], Cat. Brussels - Amsterdam - Paris Exhib., 1959, no. 68, pl. 31.

BRUGES, ATELIER OF GUILLAUME VRELANT, ca. 1455-60

203. BOOK OF HOURS

Baltimore, Md., The Walters Art Gallery. Ms. W. 197

This abundantly illustrated manuscript is characteristic of the style of illumination introduced into Bruges around the middle of the 15th century by Guillaume Vrelant. A native of Utrecht, he is recorded as being active in Bruges at least as early as 1454, and soon was at the head of a large atelier whose output was prolific during the next three decades. Typical of the atelier are the bright, hard colors and, as DELAISSÉ has pointed out, the marginal decoration of blue, rose and gold acanthus and flowers. These ornamental details were French in origin, but developed a particular, if somewhat routine character, in the Vrelant atelier. The miniatures, in addition to the series of calendar pictures of occupations of the months and signs of the zodiac include *The Crucifixion* (illustrated here) and a representation of the Holy Face, which as in many manuscripts of the Vrelant atelier, is based upon a lost painting by Jan van Eyck, and is especially fine in execution.

The book is preserved in its original binding of calf, blind stamped with plaques bearing the signature of Livinus Stuuaert, a binder who is recorded as active in Ghent in 1457.

386

Physical description: Written in Latin on vellum; 263 leaves, 8 $^1/_2$ x 6 in. (21.5 x 15 cm.); 24 full-page and 13 smaller miniatures. Bound in contemporary calf over boards.

History and Bibliography: With the bookplate of J. Capron of Ypres; his sale, Brussels, April 6, 1875, no. 38. DE RICCI, I, 1935, p. 797, no. 259; [DELAISSÉ]), Cat. Brussels - Amsterdam - Paris Exhib., 1959, no. 125.

Illuminated Manuscripts

SCHOOL OF BRUGES, ca. 1460-70

204. BOOK OF HOURS FOR ROME USE

*Baltimore, Md.,
The Walters Art Gallery
Ms. W. 208*

A little book whose miniatures reflect the influence of panel paintings in its surprisingly ambitious presentation of domestic interiors with views through open windows, elaborate landscapes with fantastic architecture and often complex figure compositions. DELAISSÉ (1959, no. 249) has pointed out the relation of its miniature style to works produced by the atelier of Liévin van Lathem. The latter, a gifted Ghent illuminator, painted a Book of Hours for Charles the Bold and later worked for the great collector, Louis de Gruuthuse of Bruges.

The miniatures include one of *The Virgin Nursing the Child in a Domestic Interior* (illustrated here).

Physical description: Written in Latin on vellum; 152 leaves, 4 ³/₈ x 3 ¹/₄ in. (11.2 x 8.3 cm.); 12 miniatures. Bound in 15th century blind stamped calf over boards.
History and Bibliography: DE RICCI, I, 1935, p. 799, no. 269; Cat. Baltimore Exhib., 1949, no. 123; Cat. Brussels - Amsterdam - Paris Exhib., 1959, no. 249.

BRUGES, WORKSHOP OF PHILIPPE DE MAZEROLLES, ca. 1470

205. JEHAN DE COURCY, CHRONIQUE UNIVERSELLE DITE LA BOUQUECHAR-DIÈRE, Vol. I

New York, N.Y., The Pierpont Morgan Library. Ms. M. 214

To Philippe de Mazerolles, the court painter of Charles the Bold, Duke of Burgundy, working probably in Bruges, are attributed the design and execution

388

Illuminated Manuscripts

of the principal miniatures of this volume of a two-volume universal history (M. 224 is volume II) compiled by Jehan de Courcy, seigneur de Bourc-Achard, who flourished from 1399 to 1431. Typical of this artist's rich pictorial style, which, as was customary, employs contemporary architectural backgrounds, costumes, and incidental details of daily life to tell the stories of the legendary and historical past, is the miniature of the scene of *King Priam Coming out of the City Gate of Troy to Meet the Spartan Princess Helen,* just arrived from Greece (fol. 84; illustrated here).

Physical description: Written in French on vellum; 178 leaves, 17 x 13 in. (44 x 33 cm.); 6 large miniatures, 9 small miniatures, illuminated initials and marginal decorations. Initials of the original owner S.A. or A.S. and two coats of arms occur in various places. Bound in late 18th century green morocco over boards.

History and Bibliography: Owned by François Baraton and Antoinette de Saint-Maure, his wife, after 1495, but perhaps earlier in the Baraton family, as DE RICCI suggests that the initials and coats of arms (as interpreted by VAN DE PUT) indicate that owner may have been Anne Feschal, widow of François Baraton, Seigneur de la Roche de Champire, allied to the houses of Sully, Craon, Saint-Maure, Valois, Nesle, Harcourt, Brittany, Flanders, Estouteville, Montmorency, and Bourbon; Duc de la Vallière sale (Paris, 1784, no. 4601) to Dusaulchoix; Comte de Mac-Carthy-Reagh sale (Paris, 1817, no. 3945) to De Karny (bought in); offered by De Bure (cat. sale, Paris, 1817, p. 46); Joseph Barrois Coll. (no. 38); sold in 1849 to the Earl of Ashburnham; his sale (London, 1901, no. 31) to Quaritch, London (cat. 211, 1902, no. 90); purchased by J. Pierpont Morgan. DE RICCI, II, 1937, p. 1405, no. 214.

FLANDERS, STYLE OF JEAN LE TAVERNIER, ca. 1470

206. RAOUL LE FÈVRE, HISTOIRE DE JASON

New York, N.Y., The Pierpont Morgan Library. Ms. M. 119

It was Raoul Le Fèvre who in 1464 at the command of his lord, Philip the Good, Duke of Burgundy, compiled for the benefit of the Duke's son, Charles, Count of Charolais, later known as Charles the Bold, a collection of the stories of Ancient Troy, which later in an English version prepared by William Caxton became the first book printed in English.

This manuscript presents the story of Jason in a text written by Raoul Le Fèvre and illustrated with twelve miniatures in grisaille in the manner frequently used by Jean Le Tavernier of Oudenaarde. The meeting of a lady and her entourage in tall hennins with a kneeling knight in armor, accompanied by many other figures in armor (fol. 25, illustrated here), is typical of the style of the illustrator of this manuscript as well as of the wealth of light such manuscript miniatures throw upon the life of the 15th century.

Jean Le Tavernier, although living in Oudenaarde, seems to have been the popular illustrator of manuscripts produced chiefly for the Burgundian court by

390

various publishing offices, such as those of Jean Miélot in Lille, David Aubert in Bruges and Brussels, and others. His distinctive style and use of grisaille left their mark on other artists not yet identified by name.

Physical description: Written in French on vellum; 104 leaves, 14 3/4 x 10 1/2 in. (37.5 x 26.7 cm.).

History and Bibliography: Jean de Montmorency, 1600; Duc de Montmorency, ca. 1740; purchased by J. Pierpont Morgan. DE RICCI, II, 1937, p. 1388.

BRUGES, PUBLISHING OFFICE OF DAVID AUBERT, STYLE OF LOYSET LIEDET, ca. 1470

207. LECTIONARY AND APOCALYPSE

New York, N.Y., The Pierpont Morgan Library. Ms. M. 68

In this volume are included lections from the Old and New Testaments (fol. 1-155) with only illuminated initials and bands, followed by a paraphrase of the Apocalypse (fol. 157-243) with sixty-eight illustrative miniatures by a member of the Ghent-Bruges School, in a style related to that of Loyset Liédet.

Typical in drawing, color, and imaginative composition is the miniature (fol. 157, illustrated here) representing *Saint John on the Island of Patmos* being shown by an angel the vision of Christ enthroned on the arc of heaven.

391

To this book is attached a special interest because the arms of Charles the Bold, which appear on the first page, indicate that it was once owned by this princely patron of the arts and ardent bibliophile.

Physical description: Written in French on vellum; 243 leaves, 14 x 10 in. (35.5 x 25.5 cm.); 68 miniatures, illuminated initials and bands. Arms of Charles the Bold appear on the first page. Bound in late 19th century pigskin over boards.

History and Bibliography: Written for Charles the Bold (1433-77), Duke of Burgundy (1467-77), as indicated by his arms appearing on first page: D. Morgand, Inv. no. 28999 bis; Ed. Rahir; purchased by J. Pierpont Morgan, 1905. DE RICCI, II, 1937, p. 1378, no. 68.

SCHOOL OF GHENT, ca. 1475

208. JEAN DE WAVRIN, CHRONIQUES D'ANGLETERRE, Vol. IV

Baltimore, Md., The Walters Art Gallery. Ms. W. 201

This is volume IV of a set of the *Chroniques,* of which volumes II, III and V belonged in 1686 to William III of Orange, eventually passing into the library of King William IV of Holland and so to their present location in the Royal Library at The Hague.

The half-page miniatures, of unusually high quality as historical illustrations, depict the Coronation of Richard II of England; the Duke of Lancaster treating

392

with the Spanish Ambassador for the Marriage of his Daughter; the Dukes of York and Lancaster and the Archbishop of York, the Bishop of London, and others on the part of the English, and the Dukes of Berry, Burgundy and others on the part of the French, treating for peace under tents pitched between Calais and Boulogne; Dispatch of Ambassadors from the Emperor of Germany to Pope Boniface at Rome and to Urban at Avignon te request both to resign so that a new Pope could be elected; the Coronation of Heny IV and the Murder of Richard II, the Smiting of Henry Percy, and the Battle of Shrewsbury.

DELAISSÉ considers that the type of marginal ornament shows a transferance of certain Brussels patterns to Ghent ateliers.

Physical description: Written in French on vellum; 283 leaves, 17 $^1/_4$ x 13 $^3/_8$ in. (43 x 34 cm.); 6 large miniatures. Bound in French early 18th century mottled calf.

History and Bibliography: Robert Blathwayt Collection, Dyrham Park, Chippenham (sold, London, Nov. 20, 1912, no. 125). DE RICCI, I, 1935, p. 851, no. 527; Cat. Baltimore Exhib., 1949, no. 135, pl. XLIV; Cat. Los Angeles Exhib., 1953-54, no. 81; [DELAISSÉ], Cat. Brussels - Amsterdam - Paris Exhib. 1959, no. 190.

Illuminated Manuscripts

BRUGES, WORKSHOP OF THE MASTER OF ANTHONY OF BURGUNDY, last quarter of the 15th Century

209. BOOK OF HOURS FOR ROME USE

New York, N.Y., The Pierpont Morgan Library. Ms. M. 493

This rare manuscript, distinctive in the execution of its text and illustrations in silver and color and some colors on black vellum, invites comparison with the other celebrated black vellum manuscript, the Book of Hours, known as the *Sforza Hours,* in the Nationalbibliothek, Vienna. In each of these two manuscripts,

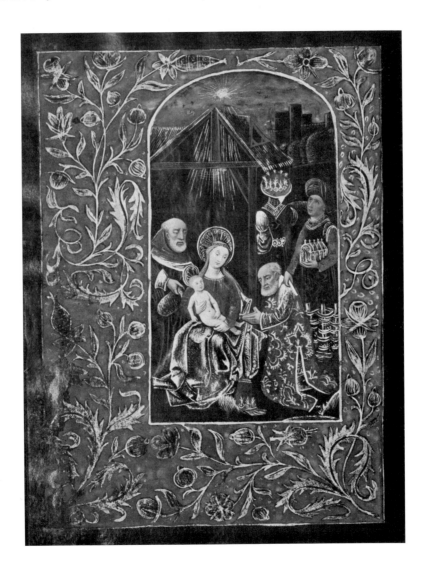

394

both produced in Bruges, the anonymous artist called the Master of Anthony of Burgundy had a large part, and it is not unlikely that it was actually Philippe de Mazerolles who was paid for the paintings in a book *ecrit en lettres d'or et d'argent sur du parchemin noir* given by the City of Bruges to Charles the Bold in 1467 (DELAISSÉ, 1959, p. 119). At least two styles can be distinguished in the miniatures of this manuscript - one, that of the Master of Anthony of Burgundy, as seen in *The Adoration of the Magi* (fol. 58 v°, illustrated here) and the other, the older and more archaic style of Guillaume Vrelant, to be seen in *The Pentecost* (fol. 18 v°).

Physical description: Written in Latin in silver and gold on vellum stained black; 121 leaves, 6 3/8 x 4 1/2 in. (16 x 11.5 cm.); 14 miniatures, illuminated initials, and 134 illuminated borders. Bound in modern pigskin.

History and Bibliography: Made for a Ghent owner, as indicated by the reference to the translation of the relics of Saint Liévin in the calendar, possibly for a widow on account of the unusual color scheme, after 1475, as shown by the presence in the litanies of Saint Bernardino da Siena, who was canonized in 1475; Nicolas Yemeniz Coll.; his sale (Paris, 1867, no. 71) to Ambroise Firmin-Didot; his sale (Paris, 1879, no. 27) to Labitte; Robert Hoe Coll. (Cat. 1909, p. 105); his sale (New York, 1912, II, no. 2465) to Quaritch, London; purchased by J. Pierpont Morgan, 1912. Cat. New York Exhib., 1933-34, no. 106; DE RICCI, II, 1937, p. 1460, no. 493; [DELAISSÉ], Cat. Brussels - Amsterdam - Paris Exhib., 1959, no. 136.

FLANDERS, ca. 1480-90

210. BOOK OF HOURS FOR ROME USE IN BRITTANY

New York, N.Y., The Pierpont Morgan Library. Ms. M. 6

This manuscript illustrates the problems often arising in the localizing of the Flemish 15th century manuscripts. Because the text of the Hours is preceded by a Calendar for Brittany (vicinity of Quimper) and the style of the main miniatures is so clearly Flemish, related to the Ghent artist known as the Master of Mary of Burgundy, the miniatures and borders have been attributed to "a Flemish artist, either working in Brittany or under the influence of Breton painting and architecture" (Cat. New York Exhib., 1933-34, p. 51).

More recently the large miniatures have reminded DELAISSÉ (1959, p. 161) of Simon Marmion and of the Master of Mary of Burgundy, though other aspects of the book are French. He cites another apparent collaboration of the painter from Valenciennes and the greatest of the Ghent miniaturists. Cases are known of books ordered from Flanders for use elsewhere; here may be an instance of a book prepared in France and sent to Flanders to receive its miniatures.

The miniatures of this manuscript with their accompanying borders of naturalistic flowers, so typical of Flemish manuscript illumination after 1475 in the hands of the schools of Ghent and Bruges, are among the most beautiful from

this period. Unusual in background details are such scenes as *The Annunciation* (fol. 21, illustrated here) apparently in a Gothic church, and *The Adoration of the Magi* (fol. 44 v°) before a neatly made bed in a ruined stable resembling a piece of modern symbolic stage setting.

Physical description: Written in Latin on vellum; 168 leaves, 6 ¼ x 4 ¼ in. (16 x 11 cm.); 11 three-quart page miniatures, 24 smaller miniatures, 24 calendar illustrations, numerous illuminated borders.

History and Bibliography: Made for a man named Peter (fol. 150), probably Pierre de Foix (1449-1490), abbot of Sainte Mélanie de Rennes, bishop of Vannes, and Cardinal in 1476 (depicted on fol. 154); Abbé Jacques de Alberte (1591); Joseph Smith Coll., Venice; his sale (London, January 25, 1773); Dr. Charles Chauncy Coll.; his sale (London, 1790, no. 2936, 2938, or 2941); Duke of Hamilton Coll. (Cat. 1882, no. 320); his sale (London, 1889, no. 80) to T.M. Whitehead; his sale (London, May 3, 1898, no. 66) to Quaritch, London; purchased by J. Pierpont Morgan. Cat. New York Exhib., 1933-34, no. 109; DE RICCI, II, 1937, p. 1365, no. 6; [DELAISSÉ], Cat. Brussels - Amsterdam - Paris Exhib., 1959.

396

z estoient les naues des romains
fortes et roides mais tardiues et
pou couuenables pour legierement
courir par mer [...] axais celles des
cartagiens estoient legieres et [...]

FLANDERS, second half of the 15th Century

211. LEONARDO BRUNI, DE LA PREMIÈRE GUERRE PUNIQUE

New York, N.Y., The Pierpont Morgan Library. Ms. M. 266

Since Bruni's Italian text was first translated into French in 1445, this manuscript dates after that year. The workshop that produced this manuscript or the name of the artist who executed the miniatures has not been determined (DELAISSÉ, 1959, p. 166). The miniatures are more than usually interesting for their depiction of ancient history in 15th century guise. The scene illustrated here shows Romans building boats.

Physical description: Written in French on vellum; 94 leaves, 9 3/4 x 6 1/2 in. (25 x 16.5 cm.); 14 miniatures. Bound in modern limp vellum.
History and Bibliography: Traces of the arms of an early owner; P. Aubert (about 1500); the Earl of Ashburnham Coll. (Appendix, no. 156); H. Yates Thompson sale (London, May 14, 1902, no. 1) to Quaritch, London, Cat. 235 (Nov. 1904), no. 109; purchased from Olschki by J. Pierpont Morgan, 1907. DE RICCI, II, 1937, p. 1416, no. 266; [DELAISSÉ], Cat. Brussels - Amsterdam - Paris Exhib., 1959, no. 220.

397

398

BRUGES, WORKSHOP OF GERARD DAVID, ca. 1500

212. THE VIRGIN AND CHILD WITH MANY FEMALE SAINTS
Single miniature (VIRGO INTER VIRGINES)

New York, N.Y., The Pierpont Morgan Library. Ms. M. 659

Sometimes referred to as a page from a Breviary or a Book of Hours, consistently attributed to Bruges, and sometimes given to Gerard David (about 1460-1523), one of the last of the great painters of the Gothic period of the School of Bruges, this miniature may have been made as a separate devotional picture, and may be by one of David's followers, reflecting the master's style. Its color and composition are charming, its preservation is excellent, and the absorbed intensity of the characterizations of all the personages is most appealing.

WINKLER (1925, p. 134) and others (like FRIEDLÄNDER, VI, 1928, pp. 99-101) have long been convinced that David as a leading panel painter of his time and a member of the Guild of Book Painters in Bruges, must have executed manuscript miniatures, or at least designed some for pupils to carry out or inspired the work of followers. No documented example of David's work as a manuscript miniaturist has come to light but WINKLER and FRIEDLÄNDER see close resemblances to the artist's style in some miniatures in the *Breviary of Isabella of Spain,* about 1495 (London, British Museum, add. ms. 18851). The present representation of the *Virgo inter Virgines* seems very close to the artist's work. In subject matter it may be compared with the larger and more elaborate painting of the same subject, formerly in the Carmelite Convent of Sion, the gift of the painter in 1509, now in the Museum in Rouen, a work of the greatest importance since it is documented and includes the self-portrait of the artist. In another style, related to David's landscape renderings, are two miniature paintings in the Bruges Museum: *Saint John the Baptist Preaching* and *The Baptism of Christ* (6 x 14 $^3/_8$ in. or 15.5 x 35 cm.), which WINKLER accepts as by the master.

Physical description: Painted in tempera on vellum; 1 leaf, 7 $^1/_8$ x 5 $^1/_4$ in. (18 x 13.4 cm.) (page); 6 $^1/_2$ x 4 $^1/_2$ in. (16.5 x 11.5 cm.) (picture).

History and Bibliography: No early history is known. Purchased by J. Pierpont Morgan. Cat. New York Exhib., 1933 - 34, no. 133. DE RICCI, II, 1937, p. 1480, no. 659; Cat. Worcester Exhib., 1951, no. 13.

SCHOOL OF BRUGES, ca. 1530

213. PRAYER BOOK

Baltimore, Md., The Walters Art Gallery. Ms. W. 426

One of the delicately executed little devotional books which were produced by the artists of the school of illumination that had its roots in innovations of Alexander Bening and his followers toward the end of the 15th century. The

399

school, which arose in Ghent, was much influenced by the great panel painters of the time, such as Hugo van der Goes. Alexander's son, Simon Bening (1484-1561), had worked closely with the Ghent artist, Gerard Horenbout, on the Grimani Breviary. In 1508 Simon registered with the guild in Bruges and was active mainly in that city for the rest of his life, assimilating notably the influence of the Bruges painter, Gerard David. The miniatures of this little book show the result of the continuation of these influences, which formed the Bruges illumination ateliers of the first half of the 16th century.

The miniatures include one of the *Virgin and Child* seated in a garden with a facing border of realistic flowers symbolic of the Virgin (illustrated here).

Physical description: Written in Latin and Flemish on vellum; 214 leaves, 3 x 2 ¼ in. (7.5 x 6 cm.); 7 full-page miniatures, 9 illuminated borders. Bound in velvet-covered boards with 16th century Flemish silver-gilt ornaments and clasps.

History and Bibliography: 17th century inscription of Jan Kominer. DE RICCI, I, 1935, p. 810, no. 332; Cat. Baltimore Exhib., 1949, no. 214, pl. XXVIII; Cat. Baltimore Exhib., 1957, no. 122.

Illuminated Manuscripts

BIBLIOGRAPHY *

ACKERMAN, P., *Recently Identified Designers of Gothic Tapestries*, in *The Art Bulletin*, IX, 1926, pp. 142-160.

ACKERMAN, P., *The Rockefeller Mc Cormick Tapestries: Three Early Sixteenth Century Tapestries*, New York, 1932*.

Algemene Geschiedenis der Nederlanden, III. *De late middeleeuwen, 1305-1477;* IV. *De Bourgondisch-Habsburgse monarchie, 1477-1567*, onder redactie van J.A. VAN HOUTTE, J.F. NIERMEYER, [...], Utrecht - Antwerp - Brussels - Ghent - Louvain, 1951-52.

ARÙ, C. and DE GERADON, E., *La Galerie Sabauda de Turin (Les Primitifs flamands, I. Corpus de la peinture des anciens Pays-Bas méridionaux au XVe siècle, 2)*, Antwerp, 1952.

AUBERT, M., *La Sculpture française au moyen âge*, Paris, (1947).

BACRI, J., *L'"Histoire d'Hercule", tapisserie du Musée des Gobelins*, in *Gazette des beaux-arts*, XII, 1934, pp. 204-211.

BALDASS, L. VON, *Die Chronologie der Gemälde des Hieronymus Bosch*, in *Jahrbuch der Preussischen Kunstsammlungen*, XXXVIII, 1917, pp. 177-195.

BALDASS, L., *Die Niederländer des 15. und 16. Jahrhunderts auf der Ausstellung Flämischer Kunst in London 1927*, in *Belvedere*, XI, 1927, pp. 80-85.

BALDASS, L., *Drei Jahrhunderte flämische Malerei*, in *Pantheon*, V, 1930, pp. 130-136.

BALDASS, L., *Die Entwicklung des Dirk Bouts. Eine Stilgeschichtliche Untersuchung*, in *Jahrbuch der kunsthistorischen Sammlungen in Wien*, N.S., VI, 1932, pp. 77-114.

BALDASS, L., *Das Ende des Weichen Stiles in der österreichischen Tafelmalerei*, in *Pantheon*, XIV, 1934, pp. 373-381.

BALDASS, L., *The Portraiture of Master Michel*, in *The Burlington Magazine*, LXVII, 1935, pp. 77-82.

BALDASS, L., *Gerard David als Landschaftsmaler*, in *Jahrbuch der kunsthistorischen Sammlungen in Wien*, N.S., X, 1936, pp. 89-96.

BALDASS, L., *Zur Entwicklungsgeschichte des Hieronymus Bosch*, in *Annuaire des Musées royaux des beaux-arts de Belgique*, I, 1938, pp. 47-71.

---

* *The asterisks at the end of certain references indicate that it was not possible to consult these works.*

BALDASS, L. VON, *Dirk Bouts, seine Werkstatt und Schule*, in *Pantheon*, XXV, 1940, pp. 93-97.

BALDASS, L. VON, *Hans Memling*, Vienna, (1942).

BALDASS, L. VON, *Hieronymus Bosch*, 1st ed., Vienna, 1943.

BALDASS, L., *The Ghent Altarpiece of Hubert and Jan van Eyck*, in *The Art Quarterly*, XIII, 1950, pp. 140-150, 182-199.

BALDASS, L., *Jan van Eyck*, London - New York, 1952.

BALDASS, L. VON, *Hieronymus Bosch*, 2nd ed., Vienna, 1959.

BARA, A., *Deux chrismatoires-tourelles aux poinçons de Louvain*, in *Bulletin des Musées royaux d'art et d'histoire*, XIII, 1941, pp. 93-95.

BARTIER, J., *Charles le Téméraire*, Brussels, (1944).

BARTIER, J., *Légistes et gens de finances au XVe siècle. Les conseillers des ducs de Bourgogne Philippe le Bon et Charles le Téméraire (Académie royale de Belgique. Classe des lettres et des sciences morales et politiques. Mémoires, L, 2-2bis)*, 2 vol., Brussels, 1955-57.

BAUDOUIN, F., *Kanttekeningen bij de catalogus van de Dieric Bouts - Tentoonstelling*, in *Bulletin des Musées royaux des beaux-arts, Bruxelles*, VII, 1958, pp. 119-140.

(BAUDOUIN, F. and BOON, K.G.), *Dieric Bouts. Palais des beaux-arts, Bruxelles 1957-1958 Museum Prinsenhof, Delft*, Brussels, 1957.

BAX, D., *Ontcijfering van Jeroen Bosch*, The Hague, 1949.

BAZIN, G., *L'Esprit d'imitation dans l'art flamand. Le thème de la Madone dans une abside*, in *L'Amour de l'art*, XII, 1931, pp. 495-500.

BAZIN, G., *Petrus Christus et les rapports entre l'Italie et la Flandre au milieu du XVe siècle*, in *Revue des arts*, II, 1952, pp. 194-208.

BEAULIEU, M. and BAYLÉ, J., *Le Costume en Bourgogne de Philippe le Hardi à la mort de Charles le Téméraire (1364-1477)*, Paris, 1956.

BEENKEN, H., *Bildnisschöpfungen Hubert van Eycks*, in *Pantheon*, XIX, 1937, pp. 116-120.

BEENKEN, H., *Hubert und Jan van Eyck*, Munich, 1941.

BEENKEN, H., *Rogier van der Weyden*, Munich, 1951.

BENESCH, O., *Die Zeichnungen der niederländischen Schulen des XV. und XVI. Jahrhunderts (Beschreibender Katalog der Handzeichnungen in der graphischen Sammlung Albertina, herausgegeben von A. SIX, Bd. II)*, Vienna, 1928.

BERGIUS, R., *Französische und belgische Konsol- und Zwickelplastik im 14. und 15. Jahrhundert*, Würzburg, 1937.

BERGSTRÖM, I., *Medicina, fons et scrinium. A study in Van Eyckean Symbolism and its Influence in Italian Art*, in *Konsthistorisk Tidskrift*, XXVI, 1957, pp. 1-20.*

BERLINER, R., *Denkmäler der Krippenkunst*, Augsburg, 1926.

BERLINER, R., *Die Weihnachtskrippe*, Munich, (1955).

BERRYER, A.M., *Evolution de la verrerie de l'époque romane à la fin du XVIIIe siècle*, in *Trois millénaires d'art verrier à travers les collections publiques et privées de Belgique. Catalogue général de l'exposition. Liège, Musée Curtius, 1958*, [s.l.], 1958, pp. 105-109.

BESANÇON, J., *Les Dessins flamands du XVe au XVIe siècle*, Paris, [1951].

BETHUNE, J.B., *Les Monuments funéraires de la ville de Furnes*, in *Gilde de Saint-Thomas et de Saint-Luc. Bulletin*, II, n° 7, 1871, pp. 101-144.

BETS, P.V., *Gids voor de bezoekers der kerk van Zout-Leeuw*, Tirlemont, 1888.

BETS, P.V., *Geschiedenis der gemeente Hakendover en van dezer mirakuleuze kerk*, 7th ed., Léau, 1907.

BIER, J., *Riemenschneider's St. Jerome and his other Works in Alabaster*, in *The Art Bulletin*, XXXIII, 1951, pp. 226-234.

BLUM, A. and LAUER, Ph., *La Miniature française aux XVe et XVIe siècles*, Paris - Brussels, 1930.

BOBER, H., *André Beauneveu and Mehun-sur-Yèvre*, in *Speculum, a Journal of Mediaeval Studies*, XXVIII, 1953, pp. 741-753.

BOCK, E. and ROSENBERG, J., *Die niederländischen Meister. Beschreibendes Verzeichnis Sämtlicher Zeichnungen (Staatliche Museen zu Berlin. Die Zeichnungen alter Meister im Kupferstichkabinett)*, 2 vol., Berlin, 1931.

BOCK, F., *Memling-Studien*, Dusseldorf, 1900.

BODE, W. and FRIEDLÄNDER, M.J., *Die Gemälde-Sammlung der Herrn Carl von Hollitscher in Berlin*, Berlin, 1912.

BODENHAUSEN, E. VON, see VON BODENHAUSEN, E.

BOES, J., *De Tinnenpotgieterij te Gent*, in *Oostvlaamsche Zanten*, X, 1935, pp. 1-22.

BOLOGNA, F., *Un "San Girolamo" lombardo del quattrocento*, in *Paragone*, no. 149, V, 1954, pp. 45-50.*

BONENFANT, P., *Philippe-le-Bon (Collection "Notre passé")*, 2nd ed., Brussels, (1944).

BONENFANT, P., *Bruxelles et la maison de Bourgogne*, in *Bruxelles au XVe siècle*, Brussels, 1953, pp. 21-32.

BONENFANT, P., *Du meurtre de Montereau au traité de Troyes (Académie royale de Belgique. Classe des lettres et sciences morales et politiques. Mémoires, LII, 4)*, Brussels, 1958.

BONENFANT-FEYTMANS, A.M., *La Corporation des orfèvres de Bruxelles au moyen âge*, in *Bulletin de la Commission royale d'histoire*, CXV, 1950, pp. 85-171.

BONENFANT-FEYTMANS, A.-M., *L'Orfèvrerie bruxelloise au XVe siècle*, in *Bruxelles au XVe siècle*, Brussels, 1953, pp. 53-72.

BOON, K.G., *Gerard David (Palet Serie)*, Amsterdam, [1938].

Boon, K.G., *De Erfenis van Aelbert van Ouwater*, in *Nederlandsch Kunsthistorisch Jaarboek,* 1947, pp. 33-46.

Boon, K.G., *Naar aanleiding van tekeningen van Hugo van der Goes en zijn school*, in *Nederlandsch Kunsthistorisch Jaarboek,* 1950-51, pp. 82-101.

Boon, K.G., *Bouts, Justus of Ghent and Berruguete*, in *The Burlington Magazine,* C, 1958, pp. 8-15.

(Boon, K.G. and Baudouin, F.), *Dieric Bouts. Palais des beaux-arts, Bruxelles 1957-1958 Museum Prinsenhof, Delft,* Brussels, 1957.

Borenius, T., *A Petrus Christus for Detroit*, in *Apollo*, I, 1925, p. 290.

Bossert, H. Th., *Geschichte des Kunstgewerbes aller Zeiten und Völker,* 6 vol., Berlin, 1928-35.

Bouchot, H., *La Gravure et l'estampe*, in *Histoire de l'art* [...], publiée sous la direction de A. Michel, III. *Le réalisme. Les débuts de la renaissance,* I, Paris, 1907, pp. 327-342.

Bouchot, H., *L'Exposition des Primitifs français. La peinture en France sous les Valois,* 2 vol., Paris, [s.d.].

Bouvy, D.R.P.A., *Middeleeuwsche Beeldhouwkunst in de Noordelijke Nederlanden,* Amsterdam, 1947.

Bouyer, R., *La Collection Pacully*, in *Revue de l'art ancien et moderne*, XIII, 1903, p. 295.

Bradley, J.W., *A Dictionary of Miniaturists Illuminators, Calligraphers and Copyists, with References to their Works, and Notices of their Patrons, from the Establishment of Christianity to the Eighteenth Century, (Burt Franklin Bibliographical Series,* VIII), 3 vol., New York, (1958).

Brans, J.V.L., *Hieronymus Bosch (El Bosco) en El Prado y en El Escorial,* Barcelona, 1948.

Brans, J.V.L., *Isabel la catolica y el arte hispano-flamenco,* Madrid, 1952.

B[reck], J., *The Esther Tapestry*, in *Minneapolis Institute of Arts Bulletin*, IV, 1915, pp. 664-666.*

Brigode, S., *Les Eglises gothiques de Belgique (L'Art en Belgique),* 2nd ed., Brussels, 1947.

Briquet, C.M., *Les Filigranes. Dictionnaire historique des marques du papier dès leur apparition vers 1282 jusque 1600,* 2nd ed., 4 vol., Leipzig, 1923.

[Brockwell, M.W.], *Flemish Art 1300-1700. Winter Exhibition, 1953-54. Royal Academy of Arts, London.*

Bruncel, V., see [Marlier, G.], alias Bruncel, V.

Bruxelles au XVe siècle, Brussels, 1953.

Burckhardt, J., *Die Kunstwerke der Belgischen Städte,* Dusseldorf, 1842.

Bürger, W., *Le Musée d'Anvers*, in *Gazette des beaux-arts*, XI, 1861, pp. 24-31.

Bürger, W., *Nouvelles études sur la galerie Suermondt à Aix-la-Chapelle,* in *Gazette des beaux-arts,* I, 1869, pp. 5-37.

Burger, W., *Roger van der Weyden,* Leipzig, 1923.

Burger, W., *Abendländische Schmelzarbeiten (Bibliothek für Kunst- und Antiquitätensammler, XXXIII),* Berlin, 1930.

Burroughs, A., *Art Criticism from a Laboratory,* Boston, 1938.

Burroughs, B. and Wehle, H.B., *The Metropolitan Museum of Art. The Michael Friedsam Collection,* New York, 1932. (Special issue of *The Bulletin of the Metropolitan Museum of Art,* XXVII, no. 11, November 1932, Section II, pp. 1-52).

Byvanck, A.W., *La Miniature dans les Pays-Bas septentrionaux,* Paris, 1937.

Byvanck, A.W., *Kroniek der Noord-Nederlandsche Miniaturen,* III, in *Oudheidkundig Jaarboek,* 4th S., IX, 1940, pp. 29-41.

Calmette, J., *L'Elaboration du monde moderne ("Clio". Introduction aux études historiques, V),* Paris, 1949.

Calmette, J., *Les grands ducs de Bourgogne,* Paris, (1949).

Cannaert, J.B., *Bijdragen tot de kennis van het oude strafrecht in Vlaenderen, verrijkt met vele tot dusverre onuitgegevene stukken,* 3rd ed., Ghent, 1835.

Cartellieri, O., *La Cour des ducs de Bourgogne (Bibliothèque historique),* Brussels, 1946.

Casier, J. and Bergmans, P., *L'Art ancien dans les Flandres (Région de l'Escaut). Mémorial de l'exposition rétrospective organisée à Gand en 1913,* 3 vol., Brussels - Paris, 1914-22.

Catalogue of the Manuscripts at Ashburnham Place, London, 1853.

Chambon, R., *L'Histoire de la verrerie en Belgique du IIe siècle à nos jours.* Préface de Mme G. Faider-Feytmans, Brussels, 1955.

Chastellain, G., *Oeuvres [...]* publiées par M. le baron Kervijn de Lettenhove, *(Publication de l'Académie royale. Collection des grands écrivains du pays,* 13), 8 vol., Brussels, 1863-66.

Châtelet, A., *Les Enluminures eyckiennes des manuscrits de Turin et de Milan-Turin,* in *Revue des arts,* VII, 1957, pp. 155-163.

Chauncey Ross, M., *Vier Evangelistenpulte aus Messina,* in *Pantheon,* XXII, 1938, pp. 290-292.

Ciselet, P. and Delcourt, M., see Monetarius de Feldkirchen, H.

Claeys, P., *Het Toreken,* in *Inventaire archéologique de Gand. Catalogue descriptif et illustré des monuments, œuvres d'art et documents antérieurs à 1830, publié par la Société d'histoire et d'archéologie de Gand,* Ghent, fasc. XLI, November 1906, p. 406.

Clemen, P. (under the direction of), *Belgische Kunstdenkmäler,* 2 vol., Munich, 1923.

COLLON-GEVAERT, S., *Histoire des arts du métal en Belgique (Académie royale de Belgique. Classe des beaux-arts. Mémoires. Collection in 8°, VII)*, 2 vol., Brussels, 1951.

COMBE, J., *Jérôme Bosch*, Paris, 1946.

COMBE, J., *Jheronimus Bosch*, London, 1946.

Commission royale des monuments [...]. Résumé des procès-verbaux. Peinture et sculpture, in *Bulletin des Commissions royales d'art et d'archéologie*, XLIV, 1905, pp. 351-358.

Commission royale des monuments [...]. Résumé des procès-verbaux. Peinture et sculpture, in *Bulletin des Commissions royales d'art et d'archéologie*, XLVII, 1908, pp. 102-106.

COMSTOCK, H., *The Connoisseur in America. Religious Paintings*, in *The Connoisseur*, CXL, 1957, pp. 204-205.

CONWAY, M., *The Van Eycks and their Followers*, London, 1921.

CONWAY, M., *Catalogue of the Loan Exhibition of Flemish and Belgian Art, Burlington House, London, 1927. A Memorial Volume*, London, 1927.

COORNAERT, E., *Les Bourses d'Anvers aux XVe et XVIe siècles*, in *Revue historique*, CCXVII, 1957, pp. 20-28.

COREMANS, P. (under the direction of), *L'Agneau mystique au laboratoire. Examen et traitement (Les Primitifs flamands*, III. *Contributions à l'étude des Primitifs flamands, 2)*, Antwerp, 1953.

COREMANS, P. and JANSSENS DE BISTHOVEN, A., *Van Eyck. L'Adoration de l'Agneau mystique (Archives centrales iconographiques d'art national, I)*, Antwerp, 1948.

COREMANS, P., GETTENS, R.J. and THISSEN, J., *La Technique des "Primitifs flamands". Etude scientifique des matériaux, de la structure et de la technique picturale*, in *Studies in (Etudes de) Conservation*, I, 1952, pp. 1-29.

COREMANS, P., SNEYERS, R. and THISSEN, J., *Memlinc's Mystiek Huwelijk van de H. Katharina, onderzoek en behandeling*, in *Bulletin de l'Institut royal du patrimoine artistique*, II, 1959, pp. 83-96.

CORNETTE, A.H., *La Peinture*, in *Trésor de l'art flamand du moyen âge au XVIIIe siècle. Mémorial de l'Exposition d'art flamand ancien à Anvers 1930*, I, Brussels, 1932, pp. 17-28.

CORNETTE, A.H., *Inleiding tot de oude meesters van het Koninklijk Museum te Antwerpen*, Antwerp, 1939.

COURAJOD, L., *Leçons professées à l'Ecole du Louvre (1887-1897)*, II. *Origines de la renaissance*, publiées par M.M. H. LEMONNIER et A. MICHEL, Paris, 1901.

COUSIN, J., *Histoire de Tournay ou quatre livres des chroniques [...], de l'évesché de Tournay*, 2 vol., Douai, 1619-20.

COUVEZ, A., see *Inventaires...*, 1852.

CRICK-KUNTZIGER, M., *Les plus anciennes tapisseries occidentales conservées en Belgique*, in *Cahiers de Belgique*, III, 1930, pp. 177-184.

CRICK-KUNTZIGER, M., *La Tapisserie bruxelloise au XVe siècle*, in *Bruxelles au XVe siècle*, Brussels, 1953, pp. 85-102.

CRICK-KUNTZIGER, M., *Un chef-d'œuvre inconnu du maître de la "Dame à la Licorne"*, in *Revue belge d'archéologie et d'histoire de l'art*, XXIII, 1954, pp. 3-20.

CRICK-KUNTZIGER, M., *Catalogue des tapisseries (XIVe au XVIIIe siècle). Musées royaux d'art et d'histoire de Bruxelles*, [Brussels, 1956].

CRICK-KUNTZIGER, M., *Les Arts décoratifs*, in *L'Art en Belgique du moyen âge à nos jours*, publié sous la direction de P. FIERENS, 3rd ed., Brussels, [1956], pp. 161-181.

CRICK-KUNTZIGER, M. and DESONAY, F., *Les "Compléments" de nos tapisseries gothiques*, I. *Un fragment inédit de l' "Histoire d'Hercule"*, in *Bulletin des Musées royaux d'art et d'histoire*, III, 1931, pp. 66-77.

CROOŸ, L. and F., *L'Orfèvrerie religieuse en Belgique depuis la fin du XVe siècle jusqu'à la révolution française*, Paris, [1911].

CROWE, J.A. and CAVALCASELLE, G.B., *The Early Flemish Painters: Notices of their Lives and Works*, London, 1857.

D'ANCONA, P. and AESCHLIMANN, E., *Dictionnaire des miniaturistes du moyen âge et de la renaissance dans les différentes contrées de l'Europe*, [...], 2nd ed. revised and enlarged, Milan, 1949.

DA SILVA FIGUEIREDO, J., *Os peninsulares nas "Guildas" de Flandres (Bruges e Antuérpia)*, Lisbon, 1941.

DAVID, H., *Au Pays de Claus Sluter*, in *Annales de Bourgogne*, IX, 1939, pp. 187-204.

DAVID, H., *Philippe le Hardi, duc de Bourgogne et co-régent de France de 1392 à 1404. Le train somptuaire d'un grand Valois*, Dijon, 1947.

DAVID, H., *Claus Sluter (Les grands sculpteurs français)*, Paris, 1951.

DAVIES, M., *The Earlier Italian Schools. National Gallery Catalogues*, London, 1951.

DAVIES, M., *The National Gallery London (Les Primitifs flamands, I. Corpus de la peinture des anciens Pays-Bas méridionaux au quinzième siècle, 3)*, 2 vol., Antwerp, 1953-54.

DAVIES, M., *Early Netherlandish School. National Gallery Catalogues*, 2nd revised ed., London, 1955.

DE BACKER, H., *L'Exercitium super Pater Noster. Contribution à l'histoire des xylotypes (Société des bibliophiles belges séant à Mons, 1)*, Mons, 1924.

DE BORCHGRAVE D'ALTENA, J., *Des Caractères de la sculpture brabançonne vers 1500,* Brussels, [s.d.] (reprint of *Annales de la Société royale d'archéologie de Bruxelles,* XXXVIII, 1934, pp. 188-214).

DE BORCHGRAVE D'ALTENA, J., *Une Scène de charité,* in *Bulletin des Musées royaux d'art et d'histoire,* VI, 1934, pp. 64-66.

DE BORCHGRAVE D'ALTENA, J., *Notes pour servir à l'inventaire des œuvres d'art du Brabant. Arrondissement de Louvain,* in *Annales de la Société royale d'archéologie de Bruxelles,* 1939-40, XLIII, pp. 121-389; XLIV, pp. 1-40.

DE BORCHGRAVE D'ALTENA, J., *Les Retables brabançons, 1450 - 1550,* Brussels, 1942.

DE BORCHGRAVE D'ALTENA, J., *Notes pour servir à l'inventaire des œuvres d'art du Brabant. Arrondissement de Bruxelles,* in *Annales de la Société royale d'archéologie de Bruxelles,* XLVII, 1944-46, (1947), pp. IX-XXIX, 1-233.

DE BORCHGRAVE D'ALTENA, J., *Le Retable de saint Georges de Jan Borman,* Brussels, (1947).

DE BORCHGRAVE D'ALTENA, J., *Les Retables brabançons conservés en Suède,* Brussels, 1948.

DE B[ORCHGRAVE D'ALTENA], J., *La Sainte Gertrude d'Etterbeek,* in *Bulletin de la Société royale d'archéologie de Bruxelles,* 1949, pp. 42-43.

DE BORCHGRAVE D'ALTENA, J., *Sculptures bruxelloises au "maillet",* in *Bulletin des Musées royaux d'art et d'histoire,* XXIV, 1952, pp. 91-95.

DE BORCHGRAVE D'ALTENA, J., *La Messe de saint Grégoire. Etude iconographique,* in *Bulletin des Musées royaux des beaux-arts de Belgique, Bruxelles,* 1959, pp. 3-34.

DE BOSSCHÈRE, J., *La Sculpture anversoise aux XVe et XVIe siècles (Collection des grands artistes des Pays-Bas),* Brussels, 1909.

DE CHAMPEAUX, A. and GAUCHERY, P., *Les Travaux d'art exécutés pour Jean de France, duc de Berry, avec une étude biographique sur les artistes employés par ce prince,* Paris, 1886.

DE COO, J., *De unieke voorstelling van de "Jozefskousen" in het veelluik Antwerpen-Baltimore van ca. 1400,* in *Oud-Holland,* LXXIII, 1958, pp. 186-198.

DE GAIFFIER, B., *Le Triptyque du Maître de la légende de sainte Barbe. Sources littéraires de l'iconographie,* in *Revue belge d'archéologie et d'histoire de l'art,* XXVIII, 1959, pp. 3-23.

DEHAISNES, *Histoire de l'art dans la Flandre, l'Artois et le Hainaut avant le XVe siècle,* Lille, 1886.

DEHAISNES, *Documents et extraits divers concernant l'histoire de l'art dans la Flandre, l'Artois et le Hainaut avant le XVe siècle,* 2 vol., Lille, 1886.

DE KONINCK, L., *De Wonderkerk van Hakendover. Volkslegende uit de 7de of 8ste eeuw in rijm gesteld,* Malines, 1896.

De Laborde, *Les Ducs de Bourgogne. Etude sur les lettres, les arts et l'industrie pendant le XVe siècle et plus particulièrement dans les Pays-Bas et le duché de Bourgogne.* Part 2, *Preuves,* 3 vol., Paris, 1849-52.

De La Grange, A. and Cloquet, L., *Etudes sur l'art à Tournai et sur les anciens artistes de cette ville,* 2 vol., Tournai, 1889.

Delaissé, L.M.J., *Les Manuscrits à peintures,* in *Bruxelles au XVe siècle,* Brussels, 1953, pp. 117-131.

Delaissé, L.M.J., *La Miniature flamande à l'époque de Philippe le Bon, (Collection de l'histoire de la miniature, 3),* Milan, (1956).

Delaissé, L.M.J., *Medieval Illuminations. From the Library of Burgundy to the Department of Manuscripts of the Royal Library of Belgium,* [...], Brussels, 1958.

(Delaissé, L.M.J.), *La Miniature flamande. Le mécénat de Philippe le Bon. Exposition organisée à l'occasion du 400e anniversaire de la fondation de la Bibliothèque royale de Philippe II le 12 avril 1559. Palais des beaux-arts, Bruxelles, avril - juin 1959 (Catalogue par* L.M.J. Delaissé), [Brussels], 1959.

Delaissé, L.M.J., *Le Siècle d'or de la miniature flamande. Le mécénat de Philippe le Bon. Exposition organisée à l'occasion du 400e anniversaire de la fondation de la Bibliothèque royale de Philippe II à Bruxelles, le 12 avril 1559. Palais des beaux-arts, Bruxelles. Rijksmuseum, Amsterdam, 26 juin - 13 septembre 1959. (Catalogue par* L.M.J. Delaissé), [Brussels], 1959.

Delaissé, L.M.J., *Miniatures médiévales. De la Librairie de Bourgogne au Cabinet des manuscrits de la Bibliothèque royale de Belgique. (Commentaires par* L.M.J. Delaissé), Brussels, 1960.

Delen, A.J.J., *Histoire de la gravure dans les anciens Pays-Bas et dans les provinces belges des origines jusqu'à la fin du XVIIIe siècle,* 3 vol., Paris-Brussels, 1924-35.

Delen, A.J.J., *Teekeningen van Vlaamsche meesters,* Antwerp - Brussels - Ghent - Louvain, [1944].

(Delen, A.J.J.), *Catalogue descriptif. Maîtres anciens. Musée royal des beaux-arts, Anvers,* 2nd ed. (revised and enlarged by M.J.J. Broeckx and G. Gepts-Buysaert), [s.l.], 1958.

Delisle, L., *Les Manuscrits du comte d'Ashburnham,* Paris, 1883.

Delisle, L., *Un nouveau manuscrit de la Fleur des Histoires de Jean Mansel possédé par M. Olschki,* in *La Bibliofilia,* V, 1903-4, pp. 269-275.

De Los, J., (Peecks), *Chronicon rerum gestarum ab anno MCCCCLV ad annum MDXIV. Accadunt Henrici de Merica et Theodorici Pauli historiae de cladibus leodiensium an. MCCCCLXV-MCCCCLXVII, cum collectione documentarum ad res Ludovici Borbonii et Joannis Hornaci temporibus gestas.* Edidit P.F.X. De Ram, *(Collection de chroniques belges inédites),* Brussels, 1844.

Demmler, Th., *Italienische Skulpturen und Plastiken in Stein, Holz, Stucco. Deutsche, niederländische, französische Skulpturen,* in *Die Sammlung Dr. Albert Figdor. Wien. Erster Teil,* herausgegeben von O. von Falcke, IV, Berlin, 1930.

Demonts, L., *Essai sur Juste de Gand à propos d'une "Adoration des Mages" et d'une "Mort de la Vierge",* in *Revue d'art,* XXV, 1925, pp. 56-74.

de Moreau, E., *Histoire de l'Eglise en Belgique,* IV. *L'Eglise aux Pays-Bas sous les ducs de Bourgogne et Charles-Quint 1378-1559 (Museum Lessianum. Section historique, 12),* Brussels, 1949.

Denis, V., *De Muziekinstrumenten in de Nederlanden en in Italië naar hun afbeelding in de 15e eeuwse kunst,* I. *Hun vorm en ontwikkeling (Universiteit te Leuven. Publicaties op het gebied der geschiedenis en der philologie,* 3rd S., 20), Louvain, 1944.

Denis, V., *Dieric Bouts (De Vlaamse Primitieven leren zien, 2),* Brussels-Amsterdam, 1957.

de Prelle de la Nieppe, E., *Un heaume de joute à l'épreuve,* in *Bulletin des Musées royaux des arts décoratifs et industriels,* II, no. 12, 1903, p. 92.

Dequid, J., *La Sainte Gertrude d'Etterbeek,* in *Bulletin de la Société royale d'archéologie de Bruxelles,* 1944, p. 44.

De Ram, P.F.X., see De Los, J.

De Renesse, J., *Dictionnaire des figures héraldiques,* 7 vol., Brussels, 1892-1903.

De Ricci, S., *Census of Medieval and Renaissance Manuscripts in the United States and Canada,* 3 vol., New York, 1935-40.

de Roddaz, C., *Mobilier,* in *L'Art ancien à l'exposition nationale belge,* publié sous la direction de C. de Roddaz, Brussels - Paris, 1882, pp. 241-260.

de Roever, N., *De Rariteiten-kamer verbonden aan 't Amsterdamsche Gemeente-archief,* in *Oud-Holland,* VI, 1888, pp. 195-224.

de Roover, R., *Money, Banking and Credit in Mediaeval Bruges. Italian Merchant-Bankers, Lombards and Money-Changers. A Study in the Origins of Banking (The Mediaeval Academy of America, 51),* Cambridge, Mass., 1948.

[de Salles], *Mémoires pour servir à l'histoire de France et de Bourgogne, contenant un journal de Paris, sous les règnes de Charles VI & de Charles VII [...],* II. *Mémoires pour l'histoire de Bourgogne,* Paris, 1729.

Descamps, J.B., *Voyage pittoresque de la Flandre et du Brabant,* Rouen, 1769.

De Schryver, A.P. and Marijnissen, R.H., *De oorspronkelijke plaats van het Lam Gods-retabel. Nieuwe gegevens betreffende het van Eyck-probleem*

(*Les Primitifs flamands*, III. *Contributions à l'étude des Primitifs flamands 1*), Antwerp, 1952.

DES MAREZ, G., *L'Organisation du travail à Bruxelles au XVe siècle (Mémoire couronné par l'Académie royale de Belgique*, LXV), Brussels, 1904.

DE SMIDT, F., *Een XVde eeuws kerkinterieur*, in *Gentse bijdragen tot de kunstgeschiedenis*, XVII, 1957-58, pp. 75-84.

DESTRÉE, Joseph, *Etude sur la sculpture brabançonne au moyen âge*, Brussels, 1894 (reprint of *Annales de la Société d'archéologie de Bruxelles*).

DESTRÉE, Joseph, *Tapisseries françaises des Musées royaux*, in *Bulletin des Musées royaux des arts décoratifs et industriels à Bruxelles*, III, 1904, pp. 51-55, 57-59, 65-67.

DESTRÉE, Joseph, *Tapisseries et sculptures bruxelloises à l'exposition d'art ancien bruxellois, organisée à Bruxelles au Cercle artistique et littéraire de juillet à octobre 1905*, Brussels, 1906.

DESTRÉE, Joseph, *Hugo van der Goes*, Brussels-Paris, 1914.

DESTRÉE, Joseph and VAN DEN VEN, P., *Les Tapisseries [des] Musées royaux du Cinquantenaire*, Brussels, 1910.

DESTRÉE, Jules, *Le Maître dit de Flémalle: Robert Campin*, in *Revue de l'art ancien et moderne*, LIII, 1928, pp. 3-14, 81-92, 137-152; LIV, 1928, pp. 113-124, 169-180; LVI, 1929, pp. 117-136.

DESTRÉE, Jules, *Roger de la Pasture - van der Weyden*, 2 vol., Paris - Brussels, 1930.

DE TOLNAY, Ch., *Hieronymus Bosch*, Basel, 1937.

DE TOLNAY, Ch., *Le Maître de Flémalle et les frères van Eyck*, Brussels, 1939.

DE TOLNAY, Ch., *History and Technique of Old Master Drawings. A Handbook*, New York, (1943).

DE TOLNAY, Ch., *Hugo van der Goes as Portrait Painter*, in *The Art Quarterly*, VII, 1944, pp. 181-190.

DE TOLNAY, Ch., *An Early Dutch Panel: A Contribution to the Panel Painting before Bosch*, in *Miscellanea Leo van Puyvelde*, Brussels, 1949, pp. 49-54.

DE VARAX, L., see *Les Tapisseries...*

DEVIGNE, M., *La Sculpture mosane du XIIe au XVIe siècle. Contribution à l'étude de l'art dans la région de la Meuse moyenne*, Paris-Brussels, 1932.

DEVIGNE, M., *Les Rapports de Claus Sluter avec le milieu franco-flamand de Paris*, in *Oud-Holland*, LIV, 1937, pp. 115-130.

DE VINCK DE WINNEZEELE, *Quelques reliques judiciaires des XVe & XVIe siècles dans le Furnambacht*, in *Annales de l'Académie royale d'archéologie de Belgique*, L, 1897, pp. 13-20.

DEVLIEGHER, L., *Enkele Brugse glasramen uit het einde der XVde eeuw,* in *Revue belge d'archéologie et d'histoire de l'art,* XXIII, 1954, pp. 197-203.

DE VORAGINE, J., *La Légende dorée, traduite du latin d'après les plus anciens manuscrits. Avec une introduction, des notes et un index alphabétique, par* T. DE WYZEWA, Paris, 1902.

DE WACHTER, L., *Repertorium van de Vlaamsche gouwen en gemeenten,* 6 vol., Antwerp, 1942-57.

DEZARROIS, A., *L'Art français à Londres,* in *Revue de l'art ancien et moderne,* LXI, 1932, pp. 73-104.

DEZARROIS, A., *Un Tableau inconnu de Jean Van Eyck?,* in *Revue de l'art ancien et moderne,* LXII, 1932, pp. 171-176.

D'HULST, R., *Le "Maître de la Vue de Ste-Gudule" et les retables de la Passion de Geel et de Strengnäs II,* in *Bruxelles au XVe siècle,* Brussels, 1953, pp. 133-153.

DIGBY-WYATT, M., *Metal-Work and its Artistic Design,* London, 1852.

DIRINGER, D., *The Illuminated Book; its History and Production,* London, 1958.

DOCHY, J., *De Schilderijen uit de 15de en de 16de eeuw [St. Salvatorskerk te Brugge],* in *West-Vlaanderen,* VIII, 1959, pp. 19-39.

DOEHAERD, R., *L'Expansion économique belge au moyen âge (Collection: "Notre passé"),* Brussels, (1946).

DOUGLAS, R.L., *Gerard David: The Blessed Virgin as Queen of Heaven,* in *Art in America,* XXXIV, 1946, pp. 161-163.

DOUILLEZ, J., *"Engels borduurwerk" in de Nederlanden,* VIII. *Aanvullende gegevens betreffende de verwerving van de koorkap van Nonnen-Mielen door het Museum Vleeshuis te Antwerpen,* in *Artes textiles,* III, 1956, pp. 12-13.

DOUTREPONT, G., *La Littérature française à la cour des ducs de Bourgogne, Philippe le Hardi, Jean sans Peur, Philippe le Bon, Charles le Téméraire (Bibliothèque du XVe siècle,* VIII), Paris, 1909.

DROUOT, H., *Sluter en Belgique,* in *Annales de Bourgogne,* VI, 1936, pp. 278-287.

DUCLOS, A., *Bruges. Histoire et souvenirs,* Bruges, 1910, (1913).

DUMONT-WILDEN, L., *Collection de M. Ch.-L. Cardon (Bruxelles),* in *Les Arts,* VIII, 1909, pp. 2-21.

DU MORTIER fils, B., *Recherches sur les principaux monuments de Tournai,* in *Bulletin de la Société historique et littéraire de Tournai,* VIII, 1862, pp. 137-369.

DUPONT, J., *Les Primitifs français (1350-1500),* Paris, 1937.

DURRIEU, P., *Heures de Turin. Quarante-cinq feuillets à peintures provenant des*

Très Belles Heures de Jean de France, duc de Berry, Paris, 1902.

DURRIEU, P., *La Peinture en France,* I. *De Jean le Bon à la mort de Charles V (1350-1380),* II. *Le règne de Charles VI,* in *Histoire de l'art* [...], publiée sous la direction de A. MICHEL, III. *Le réalisme. Les débuts de la renaissance,* 1, Paris, 1907, pp. 102-171.

DURRIEU, P., *Livre de prières peint pour Charles le Téméraire par son enlumineur en titre Philippe de Mazerolles (Le Maître de "la Conquête de la Toison d'Or"),* in *Fondation E. Piot, Monuments et mémoires,* XXII, 1916, pp. 71-130.

DURRIEU, P., *La Miniature flamande au temps de la cour de Bourgogne (1415-1530),* Brussels-Paris, 1921.

DUVERGER, J., *Brussels als kunstcentrum in de XIVe en de XVe eeuw (Bouwstoffen tot de Nederlandsche kunstgeschiedenis, III),* Antwerp-Ghent, 1935.

DUVERGER, J., *Thienen van,* in *Allgemeines Lexikon der bildenden Künstler* [...], begründet von U. THIEME und F. BECKER [...], herausgegeben von H. VOLLMER, Leipzig, 1939, XXXIII, p. 31.

DUVERGER, J., *De Meester van het grafmonument van Maria van Boergondië te Brugge,* in *Jaarboek der Koninklijke Academie van België,* VIII, 1946, p. 131.

DUVERGER, J., *Brugse schilders ten tijde van Jan Van Eyck,* in *Bulletin des Musées royaux des beaux-arts,* Bruxelles, 1955, 1-3 *(Miscellanea Erwin Panofsky),* pp. 83-120.

DUVERGER, J., *"Engels" borduurwerk in de Nederlanden,* I. *De koorkap van Nonnen-Mielen in het Vleeshuis Museum te Antwerpen,* in *Artes textiles,* II, 1955, pp. 18-27.

DVOŘÁK, M., *Das Rätsel der Kunst der Brüder van Eyck, mit einem Anhang über die Anfänge der Holländischen Malerei,* Munich, 1925.

EICHLER, H., *Flandrische gravierte Metallgrabplatten des 14. Jahrhunderts,* in *Jahrbuch der Preussischen Kunstsammlungen,* LIV, 1933, pp. 199-220.

ENGLISH, M., *De Geschiedenis van het gebouw* [St. Salvatorskerk te Brugge], in *West-Vlaanderen,* VIII, 1959, pp. 5 - 17.

ENLART, C., *Manuel d'archéologie française depuis les temps mérovingiens jusqu'à la renaissance,* III. *Le costume,* Paris, 1916.

FAIRFAX MURRAY, J. *Pierpont Morgan Collection of Drawings by the Old Masters,* I, London, 1905-12.

FEINBLATT, E., *Los Angeles County Museum. The Gothic Room,* [s.l., s.d.].

FIERENS, P., *Van der Weyden, vers 1399-1464,* in *Les Peintres célèbres,* publié sous la direction de B. DORIVAL, (Paris - Genève, 1948), pp. 62-65.

FIERENS, P., *Memling, vers 1435-1494*, in *Les Peintres célèbres*, publié sous la direction de B. DORIVAL, (Paris - Genève, 1948), pp. 68-69.

FIERENS, P. (under the direction of), *L'Art en Belgique du moyen âge à nos jours*, 3rd ed., Brussels, [1956].

FIERENS-GEVAERT, *L'Exposition des Primitifs flamands à Bruges*, in *Revue de l'art ancien et moderne*, XII, 1902, pp. 105-116, 173-182, 435-444.

FIERENS-GEVAERT, *Etudes sur l'art flamand. La renaissance septentrionale et les premiers maîtres flamands*, Brussels, 1905.

FIERENS-GEVAERT, *L'Exposition Van Eyck - Bouts à Bruxelles en 1920. Les retables de l'Agneau Mystique et du Saint-Sacrement. Notes et impressions*, Brussels-Paris, 1921.

FIERENS-GEVAERT, *La Peinture à Bruges. Guide historique et critique*, Brussels-Paris, 1922.

FIERENS-GEVAERT, *L'Art belge ancien et moderne*, Paris, 1923.

FIERENS-GEVAERT, *Histoire de la peinture flamande des origines à la fin du XVe siècle*, 3 vol., Paris-Brussels, 1927-29.

FILANGIERI DI CANDIDA, R., *Les Origines de la peinture flamande à Naples au XVe siècle*, in *Actes du XIIe Congrès international d'histoire de l'art, Bruxelles, 1930*, II, Brussels, [s.d.], pp. 560-576.

FIRMENICH-RICHARTZ, E., *Rogier van der Weyden, der Meister von Flémalle*, in *Zeitschrift für bildende Kunst*, N.S., X, 1899, pp. 1-12, 129-144.

FLIEDNER, S., *Die Brabender (ca. 1440-1520)*, in *Bulletin des musées royaux des beaux-arts*, [Bruxelles], 1958, pp. 141-214.

FLINT, R., *John N. Willys Collection*, in *International Studio*, LXXX, Feb. 1925, pp. 363-367.

FOCILLON, H., *Art d'Occident. Le moyen âge roman et gothique*, 2nd ed., Paris, 1947.

FOLIE, J., *Les Primitifs flamands dans les collections publiques des Etats-Unis*, in *Bulletin de l'Institut royal du patrimoine artistique*, I, 1958, pp. 120-124.

FORSYTH, W.H., *The Trojan War in Medieval Tapestries*, in *The Bulletin of the Metropolitan Museum of Art*, XIV, 1955, pp. 76-84.

FRÄNGER, W., *The Millennium of Hieronymus Bosch. Outlines of a new Interpretation*, London, [s.d.].

FRANCIS, H.S., *Bequest of John L. Severance, 1936. Department of Paintings*, in *The Bulletin of the Cleveland Museum of Art*, XXIX, 1942, pp. 132-136.

FRANCIS, H.S., *"The Nativity" by Gerard David*, in *The Bulletin of the Cleveland Museum of Art*, XLV, 1958, pp. 227-236.

FRANCOTTE, J., *Dieric Bouts. Zijn kunst, zijn Laatste Avondmaal, (Davidsfonds, 46)*, Louvain, 1951-52.

FRANKFURTER, A.M., *Paintings by Hans Memling in American Collections*, in

The Fine Arts, XVIII, March, 1932, pp. 18-22.

FREDERIKS, J.W., *Enkele beschouwingen naar aanleiding van het gietwerk van Reinier van Thienen*, in *Oud-Holland*, LX, 1943, pp. 118-128.

FRIEDLÄNDER, M.J., *Malerei. Niederländer und Deutsche*, in *Ausstellung von Kunstwerken des Mittelalters und der Renaissance aus Berliner Privatbesitz veranstaltet von der Kunstgeschichtlichen Gesellschaft, 20 Mai bis 3 Juli 1898*, Berlin, 1899, pp. 3-35.

FRIEDLÄNDER, M.J., *Meisterwerke der niederländischen Malerei des XV. und XVI. Jahrhunderts auf der Ausstellung zu Brügge 1902*, Munich, 1903.

FRIEDLÄNDER, M.J., *Ausstellungen. Die Brügger Leihausstellung von 1902*, in *Repertorium für Kunstwissenschaft*, XXVI, 1903, pp. 66-91, 147-175.

FRIEDLÄNDER, M.J., *Ein Madonnenbild Gerard Davids im Kaiser Friedrich Museum*, in *Jahrbuch der königlich Preussischen Kunstsammlungen*, XXVII, 1906, pp. 143-148.

FRIEDLÄNDER, M.J., *De Verzameling von Kaufmann te Berlijn*, in *Onze Kunst*, V, 1906, pp. 29-40.

FRIEDLÄNDER, M.J., *Die Leihausstellung in der Guildhall zu London*, in *Repertorium für Kunstwissenschaft*, XXIX, 1906, pp. 573-582.

FRIEDLÄNDER, M.J., Quoted in *Kunstgeschichtliche Gesellschaft, Sitzungsbericht*. Sec. II, Report of Meeting printed in *Deutsche Literaturzeitung*, February 27, 1909, pp. 551-552.

FRIEDLÄNDER, M.J., *Ein neu erworbenes Madonnenbild im Kaiser Friedrich Museum*, in *Amtliche Berichte aus den königliche Kunstsammlungen*, XXXVI, 1915, col. 117-183.

FRIEDLÄNDER, M.J., *Die Sammlung Richard von Kaufmann, Berlin. Gemälde. Versteigerung Dienstag den 4. Dezember 1917 und die folgenden Tage, unter der Leitung der Unterzeichneten P. Cassirer, Berlin und H. Helbing, München*, (Berlin), 1917.

FRIEDLÄNDER, M.J., *About some of Hans Memling's Pictures in the United States*, in *Art in America*, 1920, pp. 107-116.

FRIEDLÄNDER, M.J., *Hugo van der Goes*, in *Allgemeines Lexikon der bildenden Künstler* [...], begründet von U. THIEME und F. BECKER, XIV, ed. U. THIEME und F.C. WILLIS, Leipzig, 1921, pp. 312-213.

FRIEDLÄNDER, M.J., *Die Brüsseler Tafelmalerei gegen den Ausgang des 15. Jahrhunderts*, in *Belgische Kunstdenkmäler* [...], herausgegeben von P. CLEMEN, I, Munich, 1923, pp. 309-320.

FRIEDLÄNDER, M.J., *Der Meister der Barbaralegende*, in *Jahrbuch für Kunstwissenschaft*, 1924, pp. 20-25.

FRIEDLÄNDER, M.J., *Die altniederländische Malerei, I. Die Van Eyck-Petrus Christus*, Berlin, 1924; II. *Rogier van der Weyden und der Meister von*

Flémalle, Berlin, 1924; III. *Dierick Bouts und Joos van Gent*, Berlin, 1925; IV. *Hugo van der Goes*. Berlin, 1926; V. *Geertgen van Haarlem und Hieronymus Bosch*, Berlin, 1927; VI. *Memling und Gerard David*, Berlin, 1928; VII. *Quentin Massijs*, Berlin, 1929; VIII. *Jan Gossart - Bernart van Orley*, Berlin, 1930; IX. *Joos van Cleve - Jan Provost - Joachim Patenier*, Berlin, 1931; X. *Lucas van Leyden und andere Holländische Meister seiner Zeit*, Berlin, 1932; XI. *Die Antwerpener Manieristen, Adriaan Ysenbrant*, Berlin, 1933; XII. *Pieter Coeck - Jan van Scorel*, Leiden, 1935; XIII. *Anthonis Mor und seine Zeitgenossen*, Leiden, 1936; XIV. *Pieter Bruegel und Nachträge zu den früheren Bänden*, Leiden, 1937.

FRIEDLÄNDER, M.J., *Neues über Petrus Christus*, in *Der Kunstwanderer*, VI, 1925, pp. 297-298.

FRIEDLÄNDER, M.J., *A Drawing by Roger van der Weyden*, in *Old Master Drawings*, I, 1926-27, pp. 29-32.

FRIEDLÄNDER, M.J., *Neues über den Meister Michiel und Juan de Flandes*, in *Der Cicerone*, XXI, 1929, pp. 249-254.

FRIEDLÄNDER, M.J., *A Roger van der Weyden Altarpiece*, II, in *The Burlington Magazine*, LXIII, 1933, p. 57.

FRIEDLÄNDER, M.J., *Memling (Palet Serie)*, Amsterdam, [1949].

FRIEDLÄNDER, M.J., *Van der Goes und Memling*, in *Oud-Holland*, LXV, 1950, pp. 167-171.

FRIEDLÄNDER, M.J., *Early Netherlandish Painting from van Eyck to Bruegel*, London, 1956.

FRY, R., *Flemish Art at Burlington House*, in *The Burlington Magazine*, L, 1927, p. 62.

FRY, R., and BROCKWELL, M., *Exhibition of Old Masters, Grafton Gallery*, London, 1911.

GAILLIARD, J., *Bruges et le Franc ou leur magistrature et leur noblesse, avec des données historiques et généalogiques sur chaque famille*, 6 vol., Bruges, 1857-64.

GASPAR, C. and LYNA, F., *Les principaux manuscrits à peintures de la Bibliothèque royale de Belgique*, 2 vol., Paris, 1937-47.

GAVELLE, R., *Le Tombeau de Louis de Male et le tombeau de Jeanne de Brabant. Résumés des thèses de l'année 1934-1935. Thèse soutenue par [...]*, in *Bulletin des Musées de France*, VII, 1935, pp. 126-128.

† *Georg Swarzenski, 1876-1957*, in *Bulletin of the Museum of Fine Arts, Boston*, IV, nos. 301-302, 1957, pp. 57-119.

GERMAIN, A., *L'Influence des Pays-Bas en Bourgogne*, in *L'Art flamand et hollandais*, X, 1908, pp. 167-180.

GERMAIN, A., *Les Néerlandais en Bourgogne (Collection des grands artistes des Pays-Bas)*, Brussels, 1909.

416

GERSON, H., *Van Geertgen tot Frans Hals. De Nederlandsche Schilderkunst,* I, *(De Schoonheid van ons land. Schilderkunst),* Amsterdam, 1950.

GERSTENBERG, K., *Die Niederländische Plastik des 15. Jahrhunderts in ihrer Europäischen Auswirkung,* in *Actes du XIIIe Congrès international d'histoire de l'art, Stockholm, 1933,* (Stockholm, 1933), pp. 164-169.

GILLET, L., *Histoire artistique des ordres mendiants. Etude sur l'art religieux en Europe du XIIIe au XVIIe siècle,* Paris, 1912.

GILLIODTS-VAN SEVEREN, L. and GAILLIARD, E., *Inventaire des archives de la ville de Bruges,* 9 vol., Bruges, 1871-85.

GLÜCK, G., *The Henry VII in the National Portrait Gallery,* in *The Burlington Magazine,* LXIII, 1933, pp. 100-108.

GLÜCK, G., *Drei Jahrhunderte Flämischer Kunst,* in *Belvedere,* IX, 1939, pp. 75-81.

GÖBEL, H., *Wandteppiche,* I. *Die Niederlände,* 2 vol., Leipzig, 1923.

GOLDSCHEIDER, L., *Fünfhundert Selbstporträts,* Vienna, 1936.

GÓMEZ-MORENO, M., *La gran tapiceria de la guerra de Troya,* in *Arte español,* VIII, 4, 1919, pp. 265-282.

GORIS, J.A., *Etude sur les colonies marchandes méridionales (Portugais, Espagnols, Italiens) à Anvers de 1488 à 1567. Contribution à l'histoire des débuts du capitalisme moderne (Université de Louvain. Recueil de travaux publiés par les membres des conférences d'histoire et de philologie,* 2nd S., 4), Louvain, 1925.

GORIS, J.A., *Portraits by Flemish Masters in American Collections,* New York, 1949.

Gothic Table Appointments, in *Bulletin of the Minneapolis Institute of Arts,* XXIII, 1934, pp. 65-66.

GUESNON, A., *Le Hautelisseur Pierre Feré d'Arras, auteur de la tapisserie de Tournai (1402),* in *Revue du Nord,* I, 1910, pp. 201-215.

GUIFFREY, J., *La Guerre de Troie. A propos de dessins récemment acquis par le Louvre,* I-II, in *Revue de l'art ancien et moderne,* V, 1899, pp. 205-212, 503-516.

GUIFFREY, J., *La Tapisserie aux XIVe et XVe siècles,* in *Histoire de l'art [...],* publiée sous la direction de A. MICHEL, III. *Le réalisme. Les débuts de la renaissance,* 1, Paris, 1907, pp. 343-375.

GUIFFREY, J.J., *Histoire générale de la tapisserie. France,* Paris, [s.d.].

GUNTHER, R.T., *The Astrolabe of the World,* Oxford, 1932.

[HANNEMA, D. and VAN GELDER, J.G.], *Museum Boymans, Rotterdam 1936. Jeroen Bosch. Noord-Nederlandsche Primitieven, 10 Juli - 15 October,* [s.l.], 1936.

HAUSER, A., *The Social History of Art,* 2 vol., New York, 1952.

HEIL, W., *Catalogue of Paintings in the Permanent Collection of the Detroit Institute of Arts: European Paintings*, [Detroit], 1930.

HEILAND, P., *Dirk Bouts und die Hauptwerke seiner Schule. Ein stilkritisches Versuch, (Inaugural-Dissertation zur Erlangung der Doktorwürde bei einer Hohen Philosophischen Fakultät der Kaiser Wilhelmus-Universität Straßburg I.E.)*, Potsdam, (1902).

HEILMAIER, H., *Rundschau. Paris. Ein neuer Van Eyck?*, in *Pantheon*, XI, 1933, p. 38.

HELBIG, J., *Les Châsses de saint Domitian et de saint Mengold de l'ancienne collégiale de Huy. Le reliquaire offert en don expiatoire à la cathédrale de Saint-Lambert de Liège. Les auteurs et l'histoire de ces reliquaires*, in *Bulletin de l'Institut archéologique liégeois*, XIII, 1877, pp. 221-244.

HELBIG, J., *Une Oeuvre de Gérard Loyet, graveur de sceaux, orfèvre et valet de chambre du duc Charles de Bourgogne*, in *Revue de l'art chrétien*, XXXI, 1883, pp. 271-278.

HELBIG, J., *De Glasschilderkunst in België. Repertorium en documenten*, 2 vol., Antwerp, 1943-51.

HELD, J.S., *Book Review. Harry B. WEHLE and Margaretta M. SALINGER, A Catalogue of Early Flemish, Dutch, and German Paintings in the Metropolitan Museum of Art, New York, Metropolitan Museum, 1947, [...]*, in *The Art Bulletin*, XXI, 1949, pp. 139-143.

HELD, J.S., *Book Review. A. JANSSENS DE BISTHOVEN and R.A. PARMENTIER, Les Primitifs flamands: Corpus de la Peinture des Anciens Pays-Bas Méridionaux au Quinzième Siècle, fascicules 1-4, Le Musée Communal de Bruges [...], Antwerp, 1951, [...]*, in *College Art Journal*, XII, 1952, pp. 87-91.

HELD, J.S., *Book Review. Erwin PANOFSKY, Early Netherlandish Painting. Its Origins and Character, Cambridge, Harvard University Press, 1953 [...]*, in *The Art Bulletin*, XXXVII, 1955, pp. 205-234.

HENDY, Ph., *The Isabella Stewart Gardner Museum. Catalogue of Paintings*, Boston, 1931.

HOLMES, C., *The Holford Collection (Westonbirt), Illustrated with 101 Plates Selected from 12 Illustrated Manuscripts at Dorchester House and 107 Pictures at Westonbird in Gloustershire. Privately printed for Sir George Holford and Members of the Burlington Fine Arts Club who subscribed at the Winter Exhibition 1921-22*, London, 1924.

HOMMEL, L., *Histoire du noble Ordre de la Toison d'Or*, Brussels, (1947).

HOOGEWERFF, G.J., *De Noord-Nederlandsche schilderkunst*, 5 vol., The Hague, 1936-47.

HOSTEN, E. and STRUBBE, E.I., *Geïllustreerde catalogus. Stedelijke Museum van Schoone Kunsten, Brugge*, 2nd revised and enlarged ed., Bruges, 1938.

HOTHO, *Geschichte der Christlichen Malerei*, Stuttgart, 1867.

418

HUIZINGA, J., *The Waning of the Middle Ages*, London, 1924.

H[ULIN] DE LOO, G., *Bruges 1902. Exposition de tableaux flamands des XIVe, XVe et XVIe siècles. Catalogue critique précédé d'une introduction sur l'identité de certains maîtres anonymes*, Ghent, 1902.

H[ULIN] DE LOO, G., *Heures de Milan. Troisième partie des Très Belles Heures de Notre-Dame enluminées par les peintres de Jean de France, duc de Berry et par ceux du duc Guillaume de Bavière* [...], *Biblioteca Trivulziana à Milan. Avec une introduction historique*, Brussels - Paris, 1911.

HULIN DE LOO, G., *Stockt (Vranck Van Der)*, in *Biographie nationale* [...] *de Belgique*, XXIV, Brussels, 1926-29, col. 66-76.

HULIN DE LOO, G., *Weyden (Rogier De Le Pasture, alias Van Der)*, in *Biographie nationale* [...] *de Belgique*, XXVII, Brussels, 1938, col. 222-245.

HUMBERT, A., *La Sculpture sous les ducs de Bourgogne (1361-1483)*. Préface de H. ROUJON, Paris, 1913.

HUNTER, G.L., *The Practical Book of Tapestries*, Philadelphia - London, 1925.

HYMANS, H., *L'Exposition des Primitifs flamands à Bruges*, in *Gazette des beaux-arts*, XXVIII, 1902, pp. 89-100, 189-207, 280-306.

Inventaire des instruments scientifiques historiques conservés en Belgique, (Centre national d'histoire des sciences), Brussels, 1959.

Inventaire des objets d'art existant dans les édifices publics des communes de l'arrondissement de Louvain, (Province de Brabant, Comité des correspondants de la Commission royale des monuments), Brussels, 1906.

Inventaires des objets d'art, qui ornent les églises et les établissements publics de la Flandre occidentale, dressés par des Commissions officielles et précédés d'une introduction ou précis de l'histoire de l'art dans cette province par A. COUVEZ, Bruges, 1852.

JANSEN, A. and VAN HERCK, C., *Kerkelijke kunstschatten. Een rijk geïllustreerd documentatie- en herdenkingsalbum, samengesteld en uitgegeven naar aanleiding van de tentoonstelling "Kerkelijke kunst" gehouden te Antwerpen van 16 october tot 15 november 1948. Met een afzonderlijke bijdrage van* kan. Dr. Fl. PRIMS, Antwerp, (1949).

JANSSENS DE BISTHOVEN, A., *Het Beeldhouwwerk van het Brugsche stadhuis*, in *Gentse bijdragen tot de kunstgeschiedenis*, X, 1944, pp. 7-81.

JANSSENS DE BISTHOVEN, A., *Musée communal des beaux-arts (Musée Groeninge), Bruges (Les Primitifs flamands, I. Corpus de la peinture des anciens Pays-Bas méridionaux au quinzième siècle, 1)*, 2nd revised and enlarged ed., Antwerp, 1959.

JOHANSEN, P., *Meister Michel Sittow, Hofmaler der Köningin Isabella von Kastilien und Bürger von Reval*, in *Jahrbuch der Preussischen Kunstsammlungen*, LXI, 1940, pp. 1-36.

419

JUBINAL, A., *Les anciennes tapisseries historiées ou collection des monuments les plus remarquables qui nous sont restés du moyen âge, à partir du XIe siècle au XVIe siècle* [...], Paris, 1838.

JUSTI, C., *Altflandrische Bilder in Spanien und Portugal*, in *Zeitschrift für bildende Kunst*, XXI, 1886, pp. 93-98, 133-140; XXII, 1887, pp. 179-186, 244-251.

KÄMMERER, L., *Hubert und Jan van Eyck, (Künstler Monographien, XXXV)*, Bielefeld-Leipzig, 1898.

KÄMMERER, L., *Memling, (Künstler Monographien, XXXIX)*, Bielefeld - Leipzig, 1898.

KAUFMANN, H., *Ein Selbstporträt Rogers van der Weyden auf den Berner Trajansteppichen*, in *Repertorium für Kunstwissenschaft*, XXXIX, 1916, pp. 15-30.

KELLEHER, P., *"Madonna and Child in a Gothic Interior" by Petrus Christus in the William Rockhill Nelson Gallery of Art*, in *The Art Quarterly*, XX, 1957, pp. 112-116.

KERN, G.J., *Die Grundzüge der linear-perspektivischen Darstellung in der Kunst der Gebrüder van Eyck und ihrer Schule*, I. *Die perspektivischen Projektion*, Leipzig, 1904.

KERVYN DE LETTENHOVE, *Histoire de Flandre. La Flandre sous les ducs de Bourgogne*, I. *1383-1453;* II. *1453-1500,* 5th ed., 2 vol., Bruges, 1898.

KLEIN, D., *St. Lukas als Maler der Maria*, Berlin, 1933.

KLEINCLAUSZ, A., *Les Peintres des ducs de Bourgogne*, in *Revue de l'art ancien et moderne*, XX, 1906, pp. 161-176, 253-268.

KOCH, F., *Ein Schüler des Meisters von Flemalle*, in *Repertorium für Kunstwissenschaft*, XXIV, 1901, pp. 290-291.

KOCH, R.A., *A Rediscovered Painting by Petrus Christus*, in *The Connoisseur*, CXL, 1957, pp. 271-276.

KOECHLIN, R., *La Sculpture belge et les influences françaises aux XIIIe et XIVe siècles*, in *Gazette des beaux-arts*, XXX, 1903, pp. 5-19, 333-348, 391-407.

KOHLHAUSSEN, H., *Niederländisch Schmelzwerk*, in *Jahrbuch der Preussischen Kunstsammlungen*, LII, 1931, pp. 153-169.

KONRAD, M., *Antwerpener Binnenräume im Zeitalter des Rubens*, in *Belgische Kunstdenkmäler*, herausgeg. von P. CLEMEN, II, Munich, 1923, pp. 185-242.

KONRAD, M., *Meisterwerke der Skulptur in Flandern und Brabant*, Berlin, 1928.

Krieg (Der Trojanische). Text zu französischen Originalzeichnungen [...], von D.P. SCHUMANN, Dresden, 1898.

KRONIG, J.-O., *Deux tableaux de maîtres néerlandais dans les collections de S.M. le Roi de Portugal*, in *Les Arts*, 1910, p. 28.

420

KUGLER, F. and BURCKHARDT, J., *Handbuch der Malerei seit Constantin dem Großem*, 2nd ed., 2 vol., Berlin, 1847.

KURTH, B., *Die Blütezeit der Bildwirkerkunst zu Tournai und der burgundische Hof*, in *Jahrbuch der kunsthistorischen Sammlungen des Allerhöchsten Kaiserhauses*, XXXIV, 1917, pp. 53-110.

KUYL, P.D., *Gheel vermaerd door den eerdienst der Heilige Dimphna. Geschieden oudheidskundige beschrijving der kerken gestichten en kapellen dier oude vrijheid*, Antwerp, 1863.

LABANDE, L.H., *Les Primitifs français, peintres et peintres verriers de la Provence occidentale*, 2 vol., Marseille, 1932.

LAFOND, P., *Roger van der Weyden*, Brussels, 1912.

LAFOND, P., *Hieronymus Bosch. Son art, son influence, ses disciples*, Brussels-Paris, 1914.

LAURENT, H., *Un grand commerce d'exportation au moyen âge. La draperie des Pays-Bas en France et dans les pays méditerranéens (XII-XVe siècles)*, Paris, 1935.

LAURENT, M., *L'Architecture et la sculpture en Belgique, (Bibliothèque d'histoire de l'art)*, Paris - Brussels, 1928.

LAURENT, M., *Claes Sluter et la sculpture brabançonne*, in *XXXe Congrès de la Fédération archéologique et historique de Belgique, Bruxelles 1935*, Brussels, 1936, pp. 257-270.

LAVALLEYE, J., *Le Château de Courtrai*, in *Annales de la Société royale d'archéologie de Bruxelles*, XXXV, 1930, pp. 157-168.

LAVALLEYE, J., *Le Problème Maître de Flémalle - Rogier van der Weyden*, in *Revue belge de philologie et d'histoire*, XII, 1933, pp. 791-805.

LAVALLEYE, J., *Essai de classement de quelques œuvres de jeunesse de Rogier van der Weyden*, in *XXXe Congrès de la Fédération archéologique et historique de Belgique, Bruxelles 1935*, Brussels, 1936, pp. 32-40.

LAVALLEYE, J., *Juste de Gand, peintre de Frédéric de Montefeltre, (Université de Louvain. Recueil de travaux publiés par les membres des conférences d'histoire et de philologie*, 2nd S., 37), Louvain, 1936.

LAVALLEYE, J., *De Vlaamsche schilderkunst van Memlinc tot Metsys en zijn onmiddelijke omgeving*, in *Geschiedenis van de Vlaamsche kunst*, onder leiding van I.S. LEURS, I, Antwerp, [1936], pp. 374-408.

LAVALLEYE, J., *Le Portrait au XVe siècle, (L'Art en Belgique)*, Brussels, 1943.

LAVALLEYE, J., *L'Ecole bruxelloise de peinture au XVe siècle*, in *Bruxelles au XVe siècle*, Brussels, 1953, pp. 165-186.

LAVALLEYE, J., *Memlinc à l'hôpital Saint-Jean (Bruges)*, Brussels, (1953).

LAVALLEYE, J., *Collections d'Espagne, 1-2 (Les Primitifs flamands, II. Répertoire des peintures flamandes des quinzième et seizième siècles)*, Antwerp, 1953-58.

LAVALLEYE, J., *La Peinture et l'enluminure des origines à la fin du XVe siècle*, in *L'Art en Belgique du moyen âge à nos jours*, publié sous la direction de P. FIERENS, 3rd ed., Brussels, [1956].

LAVALLEYE, J., *Considérations sur les Primitifs flamands conservés à la Capilla Real de Grenade*, in *Bulletin de l'Académie royale de Belgique. Classe des beaux-arts*, XLI, 1959, pp. 21-29.

LEBEER, L., 1938, see *Spirituale Pomerium*...

LEBEER, L., *L'Esprit de la gravure au XVe siècle*, Brussels, 1943.

LEBEER, L., *Nog enkele wetenswaardigheden in verband met Pieter Bruegel den Oude*, in *Gentsche bijdragen tot de kunstgeschiedenis*, IX, 1943, pp. 217-236.

LEBEER, L., *Le Dessin, la gravure, le livre xylographique et typographique*, in *Bruxelles au XVe siècle*, Brussels, 1953, pp. 187-217.

LEBEER, L., *Propos sur les dessins de Roger van der Weyden et de Vrancke van der Stockt*, in *Annales de la Société royale d'archéologie de Bruxelles*, XLIX, 1956-57, pp. 73-99.

LECLERC, A., *Flemish Drawings XV-XVI Centuries*, London - Paris - New York, [1950].

LEDERLE, U., *Gerechtigkeitsdarstellungen in deutschen und niederländischen Rathäusern (Heidelberger Dissertation, 1936)*, Philippsburg, 1937.

LEEUWENBERG, J., *De tien bronzen plorannen in het Rijksmuseum te Amsterdam, hun herkomst en de voorbeelden waaraan zij zijn ontleend*, in *Gentse bijdragen tot de kunstgeschiedenis*, XIII, 1951, pp. 13-59.

LEFÈVE, R. and VAN MOLLE, F., *De oorspronkelijke schikking van de luiken van Bouts' Laatste Avondmaal*, in *Bulletin de l'Institut royal du patrimoine artistique*, III, 1960, pp. 5-19.

LEHRS, M., *Geschichte und kritischer Katalog des deutschen, niederländischen und französischen Kupferstichs im XV. Jahrhundert*, Vienna, 1908.

LEJEUNE, J., *La Principauté de Liège*. Préface de P. HARSIN, (Liège), 1948.

LEJEUNE, J., *Les Van Eyck, peintres de Liège et de sa cathédrale*, Liège, 1956.

LELAND HUNTER, G., see HUNTER, G.L.

LEMAIRE, R., *Beknopte geschiedenis van de meubelkunst*, 2nd enlarged ed., Antwerp, 1942.

LEMAIRE, R., *De Madonna in de kerk uit het Berlijnse Museum (Mededelingen van de Koninklijke Vlaamse Academie voor Wetenschappen, Letteren en*

422

Schone Kunsten van België. Klasse der Schone Kunsten, XII, no. 2), Brussels, 1950.

LEMAIRE, R.M., *L'Architecture romane et gothique,* in *L'Art en Belgique du moyen âge à nos jours,* publié sous la direction de P. FIERENS, 3rd ed., Brussels, [1956], pp. 37-100.

LEMOISNE, P.A., *La Peinture française à l'époque gothique, XIVe et XVe siècles,* Paris, 1931.

LEPRIEUR, P., *Ecoles du Nord,* in *Collection Emile Pacully. Tableaux anciens et modernes des écoles allemande, espagnole, flamande, française, hollandaise, italienne, dont la vente aura lieu galerie Georges Petit [...], le lundi 4 mai 1903,* [s.l.], 1903, pp. 33-34.

LEROQUAIS, V., *Le Bréviaire de Philippe le Bon, bréviaire parisien du XVe siècle. Etude du texte et des miniatures,* 2 vol., Brussels, 1929.

LEROQUAIS, V., *Un livre d'Heures de Jean sans Peur, duc de Bourgogne (1404-1419),* Paris, 1939.

LESTOQUOY, J., *Le Commerce des œuvres d'art au moyen âge,* in *Mélanges d'histoire sociale,* III, 1943, pp. 19-26.

LESTOQUOY, J., *Aux Origines de la bourgeoisie: les villes de Flandre et d'Italie sous le gouvernement des patriciens (XIe-XVe siècles),* Paris, 1952.

LEURS, I.S. (under the direction of), *Geschiedenis van de Vlaamsche Kunst,* 2 vol., Antwerp, [s.d.].

LEVETUS, A.S., *Ancient Bedsteads and Cradles,* in *The Studio,* XXXVI, 1906, pp. 131-138.

LEX, L., *Chronique. Bibliothèques. Mâcon. Rapport de M. LEX, [...] relatif à la réorganisation de la bibliothèque de la ville,* in *Bulletin des bibliothèques et des archives,* III, 1886, pp. 119-134.

LIEBREICH, A., *Claus Sluter,* Brussels, 1936.

LINDEMAN, C.M.A.A., *De Dateering, herkomst en identificatie der "Gravenbeeldjes" van Jacques de Gérines,* in *Oud-Holland,* LVIII, 1941, pp. 49-58, 97-105, 161-169, 193-219.

LOUIS, A., *Les Consoles de l'hôtel de ville de Bruges,* in *Revue belge d'archéologie et d'histoire de l'art,* VII, 1937, pp. 199-210.

LUGT, F., *Répertoire des catalogues de ventes publiques intéressant l'art ou la curiosité [...], I. Première période, vers 1600-1825; II. Deuxième période, 1825-1860, (Publications du Rijksbureau voor Kunsthistorische Documentatie, La Haye),* 2 vol., The Hague, 1938-53.

LYNA, F., *De Vlaamsche miniatuur van 1200 tot 1530, (Eigen schoon, 12),* Brussels - Amsterdam, 1933.

MAC DONNELL, E.W., *Beguins and Beghards in Medieval Culture with Special Emphasis on the Belgian Scene,* New Jersey, 1954.

423

MAERE, R., *Le Retable d'Haekendover*, in *Annales de l'Académie royale d'archéologie de Belgique*, LXVIII, 1920, pp. 70-97.

MAERE, R., *Over het afbeelden van bestaande gebouwen in het schilderwerk van Vlaamsche Primitieven*, in *De Kunst der Nederlanden*, I, 1930-31, pp. 201-212.

MAERE, R., *Maquettes des tours de l'église Saint-Pierre à Louvain et l'emploi des maquettes en architecture*, in *Annales de la Société royale d'archéologie de Bruxelles*, XL, 1936, pp. 48-88.

MAERE, R., *Over iconografie van kribbe en Christus-Kind in de Christelijke-Kunst*, in *Winterhulp-Kerstmis, 1943*, [s.l.], 1943, pp. 81-84.

MAETERLINCK, L., *Le Genre satirique dans la peinture flamande*, 2nd revised and enlarged ed., Brussels, 1907.

MAETERLINCK, L., *Les Imitateurs de Hieronymus Bosch. A propos d'une œuvre inconnue d'Henri met de Bles*, in *Revue de l'art ancien et moderne*, XXIII, 1908, pp. 145-156.

MAETERLINCK, L., *Une Ecole primitive méconnue. Nabur Martins ou le Maître de Flémalle (nouveaux documents)*, Brussels - Paris, 1913.

MAFFEI, E., *La Réservation eucharistique jusqu'à la renaissance*, Brussels, 1942.

MAFFEI, E., *Le Mobilier civil en Belgique au moyen âge*, Namur, [s.d.].

MÂLE, E., *L'Art religieux du XIIIe siècle en France. Etude sur l'iconographie du moyen âge et sur ses sources d'inspiration*, Paris, 1902.

MÂLE, E., *L'Art religieux de la fin du moyen âge en France. Etude sur l'iconographie du moyen âge et sur ses sources d'inspiration*, 2nd ed., Paris, 1925.

MARÉCHAL, J., *Bruges centre du commerce de l'argent aux derniers siècles du moyen âge*, in *Revue de la banque*, XIV, 1950, pp. 389-404.

MARIJNISSEN, R. and SAWKO-MICHALSKI, M., *De twee gotische retabels van Geel. Een onderzoek van materiële feiten*, in *Bulletin de l'Institut royal du patrimoine artistique*, III, 1960, pp. 143-162.

MARILLIER, H.C., *The Tapestries of the Painted Chamber, the "Great History of Troy"*, in *The Burlington Magazine*, XLVI, 1925, pp. 35-42.

MARIX, J., *Histoire de la musique et des musiciens de la cour de Bourgogne sous le règne de Philippe le Bon (1420-1467)*, *(Sammlung Musikwissenschaftlicher Abhandlungen. Collection d'études musicologiques*, XXVIII), Strasburg, 1939.

M[ARLIER], G., *Un Christ en croix de Gérard David*, in *Les Beaux-Arts*, 2 mars 1956, p. 11.

[MARLIER, G.], alias BRUNCEL, V., *Une Découverte sensationnelle. Un chef-d'œuvre inconnu de Petrus Christus au Musée de Kansas City*, in *Les Beaux-Arts*, 12 avril 1957, p. 5.

MATHIEU, C., *Le Métier des peintres à Bruxelles aux XIVe et XVe siècles*, in *Bruxelles au XVe siècle*, Brussels, 1953, pp. 219-235.

MAYER, A.L., *Die Fürstlich - Hohenzollernschen Sammlungen in Sigmaringen,* in *Pantheon,* I, 1928, pp. 59-65.

MEDER, J., *Die Handzeichnung,* Vienna, 1919.

MEINANDER, K.K., *Medeltida Altarskåp och Träsniderier i Finlands Kyrkor,* Helsinki, 1908.

MEINANDER, K.K., *Oeuvres d'art flamand du moyen âge en Finlande,* Helsinki, 1930, pp. 18-40.

MEISS, M., *The Madonna of Humility,* in *The Art Bulletin,* XVIII, 1936, pp. 434-464.

MEISS, M., *Light as Form and Symbol in some Fifteenth-Century Paintings,* in *The Art Bulletin,* XXVII, 1945, pp. 175-187.

MICHEL, A., *La Sculpture en France et dans les pays du Nord,* in *Histoire de l'art [...],* publiée sous la direction de A. MICHEL, III. *Le réalisme. Les débuts de la renaissance,* 1, Paris, 1907, pp. 375-421.

MICHEL, E., *La Collection Mayer van den Bergh à Anvers,* in *Gazette des beaux-arts,* X, 1924, pp. 41-58.

MICHEL, E., *Musée national du Louvre. Catalogue raisonné des peintures du moyen âge, de la renaissance et des temps modernes. Peintures flamandes du XVe et du XVIe siècle,* Paris, 1953.

MICHELANT, M., *Inventaire des joyaux, ornements d'église, vaisselles, tapisseries, livres, tableaux, etc. de Charles-Quint, dressé à Bruxelles au mois de mai 1536,* in *Compte-rendu des séances de la Commission royale d'histoire ou Recueil de ses bulletins,* 3rd S., XIII, 1872, pp. 199-368.

MICHIELS, A., *Histoire de la peinture flamande et hollandaise,* 4 vol., Brussels, 1845-48.

MICHIELS, A., *Histoire de la peinture flamande depuis ses débuts jusqu'en 1864,* 10 vol., Paris, 2nd ed., 1865-76.

MIGEON, G., *Les Arts du tissu (Manuels d'histoire de l'art),* new revised and enlarged ed., Paris, 1929.

MILLIER, A., in *Art Digest,* Jan. 1948, p. 9.*

MILLIKEN, W.M., *The Art of the Goldsmith,* in *The Journal of Aesthetics and Art Criticism,* VI, 1948, pp. 311-322.*

MIREUR, H., *Dictionnaire des ventes d'art faites en France et à l'étranger pendant les XVIIIe et XIXe siècles,* 7 vol., Paris, 1901-12.

MONETARIUS DE FELDKIRCHEN, H., *Monetarius. Voyage aux Pays-Bas (1495),* traduit pour la première fois, introduit et annoté par P. CISELET et M. DELCOURT, *(Collection nationale,* 22), Brussels, 1942.

MONGAN, A., *A Pieta by Simon Marmion,* in *Bulletin of the Fogg Museum of Art,* IX, 1942, pp. 115-120.

MONGAN, A., *One hundred Master Drawings,* Cambridge, Mass., 1949.

Monget, C., *La Chartreuse de Dijon d'après les documents des archives de Bourgogne*, 3 vol., Montreuil-sur-Mer, 1898-1905.

Morelli, J., *Notizia d'opere di disegno della prima metà del secolo XVI esistenti in Padova, Cremona, Milano, Pavia, Bergamo, Crema, Venezia, scritta da un anonimo di quel tempo*, publicata e illustrata da Jacopo Morello, custode della Regia Biblioteca di San Marco di Venezia, Bassano, 1800.

Morelli, J., *Notizia d'opere di disegno publicata e illustrada*, 2nd ed., revised and enlarged by G. Frizzoni, Bologna, 1884.

Mosmans, J., *Jheronimus Anthonis-zoon van Aken, alias Hieronymus Bosch, zijn leven en zijn werk*, 's-Hertogenbosch, 1947.

Müller, T. and Steingräber, E., *Die französische Goldemailplastik um 1400*, in *Münchner Jahrbuch der bildenden Kunst*, 3rd S., V, 1954, pp. 29-79.

Müntz, E., *Les Origines du réalisme. L'art flamand et l'art italien au XVe siècle*, in *Revue des deux mondes*, 1886, pp. 557-590.

Müntz, E., *Les Collections des Médicis au XVe siècle*, Paris, 1888.

Müntz, E., *Bibliographie*. P. Schumann, *Der trojanische Krieg (La guerre de Troie). Dessins de tapisserie français du XVe siècle, Dresde, libr. Gutbier, 1898, [...]*, in *Chronique des arts et de la curiosité, supplément à la Gazette des beaux-arts*, 1898, 20 August, pp. 263-264.

Münzenberger, E.F.A. and Beissel, *Zur Kenntnis und Würdigung der Mittelalterlichen Altäre Deutschlands. Ein Beitrag zur Geschichte des vaterländischen Kunst*, 2 vol., Frankfort on-Main, 1885-1905.

Musper, H. Th., *Untersuchungen zu Rogier van der Weyden und Jan van Eyck*, Stuttgart, [1948].

Musper, H. Th., *Die Brüsseler Gregorsmesse. Ein Original*, in *Bulletin des Musées royaux des beaux-arts de Belgique*, Bruxelles, 1952, pp. 89-94.

Neefs, E., *Histoire de la peinture et de la sculpture à Malines, I. La gilde de St-Luc. L'Académie des beaux-arts. Les peintres malinois; II. Les sculpteurs malinois*, 2 vol., Ghent, 1876.

Niederstein, A., *Die Lukas-Madonna des Rogier van der Weyden*, in *Pantheon*, XII, 1933, pp. 361-366.

Nieuwenhuys, C.J., *Description de la collection des tableaux qui ornent le palais de S.A.R. Mgr le Prince d'Orange, à Bruxelles*, Brussels, 1837.

Nieuwenhuys, C.J., *Description de la galerie de S.M. le Roi des Pays-Bas*, Brussels, 1843.

Niffle-Anciaux, E., *Les Repos de Jésus et les berceaux reliquaires*, Namur, 1890.

Niffle-Anciaux, E., *Les Repos de Jésus et les berceaux reliquaires*, new ed., Namur, 1896.

Oberlin College, "*Exhibition of Flemish Book Illumination*", in *Allen Memorial Art Museum Bulletin*, XVII, 1960, p. 108.

OETTINGER, K., *Das Rätsel der Kunst des Hugo van der Goes*, in *Jahrbuch der kunsthistorischen Sammlungen in Wien*, XII, 1938, pp. 43-76.

OMAN, C.C., *Medieval Brass Lecterns in England*, in *Archaeological Journal*, LXXXVII, 1930, pp. 117-149.

OMAN, C.C., *Niederländische Messingpulte in Italiën*, in *Pantheon*, XX, 1937, pp. 274-277.

ONGHENA, M.J., *De Iconografie van Philips de Schone (Académie royale de Belgique. Classe des beaux-arts. Mémoires, Collection in 8°, X, 5)*, 2 vol., Brussels, 1959.

PÄCHT, O., M.J. FRIEDLÄNDER, *Dierick Bouts - Joos van Gent. P. Cassirer, Berlin, 1925*, in *Kritische Berichte zur Kunstgeschichtlichen Literatur*, I, 1927-28, pp. 37-54.

PÄCHT, O., *The Master of Mary of Burgundy*, London, [1948].

PALLIOT, P., *La vraye et parfaite science des armoiries, ou l'Indice armorial de feu Maître Louvan Geliot, advocat au Parlement de Bourgogne, apprenant et expliquant sommairement les mots et figures dont on se sert au blason des Armoiries et l'origine d'icelles*, Paris, 1661.

PANOFSKY, E., *Die Perspektive als "symbolische Form"*, in *Vorträge der Bibliothek Warburg, Vorträge 1924-25*, pp. 258-330.

PANOFSKY, E., *Studies in Iconology. Humanistic Themes in the Art of the Renaissance*, New York, 1939.

PANOFSKY, E., in *Beiträge für Swarzenski*, Berlin, 1951.*

PANOFSKY, E., *Early Netherlandish Painting. Its Origins and Character*, 2 vol., Cambridge, Mass., 1953.

PANOFSKY, E., *A Letter to St. Jerome. A Note on the Relationship between Petrus Christus and Jan van Eyck*, in *Studies in Art and Literature for Bella da Costa Greene*, Princeton, 1954, pp. 102-108.

PAQUAY, J., *Aperçu historique sur le trésor de l'église Notre-Dame à Tongres*, in *Bulletin de la Société scientifique et littéraire du Limbourg*, XXII, 1904, pp. 107-168.

PAQUAY, J., *Eglise Notre-Dame à Tongres*, in *Bulletin de la Société scientifique et littéraire du Limbourg*, XXIX, 1911, pp. 81-275.

PARMENTIER, R.A., *Indices op de Brugsche Poorterboeken. I. Poorterboeken over 1418-1450; II. Poorterboeken over 1450-1794, (Geschiedkundige publicatiën der stad Brugge, II, 1-2)*, 2 vol., Bruges, 1938.

PASSAVANT, J.D., *Die Christliche Kunst in Spanien*, Leipzig, 1853.

PASSAVANT, J.D., *Die Maler Roger van der Weyden*, in *Zeitschrift für Christliche Archäologie und Kunst*, II, 1858, pp. 1-20.

PEETERS, F., *Le Triptyque eucharistique de Thierry Bouts à l'église Saint-Pierre, Louvain*, 3rd ed., Léau, 1926.

PFISTER, K., *Hugo van der Goes*, Basel, 1923.

PINCHART, A., *Archives des arts, sciences et lettres, documents inédits publiés et annotés*, 3 vol., Ghent, 1860-81.

PINCHART, A., *Jacques de Gérines, batteur de cuivre du XVe siècle, et ses œuvres*, in *Bulletin des Commissions royales d'art et d'archéologie*, V, 1866, pp. 114-136.

PINCHART, A., *Dinanderie*, in *L'Art ancien à l'exposition nationale belge*, publié sous la direction de C. DE RODDAZ, Brussels - Paris, 1882, pp. 71-102.

(PINCHART, A.), *Histoire générale de la tapisserie. Pays-Bas*, (Paris), [1883].

PIOT, C., *Renier van Thienen, fondeur-ciseleur*, in *Revue universelle des arts*, I, 1855, pp. 280-283.

PIOT, C., *Notice historique sur la ville de Léau*, II, in *Revue d'histoire et d'archéologie*, II, 1860, pp. 52-76.

PIOT, C., *Essai sur le type et le caractère de la sculpture en Belgique pendant le moyen âge*, in *Annales de la Société d'émulation pour l'étude de l'histoire de l'art et des antiquités de la Flandre*, 3rd S., II, 1867, pp. 179-260.

PIRENNE, H., *Les Villes et les institutions urbaines*, 3rd ed., 2 vol., Paris - Brussels, 1939.

PIRENNE, H., *Histoire de Belgique*, II. *Du commencement du XVe siècle à la mort de Charles le Téméraire*, 4th ed., Brussels, 1947; III. *De la mort de Charles le Téméraire à l'arrivée du duc d'Albe dans les Pays-Bas (1567)*, 4th ed., Brussels, 1953.

P[OPHAM], A.E., *Memling*, in *The Oppenheimer Collection*, in *The Vasari Society*, 2nd S., II, 1921, no. 11, p. 23.

POPHAM, A.E., *Drawings of the Early Flemish School*, (*Drawings of the Great Masters*), London, 1926.

POPHAM, A.E., *Simon Marmion (after) - (working 1449-1489). Pietà. - Coll. of the Rev. Canon Lewis Gilbertson, London. - Silverpoint on prepared cream coloured ground. 15.4 x 11.5 cm.*, in *Old Master Drawings*, I, 1926, pp. 21-22.

POPHAM, A.E., *Notes on Flemish Domestic Glass Painting*, I, in *Apollo*, VII, 1928, pp. 175-179.

POPHAM, A.E., *Catalogue of Drawings by Dutch and Flemish Artists preserved in the Department of Prints and Drawings in the British Museum*, V. *Dutch and Flemish Drawings of the XV and XVI Centuries*, (London), 1932.

PORCHER, J., *L'Enluminure française*, (Paris, 1959).

POST, C.R., *A History of Spanish Painting*, 12 vol., Cambridge, Mass., 1930-58.

428

Poupeye, C., *Les Jardins clos et leurs rapports avec la sculpture malinoise,* in *Bulletin du Cercle archéologique, littéraire et artistique de Malines,* XXII, 1912, pp. 51-114.

Prenau, S.L., *Zout-Leeuw. De "stad" en de kerk,* Antwerp, 1901.

Prims, F., *Altaarstudien,* in *Antwerpiensia,* XIII, 1939, pp. 278-447.

Quicke, F., *Les Chroniqueurs des fastes bourguignons, (Collection nationale,* 4th S., 40), Brussels, 1943.

Quicke, F., *Les Pays-Bas à la veille de la période bourguignonne 1356-1384. Contribution à l'histoire politique et diplomatique de l'Europe occidentale dans la seconde moitié du XIVe siècle,* Brussels, (1947).

Rackham, B., *Victoria and Albert Museum Department of Ceramics. A Guide to the Collections of Stained Glass,* London, 1936.

Rankin, W., *Il quadro di Ruggero van der Weyden nel Museo di Belle Arti a Boston,* in *Rassegna d'arte,* IV-V, 1905, pp. 24-25.

Rare mille-fleur Tapestry added to Martin Collection, in *Bulletin of the Minneapolis Institute of Arts,* XXIII, 1934, pp. 41-51.

Raymaekers, F.J., *Notice historique sur l'église primaire de Saint-Sulpice à Diest,* III, in *Messager des sciences historiques, des arts et de la bibliographie de Belgique,* 1856, pp. 487-499.

Réau, L., *Iconographie de l'Art chrétien,* 6 vol., Paris, 1955-59.

Reinach, S., *Répertoire des peintures du moyen âge et de la renaissance (1280-1580),* 5 vol., Paris, 1905-22.

Renders, E., *La Solution du problème Van der Weyden - Flémalle - Campin,* avec la collaboration de J. De Smet et L. Beyaert-Carlier, 2 vol., Bruges, 1931.

Renders, E., *St Luc peignant la Vierge par Rogier van der Weyden,* in *Bulletin of the Museum of Fine Arts, Boston,* XXXI, 1933, pp. 70-74.

Renders, E., *Jean van Eyck, son œuvre, son style, son évolution et la légende d'un frère peintre,* Bruges, 1935.

Répertoire des biens culturels importants. Royaume de Belgique. Ministère de l'Instruction publique. Administration des Arts, des Lettres et de l'Education populaire. Ministère de l'Intérieur. Administration de la Protection civile, duplicated, [Brussels, 1956-.]; *Repertorium van het belangrijk cultuurbezit. Koninkrijk België. Ministerie van Openbaar Onderwijs. Algemene Directie voor Kunst, Letteren en Volksopleiding. Ministerie van Binnenlandse Zaken. Bestuur der Burgerlijke Bescherming,* duplicated, [Brussels, 1956-.].

Reusens, E., *Eléments d'archéologie chrétienne,* 2 vol., Louvain, 1871-75.

Reusens, E., *Ferronnerie,* in *L'Art ancien à l'exposition nationale belge,* publié sous la direction de C. de Roddaz, Brussels - Paris, 1882, pp. 183-194.

REUSENS, E., (under the direction of), *Exposition rétrospective d'art industriel organisée par le gouvernement* [...]. *Ministère de l'Agriculture, de l'Industrie et des Travaux publics. Bruxelles, 1888. Catalogue officiel* [...], Brussels, 1888.

RICHARDSON, E.P., *The Detroit Institute of Arts. Flemish Painting of the Fifteenth and Sixteenth Centuries*, Detroit, 1936.

RICHARDSON, E.P., *Three Paintings by Master Michiel*, in *The Art Quarterly*, II, 1939, pp. 103-111.

RICHARDSON, E.P., *The Rest on the Flight into Egypt*, in *Journal of the Walters Art Gallery*, II, 1939, pp. 37-42.

RICHARDSON, E.P., *Catherine of Aragon as the Magdalen by Master Michiel*, in *Bulletin of the Detroit Institute of Arts*, XIX, 1940, pp. 81-83.

RICHARDSON, E.P., in *Art News*, XL, 1941, no. 6, p. 17.*

[RICHARDSON, E.P.], *The Detroit Institute of Arts. Catalogue of Paintings*, 2nd ed., Detroit, 1944.

RICHARDSON, E.P., *St. Jerome in the Desert by Rogier van der Weyden*, in *Bulletin of the Detroit Institute of Arts*, XXVI, 1947, pp. 53-56.

[RICHARDSON, E.P.], *Catalogue of the Paintings and Sculpture Given by Edgar B. Whitcomb and Anna Scripps Whitcomb to the Detroit Institute of Arts*, Detroit, 1954.

RICHARDSON, E.P., *The Detroit "St-Jerome" by Jan van Eyck*, in *The Art Quarterly*, XIX, 1956, pp. 226-235.

RICHARDSON, E.P., *Portrait of a Man in a Red Hat by Master Michiel*, in *Bulletin of the Detroit Institute of Arts*, XXXVIII, 1958-59, pp. 79-83.

RICHARDSON, E.P., *A Fifteenth Century Altarpiece from Bruges*, in *Bulletin of the Detroit Institute of Arts*, XXIX, 1959-60, no. 1, pp. 3-7.

RIEFFEL, F., *Das Fürstlich Hohenzollernsche Museum zu Sigmaringen. Gemälde und Bildwerke*, in *Städel-Jahrbuch*, III-IV, 1924, pp. 55-74.

RIETSTAP, J.B., *Armorial général*, 2nd ed., 2 vol., Gouda, 1884.

RING, G., *Ein Diptychon des Hugo van der Goes*, in *Zeitschrift für bildende Kunst*, N.S., XXIV, 1913, pp. 85-88.

RING, G., *Beiträge zur Geschichte Niederländischer Bildnismalerei im 15. und 16. Jahrhundert*, Leipzig, 1913.

RING, G., *Beiträge zur Plastik von Tournai im 15. Jahrhundert*, in *Belgische Kunstdenkmäler*, herausgegeben von P. CLEMEN, I, Munich, 1923, pp. 269-291.

RING, G., *St. Jerome Extracting the Thorn from the Lion's Foot*, in *The Art Bulletin*, XXVII, 1945, pp. 188-194.

RING, G., *A Century of French Painting, 1400-1500*, London, 1949.

Robb, D.M., *The Iconography of the Annunciation in the Fourteenth and Fifteenth Centuries*, in *The Art Bulletin*, XVIII, 1936, pp. 480-526.

Robinson, J.C., *The "Maître de Flémalle" and the Painters of the School of Salamanca*, in *The Burlington Magazine*, VII, 1905, pp. 387-393.

Roggen, D., *Het Retabel van Hakendover*, in *Gentsche bijdragen tot de kunstgeschiedenis*, I, 1934, pp. 108-121.

Roggen, D., *Beeldhouwkunst, einde der XIVe en XVe eeuw*, in *Geschiedenis van de Vlaamsche kunst* [...], onder leiding I.S. Leurs, I, Antwerp, [1937], pp. 236-284.

Roggen, D., *Klaas Sluter vóór zijn vertrek naar Dijon in 1385*, in *Gentse bijdragen tot de kunstgeschiedenis*, XI, 1945-48, pp. 7-40.

Roggen, D., *Prae-sluteriaanse, sluteriaanse, post-sluteriaanse Nederlandsche sculptuur*, in *Gentse bijdragen tot de kunstgeschiedenis*, XVI, 1955-56, pp. 111-191.

Roggen, D., and Verleyen, L., *De Portaalsculpturen van het Brusselsche stadhuis*, in *Gentsche bijdragen tot de kunstgeschiedenis*, I, 1934, pp. 123-148.

Roggen, D. and Withof, J., *Grondleggers en grootmeesters der Brabantsche Gotiek*, in *Gentsche bijdragen tot de kunstgeschiedenis*, X, 1944, pp. 88-208.

Rolfs, W., *Geschichte der Malerei Neapels*, Leipzig, 1910.

Rolland, P., *Les Primitifs tournaisiens, peintres et sculpteurs*, Brussels - Paris, 1932.

Rolland, P., *L'Architecture et la sculpture gothiques*, in *L'Art en Belgique*, publié sous la direction de P. Fierens, Brussels, (1939) pp. 43-90.

Rolland, P., *La Sculpture tournaisienne (L'Art en Belgique)*, Brussels, 1944.

Rolland, P., *La Madone italo-byzantine de Frasnes-lez-Buissenal*, in *Revue belge d'archéologie et d'histoire de l'art*, XVII, 1948, pp. 97-106.

Roosval, J., *Schnitzaltäre in Schwedischen Kirchen und Museen aus der Werkstatt der Brüsseler Bildschnitzers Jan Bormann (Zur Kunstgeschichte der Auslander, XIV)*, Strasburg, 1903.

Roosval, J., *Retables d'origine néerlandaise dans les pays nordiques*, in *Revue belge d'archéologie et d'histoire de l'art*, III, 1933, pp. 136-158.

Rorimer, J.J., *A Fifteenth Century Tapestry with Scenes of the Trojan War*, in *Bulletin of the Metropolitan Museum of Art*, XXXIV, 1939, pp. 224-227.

Ross, M. Ch., *Vier Evangelistenpulte aus Messina*, in *Pantheon*, XXII, 1938, pp. 290-292.

Rousseau, F., *La Meuse et le pays mosan en Belgique, leur importance historique avant le XIIIe siècle*, in *Annales de la Société archéologique de Namur*, XXXIX, 1930, pp. 1-248.

Rousseau, H., *Notes pour servir à l'histoire de la sculpture en Belgique. Les retables*, in *Bulletin des Commissions royales d'art et d'archéologie*, XXIX,

1890, pp. 425-461; XXX, 1891, pp. 29-65, 79-115, 123-168, 209-252; XXXI, 1892, pp. 473-510; XXXII, 1893, pp. 203-250; XXXIII, 1894, pp. 90-105; XXXIV, 1895, pp. 20-48.

ROUSSEAU, J., *La Sculpture flamande et wallonne du XIe au XIXe siècle*, IV, in *Bulletin des Commissions royales d'art et d'archéologie*, XVI, 1877, pp. 19-67.

RUBBRECHT, O., *L'Origine du type familial de la Maison de Habsbourg*, Brussels, 1910.

RUHEMANN, H., *A Record of Restoration*, in *Technical Studies in the Field of the Fine Arts*, III, 1934, pp. 3-15.

SABBE, E., *La Guerre de Cent ans et la primauté de l'art flamand à la fin du moyen âge*, in *Revue belge d'archéologie et d'histoire de l'art*, XXI, 1952, pp. 221-252.

SANDER PIERRON, *L'Eglise Saint-Léonard. L'édifice et ses trésors d'art*, in *Léau et son exposition d'art, d'archéologie et de folklore, 6-28 juillet 1924*. (Special issue of the *Folklore brabançon*, IV, nos. 20-22, 1924-25, pp. 97-119).

SCHEEWE, L., *Die neueste Literatur über Roger van der Weyden*, in *Zeitschrift für Kunstgeschichte*, III, 1934, pp. 208-212.

SCHMARSOW, A., *Robert van der Kampine und Roger van der Weyden*, (*Philologisch-historischen Klasse der Sächsischen Akademie der Wissenschaften*, XXXIX, 11), Leipzig, 1928.

SCHMITZ, H., *Bildteppiche. Geschichte der Gobelinwirkerei*, 2nd ed., Berlin, 1921.

SCHNEIDER, R. and COHEN, G., *La Formation du génie moderne dans l'art de l'Occident. Arts plastiques. Art littéraire*, (*L'évolution de l'humanité. Synthèse collective*, XLVIII), Paris, 1936.

SCHÖNE, W., *Über einige altniederländische Bilder, vor allem in Spanien*, in *Jahrbuch der Preussischen Kunstsammlungen*, LVIII, 1937, pp. 153-182.

SCHÖNE, W., *Dieric Bouts und seine Schule*, Berlin-Leipzig, 1938.

SCHÖNE, W., *Hans Memling zur Ausstellung seines Lebenswerkes in Brügge*, in *Pantheon*, XXIV, 1939, pp. 291-299.

SCHOPENHAUER, J., *Johann van Eyck und seine Nachfolger*, 2 vol., Frankfort on Main, 1822.

SCHRADE, H., *Malerei des Mittelalters: Gestalt, Bestimmung, Macht, Schicksal*, Cologne, 1958.

SCHUMANN, P., see *Krieg...*

SCHWARTZ, H., *The Mirror of the Artist and the Mirror of the Devot. Observations on some Paintings, Drawings and Prints of the fifteenth Century*, in *Studies in the History of Art dedicated to William E. Suida on his eightieth Birthday*, London, 1959, pp. 90-105.

SIMOND, Ch., *Les Origines de nos tapisseries*, in *Revue des revues*, XXVI, 1898, July, pp. 82-91.

SIX, J., *Les Bronzes de Jacques de Gérines au Musée national d'Amsterdam*, in *Gazette des beaux-arts*, XV, 1896, pp. 388-404.

SMITS, K., *De Iconografie van de Nederlandsche Primitieven*, Amsterdam - Brussels - Antwerp - Louvain, 1933.

SNYDER, J.E., *The Early Haarlem School of Painting*, in *The Art Bulletin*, XLII, 1960, pp. 39-55.

[SOIL, E.], *Tapisseries du quinzième siècle conservées à la cathédrale de Tournay. Leur fabrication à Arras en 1402. Histoire, description, précédées d'une notice sur la fabrication des tapisseries en Flandre et particulièrement à Arras [...]*, Tournai - Lille, 1883.

SOIL, E., *Les Tapisseries de Tournai. Les tapissiers et les hautelisseurs de cette ville. Recherches et documents sur l'histoire, la fabrication et les produits des ateliers de Tournai*, Tournai - Lille, 1892.

SOIL DE MORIAME, E., *Exposition des anciennes industries d'art tournaisiennes. Catalogue. Ville de Tournai, juillet - octobre 1911*, [s. l.], 1911.

SOMMER, C., *The Prophets of Saint-Antoine en Viennois*, in *The Journal of the Walters Art Gallery*, XIII-XIV, 1950-51, pp. 9-19.

SPENCER, E.P., *The International Style and Fifteenth Century Illuminations*, in *Parnassus*, XII, 1940, pp. 30 ff.*

Spirituale Pomerium (Bibliothèque royale de Belgique. Manuscrit 12.070). Etude critique par L. LEBEER *(Société des bibliophiles et iconophiles de Belgique)*, Brussels, 1938.

SQUILBECK, J., *La Sculpture de l'ancienne maison échevinale de Malines*, in *Revue belge d'archéologie et d'histoire de l'art*, V, 1935, pp. 329-333.

SQUILBECK, J., *Les Lutrins dinantais de Venise et de Gênes*, in *Bulletin de l'Institut historique belge de Rome*, XXI, 1940-41, pp. 347-356.

SQUILBECK, J., *Notices sur les artistes de la famille Van Mansdale, dite Keldermans*, in *Handelingen van de Koninklijke Kring voor Oudheidkunde, Letteren en Kunst van Mechelen*, LVI, 1952, pp. 90-137; LVII, 1953, pp. 99-140.

SQUILBECK, J., *Le Travail du métal à Bruxelles*, in *Bruxelles au XVe siècle*, Brussels, 1953, pp. 245-271.

SQUILBECK, J., *Nos collections d'armes et d'armures, I. Un plastron de cuirasse gothique trouvé à Tongres*, in *Bulletin des Musées royaux d'art et d'histoire*, XXVI, 1954, pp. 68-77.

SQUILBECK, J., *Pour une nouvelle orientation des recherches sur la dinanderie en Belgique*, in *Revue belge d'archéologie et d'histoire de l'art*, XXVII, 1958, pp. 117-171.

STALPAERT, H., *In de keuken van Gruuthuse*, in *West-Vlaanderen*, VI, 1957, pp. 24-27.

STANGE, A., *Deutsche Malerei der Gotik*, 10 vol., Berlin - Munich, 1934-60.

STEPPE, J., *Het Koordoksaal in de Nederlanden* (*Verhandelingen van de koninklijke Vlaamse Academie voor Wetenschappen, Letteren en Schone Kunsten van België. Klasse der Schone Kunsten, 7*), Brussels, 1952.

STEPPE, J., *Een Binnenzicht van de voormalige Sint-Donaaskerk te Brugge op een schilderij van Memling*, in *Bulletin de la Commission royale des monuments et des sites*, IV, 1953, pp. 187-200.

STEPPE, J. and VAN MOLLE, F., *De Koorbanken van de Onze Lieve Vrouwkerk te Aarschot. Een bijdrage tot de studie van de laat-gotische koorbanken in Brabant*, in *Bulletin de la Commission royale des monuments et des sites*, II, 1950, pp. 197-250.

STERLING, Ch., *La Peinture française. Les Primitifs*, Paris, 1938.

STERLING, Ch., *La Peinture française. Les peintres du moyen âge*, Paris, 1942.

STOUT, G.L., *The Grip of the Artist's Brush*, in *Technical Studies in the Field of the Fine Arts*, X, 1941, pp. 3-17.

STRIEDER, P., *Hans Holbein der Ältere und die deutschen Wiederholungen des Gnadenbildes von Santa Maria del Popolo*, in *Zeitschrift für Kunstgeschichte*, XXI, 1959, pp. 252-267.

STRUBBE, E.I., *Een opstandige schuldenaar te Westvleteren. De plaat en de vuist te Veurne*, in *Biekorf*, XLVI, 1940, pp. 1-7.

STRUBBE, E., *Rond David's Oordeel van Cambyzes*, unpublished study. Lecture at the Groeningemuseum in Bruges, March 18, 1956. Typewritten manuscript.

STRÜMPELL, A., *"Hieronymus im Gehäuse"*, in *Marburger Jahrbuch für Kunstwissenschaft*, II, 1925-26, pp. 173-252.

STRZYGOWSKI, J., *Ikonographie der Taufe Christi*, Munich, 1885.

SULZBERGER, S., *Autoportraits de Gérard David*, in *Bulletin des Musées royaux des beaux-arts, Bruxelles*, 1955, 1-3 (*Miscellanea Erwin Panofsky*), pp. 176-178.

SWARZENSKI, H., *An Unknown Bosch*, in *Bulletin of the Museum of Fine Arts, Boston*, LIII, 1955, pp. 2-10.

S.z.S., *Der Weimarer Bilderverkauf*, in *Kunstchronik*, N.S., XXXIV, 1923, pp. 547-548.

Les Tapisseries du cardinal de Clugny (1480-1483). Mémoire du XVIIIe siècle, publié par le vicomte L. DE VARAX, Lyon, 1926.

TARLIER, J. and WAUTERS, A., see WAUTERS, A., 1874.

TAVENOR PERRY, J., *Dinanderie. A History and Description of Mediaeval Art Work in Copper, Brass and Bronze*, London, 1910.

TEIXEIRA DE VASCONCELLOS, A.A., *Les Contemporains portugais, espagnols et brésiliens*, I, Paris, 1859.

TEMPLE, A.G., *Illustrated Catalogue of the Exhibition of Works by the Early*

Flemish Painters. Art Gallery of the Corporation of London (Guildhall Gallery), (London), 1906.

THIEME, U., BECKER, F. und VOLLMER, H. (under the direction of), *Allgemeines Lexikon der bildenden Künstler von der Antike bis zur Gegenwart*, 37 vol., Leipzig, 1907-1950.

[THIMISTER, O.J.], *Essai historique sur l'église de St-Paul, ci-devant collégiale, aujourd'hui cathédrale de Liège*, Liège, 1867.

THOMSON, W.G., *A History of Tapestry from the Earliest Times until the Present Day*, London, 1906.

THORLACIUS-USSING, V., *La Sculpture belge au Danemark de la fin du moyen âge au commencement du XVIIIe siècle*, in *Actes du XIIe Congrès international d'histoire de l'art, Bruxelles, 1930*, II, Brussels, [s.d.], pp. 538-543.

THYS, Ch.-M.-T., *L'Eglise de Notre-Dame à Tongres. Mémoire*, in *Annales de l'Académie d'archéologie de Belgique*, XXII, 1866, pp. 169-415.

TIETZE, H., *Meisterwerke Europäischer Malerei in Amerika*, Vienna, (1935).

TIETZE, H., *European Master Drawings in the United States*, London, (1947).

TOLNAY, Ch., see DE TOLNAY, Ch.

TOVELL, R.M., *Flemish Artists of the Valois Courts*, Toronto, 1950.

TOVELL MASSEY, R., *Roger van der Weyden and the Flémalle Enigma*, Toronto, 1955.

T[OWNSEND], G., *Eight Fragments of fifteenth Century Tapestry*, in *Bulletin of the Museum of Fine Arts, Boston*, XXVII, 1929, pp. 2-10.

TRÖSCHER, G., *Claus Sluter und die Burgundische Plastik um die Wende des XIV. Jahrhunderts, I. Die herzogliche Bildhauerwerkstatt im Dijon unter ihren Leitern Jean de Marville, Claus Sluter und Claus de Werve*, Freiburg in Breisgau, (1932).

TRÖSCHER, G., *Weltgerichtsbilder in Rathäusern und Gerichtsstätten*, in *Wallraf-Richartz Jahrbuch*, XI, 1939, pp. 139-214.

TRÖSCHER, G., *Die Burgundische Plastik des ausgehenden Mittelalters und ihre Wirkungen auf die Europäische Kunst*, 2 vol., Frankfort on Main, 1940, (1941).

V[ALENTINER], W.R., *Saint Jerome by Petrus Christus*, in *Bulletin of the Detroit Institute of Arts*, VI, 1924-25, pp. 57-59.

V[ALENTINER], W.R., *The Annunciation by Gerard David*, in *Bulletin of the Detroit Institute of Arts*, VIII, 1927, pp. 92-93.

V[ALENTINER], W.R., *Masterpieces of Art, New York World's Fair. Catalogue of European Paintings and Sculpture from 1300-1800*, compiled by George Henry MC CALL under the Editorship of William R. VALENTINER. *May to October 1939*.

435

VALENTINER, W.R., *Aelbert van Ouwater*, in *The Art Quarterly*, VI, 1943, pp. 74-91.

VALENTINER, W.R., *Rogier van der Weyden, "The Mass of St-Gregory"*, in *The Art Quarterly*, VIII, 1945, pp. 240-243.

VAN CAUWENBERGH, E., *De Kleinkunst te Leuven en in Vlaanderen*, in *Kunst te Leuven*, Louvain, [1946], pp. 61-76.

VAN DEN NIEUWENHUYZEN, J., *Gids voor de kathedraal van Antwerpen*, Antwerp, 1957.

VAN DEN STEEN DE JEHAY, X., *Essai historique sur l'ancienne cathédrale de Saint-Lambert à Liége et sur son chapitre de Chanoines-Tréfonciers*, Liège, 1846.

VAN DEN STEEN DE JEHAY, X., *La Cathédrale de Saint-Lambert à Liège et son chapitre de Tréfonciers*, 2nd ed., Liège, 1880.

VAN DER ELST, J., *The Last Flowering of the Middle Ages, People and Painters of Flanders*, New York, 1944.

VAN DER HAEGHEN, V., *Archives gantoises, I. Brasseries à Gand au XVe et XVIIe siècle*, in *Messager des sciences historiques*, 1886, pp. 125-133.

V[AN] D[ER] LINDEN, G., *De Collegiale kerk van de H. Sulpitius te Diest*, in *Jaarboek van de Diestersche kunstkring*, VIII, 1936, pp. 76-92.

VAN DER LINDEN, G., *De Hoofdkerk van de H.H. Sulpitius en Dionysius te Diest*, in *Eigen Schoon en de Brabander*, N.S., XI, 1936, pp. 120-136.

V[AN] D[E] V[ELDE], H., *Monuments d'ancien droit criminel. Têtes et poings de métal*, in *Annales de la Société d'émulation pour l'étude de l'histoire et des antiquités de la Flandre*, 2nd S., I, 1843, pp. 186-192.

VAN DOORSLAER, G., *Marques de sculpteurs et de polychromeurs malinois*, in *Revue belge d'archéologie et d'histoire de l'art*, III, 1933, pp. 159-176.

VAN DUYSE, H., *Cimarre du magistrat de Gand*, in *Inventaire archéologique de Gand. Catalogue descriptif et illustré des monuments, œuvres d'art et documents antérieurs à 1830 […]*, Ghent, 1897, p. 31.

VAN DUYSE, P. and DE BUSSCHER, E., *Inventaire analytique des chartes et documents appartenant aux archives de la ville de Gand*, Ghent, 1867.

VAN EEGHEM, W., *Le Théâtre bruxellois d'expression néerlandaise*, in *Bruxelles au XVe siècle*, Brussels, 1953, pp. 291-297.

VAN EVEN, E., *Monographie de l'église de Saint-Pierre à Louvain*, Brussels - Louvain, 1858.

VAN EVEN, E., *L'Ancienne école de peinture de Louvain*, Brussels-Louvain, 1870.

VAN EVEN, E., *Maître Jean Borman, le grand sculpteur belge de la fin du XVe siècle*, in *Bulletin des Commissions royales d'art et d'archéologie*, XXIII, 1884, pp. 397-414.

VAN EVEN, E., *Louvain dans le passé et dans le présent. Formation de la ville.*

Evénements mémorables. Territoire. Monuments. Oeuvres d'art, Louvain, 1895.

VAN EVEN, E., *Le Contrat pour l'exécution du triptyque de Thierry Bouts de la collégiale Saint-Pierre à Louvain (1464),* in *Bulletin de l'Académie royale des sciences, des lettres et des beaux-arts de Belgique,* LXVIII, 1898, pp. 469-478.

VAN GELDER, H.E. and DUVERGER, J. (under the direction of), *Kunstgeschiedenis der Nederlanden. De Middeleeuwen en de zestiende eeuw,* I, 3rd ed., Utrecht - Antwerp - Brussels - Ghent - Louvain, 1954.

VAN GELDER, J.G., *The Gerard David Exhibition at Bruges,* in *The Burlington Magazine,* XCI, 1949, pp. 253-254.

VAN GELDER, J.G., *Het zogenaamde portret van Dieric Bouts op "het werck van de Heilichen Sacrament",* in *Oud-Holland,* LXVI, 1951, pp. 51-52.

VAN HALL, H., *Repertorium voor de geschiedenis der Nederlandsche schilder- en graveerkunst sedert het begin der 12de eeuw* [...], 2 vol., The Hague, 1936-49.

VAN HERCK, J., *Het Passie-retabel van Geel,* Antwerp, 1951.

VAN HOUTE, J.A., *La Genèse du grand marché international d'Anvers à la fin du moyen âge,* in *Revue belge de philologie et d'histoire,* XIX, 1940, pp. 87-126.

VAN KALKEN, F., *Histoire de Belgique des origines à nos jours,* 5th ed., Brussels, 1946.

VAN MANDER, C., *Dutch and Flemish Painters.* Translation from the Schilderboek and Introduction by C. VAN DE WALL, New York, 1936.

VAN MOLLE, F., *De Edelsmeedkunst te Leuven,* Louvain, 1957 (Typewritten Doctoral Thesis at University of Louvain).

VAN MOLLE, F., *La Justice d'Othon de Thierry Bouts. Sources d'archives,* in *Bulletin de l'Institut royal du patrimoine artistique,* I, 1958, pp. 7-17.

(VAN MOLLE, F.), *St. Gertrudis. Tentoonstelling. St.-Gertrudiskerk te Leuven, 16 augustus - 13 september 1959,* (Heverlee), 1959.

VAN MOLLE, F., *Identification du portrait de Gilles Joye attribué à Memlinc, (Les Primitifs flamands,* III. *Contributions à l'étude des Primitifs flamands),* Brussels, 1960.

van PUYVELDE, L., *Les Primitifs flamands. Catalogue. Musée de l'Orangerie, Paris, 5 juin - 7 juillet 1947,* Brussels, 1947.

van PUYVELDE, L., *La Peinture flamande au siècle des Van Eyck,* Paris-Brussels-New York - Amsterdam - London, 1953.

van PUYVELDE, L., *The Flemish Primitives,* Brussels, (1958).

VAN SCHOUTE, R., *Le Portement de croix de Jérôme Bosch au Musée de Gand.*

Considérations sur l'exécution picturale, in *Bulletin de l'Institut royal du patrimoine artistique,* II, 1959, pp. 47-58.

VAN WEDDINGEN, R., *De Diestersche Misericordiën,* in *Diestersche kunstkring. Vereeniging voor kunst, geschiedenis, oudheidkunde en folklore. Jaarboek,* VI, 1935-36, pp. 53-60.

VAN WERVEKE, H., *Bruges et Anvers, huit siècles de commerce flamand,* revised and enlarged ed., Brussels, 1944.

VAN WERVEKE, H., *De zwarte dood in de Zuidelijke Nederlanden (1349-1351) (Mededelingen van de koninklijke Vlaamse Academie voor Wetenschappen, Letteren en Schone Kunsten van België. Klasse der Letteren, XII, 3),* Brussels, 1950.

VENTURI, L., *The Rabinowitz Collection,* New York, 1945.

VERHAEGEN, N., *Le Maître de la légende de sainte Lucie. Précisions sur son œuvre,* in *Bulletin de l'Institut royal du patrimoine artistique,* II, 1959, pp. 73-82.

VERLANT, E., *La Peinture ancienne à l'exposition de l'art belge à Paris en 1923,* Brussels-Paris, 1924.

VERLET, P., *La Tapisserie française du moyen âge à nos jours,* [*Introduction de ...*], *Bruxelles, Palais des beaux-arts, janvier - février 1947,* [Brussels], 1947.

VERSCHELDE, K., *De Kathedrale van S.-Salvator te Brugge, geschiedkundige beschrijving,* Bruges, 1863.

VERSCHELDE, K., *Exposition d'objets d'art et d'antiquités organisée par la Société archéologique de Bruges. Ville de Bruges, 25 août - 25 septembre 1867,* 2nd ed., Bruges, 1867.

VERSYP, J., *"Engels" borduurwerk in de Nederlanden, V. Een laat-vijftiend' eeuwse kazuifel in de St.-Rochuskerk te Blankenberge,* in *Artes Textiles,* III, 1956, pp. 3-4.

VIAENE, A., *Het Portret van Margareta van Eyck,* in *Biekorf,* LIV, 1953, pp. 17-20.

VITRY, P., *Michel Colombe et la sculpture française de son temps,* Paris, 1901.

VITRY, P., *La Sculpture dans les Pays-Bas au XVe et au XVIe siècle,* in *Histoire de l'art* [...], publiée sous la direction de A. MICHEL, V. *La renaissance dans les pays du Nord. Formation de l'art classique,* 1, Paris, 1912, pp. 313-334.

VOGELSANG, W., *Holländische Miniaturen des späteren Mittelalters, (Studien zur deutschen Kunstgeschichte,* 18), Strasburg, 1899.

VOISIN, E., *Notice sur les anciennes tapisseries de la cathédrale de Tournai,* in *Bulletin de la Société historique et littéraire de Tournai,* IX, 1863, pp. 213-245.

VOLL, K., *Rogier van der Weyden,* in *Süddeutsche Monatsheft,* III, 1906, pp. 294-314.

VOLL, K., *Memling. Des Meisters Gemälde, (Klassiker der Kunst in Gesamtausgaben, XIV)*, Stuttgart - Leipzig, 1909.

VOLL, K., *Die altniederländische Malerei von Jan van Eyck bis Memling. Ein Entwicklungsgeschichtlicher Versuch*, 2nd ed., Leipzig, 1928.

VON BALDASS, L., see BALDASS, L. VON.

VON BODENHAUSEN, E., *Gerard David und seine Schule*, Munich, 1905.

VON LEHNER, F.A., *Fürstlich Hohenzollern'sches Museum zu Sigmaringen. Verzeichnis der Gemälde*, 2nd ed., Sigmaringen, 1883.

VON SCHLOSSER, J., *Der Burgundische Paramentenschatz des Ordens Goldenen Vliesse*, Vienna, 1912.

VON TSCHUDI, H., *Der Meister von Flémalle*, in *Jahrbuch der königliche Preussischen Kunstsammlungen*, XIX, 1898, pp. 8-34, 89-116.

VON WURZBACH, A., *Niederländisches Künstler-Lexikon auf Grund archivalischer Forschungen bearbeitet*, 3 vol., Vienna - Leipzig, 1906 - 11.

VORENKAMP, A.P.A., *A Silverpoint by Dieric Bouts*, in *Bulletin of the Smith College Museum of Art, Northampton, Massachusetts*, XX, 1939, pp. 3-10.

VORENKAMP, A.P.A., *A Silverpoint by Dieric Bouts*, in *Bulletin of the Smith College Museum of Art, Northampton, Massachusetts*, XXVIII, 1958, pp. 1-7.

WAAGEN, G.F., *Kunstwerke und Künstler in England und Paris*, 3 vol., Berlin, 1837-39.

WAAGEN, G.F., *Manuel de l'histoire de la peinture. Ecoles allemande, flamande et hollandaise*, 3 vol., Brussels - Leipzig - Ghent - Paris, 1863.

WAAGEN, G.F., *Über in Spanien vorhandene Bilder, Miniaturen und Handzeichnungen*, in *Jahrbücher für Kunstwissenschaft*, 1868-69, pp. 32-55.

WAAGEN, G.F., *Die Gemäldesammlung in der Kaiserlichen Eremitage zu St. Petersburg*, St. Peterburg, 1870.

WALDMANN, *Die Ehemalige Sammlung von Hollitscher*, in *Kunst und Künstler*, XVIII, 1920, p. 531.

WANGERMÉE, R., *Notes sur la vie musicale à Bruxelles au XVe siècle*, in *Bruxelles au XVe siècle*, Brussels, 1953, pp. 299-311.

WAUTERS, A., *Roger Vanderweyden, ses œuvres, ses élèves et ses descendants. Etude sur l'histoire de la peinture au XVe siècle*, Brussels, 1855, (reprint of *Revue universelle des arts*, II, 1855).

WAUTERS, A., *La Belgique ancienne et moderne. Géographie et histoire des communes belges*. Continuation par A. WAUTERS [...]. *Arrondissement de Louvain. Ville de Tirlemont*, Brussels, 1874.

WAUTERS, A., *Malouel (Alphonse)*, in *Biographie nationale [...] de Belgique*, XIII, Brussels, 1894-95, col. 262-264.

WEALE, W.H.J., *Catalogue du Musée de l'Académie de Bruges. Notices et descriptions avec monogrammes, etc.*, Bruges - London, 1861.

WEALE, W.H.J., *Bruges et ses environs. Description des monuments, objets d'art et antiquités, précédée d'une notice historique*, Bruges - London, 1862.

WEALE, W.H.J., *Notice sur la collection de tableaux anciens faisant partie de la galerie de Mr J.P. Weyer*, in *Messager des sciences historiques de Belgique*, 1864, pp. 447-488.

WEALE, W.H.J., *Catalogue des objets d'art religieux du moyen âge, de la renaissance et des temps modernes exposés à l'hôtel de Liedekerke à Malines, 1864*, Brussels, 1864.

WEALE, W.H.J., *Instrumenta ecclesiastica. Choix d'objets d'art religieux du moyen âge et de la renaissance exposés à Malines en septembre 1864* [...], Brussels - London - Paris, 1867.

WEALE, W.H.J., *Portrait de Hans Memlinc peint par lui-même, eau-forte de Jacques van Oost dit le vieux*, in *Beffroi*, IV, 1872-73, p. 45.

[WEALE, W.H.J.], *Exhibition of Pictures by Masters of the Flemish and British Schools including a selection from the Works of Sir Peter Paul Rubens. The New Gallery, Regent Street*, [London], 1899-1900.

WEALE, W.H.J., *Hans Memlinc, (The Great Masters in Painting and Sculpture)*, London, 1901.

WEALE, W.H.J., *Hans Memlinc. Biographie. Tableaux conservés à Bruges*, Bruges, 1901.

WEALE, W.H.J., *The Early Painters of the Netherlands as Illustrated by the Bruges Exhibition of 1902*, in *The Burlington Magazine*, I, 1903, pp. 41-52.

WEALE, W.H.J., *Hubert and John van Eyck. Their Life and Work*, London, 1908.

WEALE, W.H.J. and BROCKWELL, M.W., *The van Eycks and their Art*, London - New York - Toronto, 1912.

WEESE, A., *Skulptur und Malerei in Frankreich im XV. und XVI. Jahrhundert, (Handbuch der Kunstwissenschaft)*, Potsdam, 1927.

WEHLE, H.B., *A Painting by Joos van Gent*, in *The Metropolitan Museum of Art Bulletin*, II, 1943-44, pp. 133-139.

WEHLE, H.B. and SALINGER, M., *The Metropolitan Museum of Art. A Catalogue of Early Flemish, Dutch and German Paintings*, New York, 1947.

[WEIBEL, A.C.], *A Pair of Mille Fleurs Tapestries*, in *Bulletin of the Detroit Institute of Arts*, XXXIX, 1960, pp. 96-97.

WEINBERGER, M., *Notes on Maître Michiel*, in *The Burlington Magazine*, XC, 1948, pp. 247-253.

WERNER, A., *Berichte Amerika*, in *Pantheon*, XVIII, 1960, p. XVIII.

440

WESCHER, P., *Berlin, Versteigerungen,* in *Pantheon,* VIII, 1931, p. 436.

WESCHER, P., *The Drawings of Vrancke Van der Stoct (The Master of the Cambrai Altar),* in *Old Master Drawings,* XIII, 1938-39, pp. 1-5.

WESCHER, P., *Das Höfische Bildnis von Philipp dem Gutem bis zu Karl V,* in *Pantheon,* XXVIII, 1941, pp. 195-202, 272-277.

WINKLER, F., *Der Meister von Flemalle und Rogier van der Weyden,* Strasburg, 1913.

WINKLER, F., *Über verschollene Bilder der Brüder van Eyck,* in *Jahrbuch der königlich Preussischen Kunstsammlungen,* XXXVII, 1916, pp. 287-301.

WINKLER, F., *Der Meister der Anna Selbdritt im Louvre,* in *Kunstchronik und Kunstmarkt,* N.S., XXXIII, 1922, pp. 611-617.

WINKLER, F., *Die altniederländische Malerei. Die Malerei in Belgien und Holland von 1400-1600,* Berlin, 1924.

WINKLER, F., *Die Flämische Buchmalerei des XV. und XVI. Jahrhunderts. Künstler und Werke von den Brüdern van Eyck bis zu Simon Bening,* Leipzig, 1925.

WINKLER, F., *Neues von Hubert und Jan van Eyck,* in *Festschrift für Max J. Friedländer zum 60. Geburtstage,* Leipzig, 1927, pp. 91-102.

WINKLER, F., *Malouel (Maelwael, Maluel usw.),* in *Allgemeines Lexikon der bildenden Künstler [...],* begründet von U. THIEME und F. BECKER, XXXIII, ed. H. VOLLMER, Leipzig, 1929, pp. 599-600.

WINKLER, F., *Master Michiel,* in *Art in America and Elsewhere,* XIX, 1930-31, pp. 247-257.

WINKLER, F., *Neue Werke des Meisters Michiel,* in *Pantheon,* VII, 1931, pp. 175-178.

[WINKLER, F.], *Ein neuer Memling ?,* in *Pantheon,* XXVI, 1940, p. VI.

W[INKLER], F., *Ein neuer Memling ?,* in *Pantheon,* XXVI, 1940, p. 249.

WINKLER, F., *Die Prado - Bilder in Genf. Zur Ausstellung 1938,* in *Zeitschrift für Kunstgeschichte,* IX, 1940, pp. 66-70.

WINKLER, F., *Weyden, Rogier van der (Rogier de le Pasture),* in *Allgemeines Lexikon der bildenden Künstler [...],* begründet von U. THIEME und F. BECKER, XXXV, ed. H. VOLLMER, Leipzig, 1942, pp. 468-476.

WINKLER, F., *Das Berliner "Tüchlein" des Hugo van der Goes und sein Gegenstück,* in *Berliner Museen,* V, 1955, pp. 2-8.

WINKLER, F., *Dieric Bouts und Joos van Gent. Ausstellungen in Brüssel und Gent,* in *Kunstchronik,* XI, 1958, pp. 1-11.

W[ISHY], C., *Great Master Drawings of Seven Centuries. Benefit Exhibition of Columbia University for the Scholarship Fund of the Department of Fine Arts and Archaeology. New York. Knoedler & Co, October 13-November 7, 1959.**

[Woermann, K.], *Galerie Weber, Hamburg. Versteigerung: Dienstag, den 20., Mittwoch, den 21. und Donnerstag, den 22. Februar 1912. Rudolph Lepke's Kunst-Auctions-Haus, Berlin.*

X., *Tableau de Hans Memling, de la collection de M. le chev. Florent van Ertborn, ancien bourguemaître d'Anvers, gouverneur de la province d'Utrecht,* in *Messager des sciences et des arts,* 1829-30, pp. 61-62, 399-406.

X., *Résumé des procès-verbaux. Séances des 1, 8, 15 et 29 juillet; des 5, 12, 19 et 26 août 1905. Peinture et sculpture,* in *Bulletin des Commissions royales d'art et d'archéologie,* XLIV, 1905, pp. 85-96.

Zanettacci, H., *Les Ateliers picards de sculptures à la fin du moyen âge (Etudes d'art publiées par le Musée national des beaux-arts d'Alger),* Paris, 1954.

Zanotto, F., *Novissima guida di Venezia,* Venice, 1856.

Zeri, F., *Un Trittico del Maestro della Leggenda di Santa Barbara,* in *Paragone,* 1960, pp. 41-45.*

1773   London Sale. - *Bibliotheca Smithiana, ou catalogue de la rare et précieuse bibliothèque de feu Joseph Smith [...], vente chez S. Barker et G. Leigh, 25 janvier 1773,* London, 1773.

1784   Paris Sale. - Catalogue de la vente duc de la Vallière, Paris, 1784.

1790   London Sale. - Dr. Charles Chauncy Collection. Sale, London, 1790.

1815   London Sale. - *Catalogue of the Splendid Collection of Pictures belonging to Prince Lucien Buonaparte; which will be Exhibited for Sale by Private Contract, on Monday the Sixth Day of February, 1815, and Following Days at the New Gallery,* London, 1815.

1817   Paris Sale. - *Catalogue des livres rares et précieux de la bibliothèque de feu M. le comte de Mac-Carthy-Reagh,* 2 vol., Paris, 1915. *Liste des prix des livres de la bibliothèque de feu M. le comte de Mac-Carthy-Reagh, vendue à l'enchère par De Bure frère, [...] depuis le 27 janvier 1817, jusques et y compris le 6 mai suivant,* Paris, 1817.

1835   Mâcon Sale. - Catalogue de la vente Moreau, Mâcon, 1835.

1845   Ghent Exhib. - *Exposition de tableaux anciens, antiquités et objets d'art, au vestibule de l'Université [de Gand], 1845,* Ghent, (1845).

1850   The Hague Sale. - *Catalogue des tableaux anciens et modernes, de diverses écoles, dessins et statues, formant la galerie de feu Sa Majesté Guillaume II, Roi des Pays-Bas, etc. dont la vente aura lieu lundi le 12 août 1850 et jours suivants, à 10 heures du matin, au Palais de feu Sa Majesté, à la Haye,* Amsterdam, 1850.

1851   The Hague Sale. - *Catalogue des tableaux anciens et modernes de diverses écoles, dessins et estampes encadrés formant la seconde partie de la galerie de feu S.M. Guillaume, roi des Pays-Bas, Prince d'Orange, Grand-Duc de*

*Luxembourg, dont la vente aura lieu, mardi 9 septembre 1851 au Palais
de feu S.M. à la Haye sous le ministère du notaire M. Eyssel par Jeronimo
de Vries, Cornelis François Roos et Johannes Albertus Brondgeest.*

1853   LONDON Collection. - *Catalogue of the Manuscripts at Ashburnham
Place,* London, 1853.

1854   GHENT Exhib. - *Exposition de tableaux anciens et modernes, d'antiquités
et d'objets d'art au palais de l'Université [de Gand], 1854. Au profit
des indigents,* Ghent, 1854.

1861   BRUGES Museum. - WEALE, W.H.J., *Catalogue du Musée de l'Académie
de Bruges. Notices et descriptions avec monogrammes, etc.,* Bruges-Lon-
don, 1861.

1862   COLOGNE Sale. - *Catalogue illustré de la très riche et nombreuse collection
de tableaux composant la galerie de Mr J.P. Weyer, architecte honoraire
de la ville de Cologne et chevalier de l'Ordre de la Toison d'Or de
Belgique, dont la vente aux enchères publiques aura lieu, Rothgerbach
no. 1, le 25 août 1862 et jours suivants sous la direction de J.M. Heberle
(H. Lempertz) à Cologne,* [s.l.], 1862.

1864   MALINES Exhib. - WEALE, W.H.J., *Catalogue des objets d'art religieux du
moyen âge, de la renaissance et des temps modernes exposés à l'hôtel de
Liedekerke à Malines, 1864,* Brussels, 1864.

1865   PARIS Sale. - *Catalogue des tableaux [...], la galerie du Palais Vendra-
mini à Venise et appartenant à Mme la Duchesse de Berry, Paris, Hôtel
Drouot, 17-18 avril 1865,* [s.l.], 1865.

1866   LONDON Sale. - *Catalogue of the Memorable Cabinet of Drawings by the
Old Masters, and Collection of Engravings, formed with profound Taste
and Judgment by the late Rev. Dr. Wellesley, [...] which will sold by
Auction, by Messrs. Sotheby, Wilkinson and Hoolge [...], on Monday,
the 25th of June, 1866 and the following Days [...],* London, 1866.

1866   PARIS Exhib. - *Exposition rétrospective. Tableaux anciens empruntés aux
galeries particulières, Palais des Champs-Elysées,* Paris, 1866.

1867   BRUGES Exhib. - WEALE, W.H.J., *Gilde de Saint Thomas et Saint Luc.
Tableaux de l'ancienne école néerlandaise exposés à Bruges dans la grande
salle des halles. Septembre 1867. Catalogue,* Bruges, 1867.

1867   BRUGES Exhib. - VERSCHELDE, C., *Exposition d'objets d'art et d'antiquités
organisée par la Société archéologique de Bruges. Ville de Bruges, 25
août - 25 septembre 1867,* Bruges, 1867.

1867   PARIS Sale. - Catalogue de la vente Nicolas Yemeniz, Paris, 1867.

1869   PARIS Sale. - *Catalogue des tableaux [...], à M. Demidoff en son hôtel,
rue Jean-Goujon no. 35, 1-3 avril 1869,* [s.l.], 1869.

1873   AMSTERDAM Exhib. - *Tentoonstelling van voorwerpen van kunst en nijver-
heid uit vroegere eeuwen. Amsterdam, Arti et amicitiae, 1873,* Amsterdam, 1873.*

1875   BRUSSELS Sale. - Catalogue de vente, 6 avril 1875.

1876   PAU Collection. - X., *Catalogue abrégé des tableaux exposés dans les salons de l'ancien asile de Pau appartenant aux héritiers de feu Mgr. Sébastien de Bourbon et Bragance*, Pau, 1876.

1877   AMSTERDAM Exhib. - *Tentoonstelling. Catalogus van het Amsterdams museum van het koninklijk oudheidkundig genootschap in het oude Mannenhuis, 1877.*[*]

1877   PARIS Sale. - *Collection Roybet, catalogue de vente. Hôtel Drouot, Paris, 24 mars 1877,* [s.l.], 1877.[*]

1879   FRANKFORT on M. Sale. - *Prestel. Frankfurt a.M. Heimsoeth, 5 May 1879.*[*]

1879   PARIS Sale. - Catalogue de la vente Ambroise Firmin-Didot, Paris, 1879.

1880   BRUSSELS Exhib. - *Exposition nationale. 1880. Cinquantième anniversaire de l'indépendance de la Belgique. IVe Section. Industries d'art en Belgique antérieures au XIXe siècle. Catalogue officiel,* Brussels, 1880.

1881   LIÈGE Exhib. - *Exposition de l'art ancien au pays de Liège. Catalogue officiel. Cinquantième anniversaire de l'indépendance nationale,* Liège, 1881.

1882   AMSTERDAM Sale. - *Catalogue des cabinets de tableaux anciens et modernes délaissés par le Dr. P.A. Borger à Arnhem et par Mr D.J.H. Joosten, peintre-artiste à Harlem* [...], *Amsterdam, Fr. Muller & Co., 1882,* [s.l.], 1882.

1882   ... Collection. - Duke of Hamilton Collection. Catalogue, 1882.

1883   SIGMARINGEN Museum. - VON LEHNER, F.A., *Fürstlich Hohenzollern'sches Museum Sigmaringen. Verzeichnis der Gemälde,* 2nd ed., Sigmaringen, 1883.

1886   BRUSSELS Exhib. - *Exposition de tableaux de maîtres anciens organisée au profit de la Caisse centrale des artistes belges par la Classe des beaux-arts. Académie royale de Belgique. Catalogue explicatif,* Brussels, 1886.

1888   BRUSSELS Exhib. - *Exposition rétrospective d'art industriel organisée par le gouvernement* [...]. *Ministère de l'Agriculture, de l'Industrie et des Travaux publics. Bruxelles, 1888. Catalogue officiel publié sous la direction de M. le chanoine* REUSENS, Brussels, 1888.

1889   LONDON Sale. - Duke of Hamilton Collection, Sale, London, 1889.

1889   NEW YORK Sale. - *Catalogue of oil paintings, drawings and original sketches by the old masters belonging to his Highness, Don Pedro, Duque de Durcal* [...], *April 5th and 6th, American Art Sales Association, 1889,* [s.l.], 1889.

1892   LONDON Sale. - E.H. Lawrence Collection. Sale, London, 1892.

1897   PARIS Sale. - *Catalogue des objets d'art et de haute curiosité du moyen âge et de la renaissance, faïences hispano-moresques et italiennes, émaux champlevés et peints de Limoges, verrerie de Venise, grande verrière, orfèvrerie, bronzes, sculptures en ivoire, bois et pierre, peintures primitives italiennes et flamandes, polyptique de sainte Godelieve, meubles, tapisseries flamandes des XVe et XVIe siècles [...], collection de M.A. Tollin [...], vente [...], à Paris, salle Georges Petit [...], les jeudi 20 et vendredi 21 mai 1897*, [s.l.], 1897.

1898   BERLIN Exhib. - *Ausstellung von Kunstwerken des Mittelalters und der Renaissance aus Berliner Privatbesitz veranstaltet von der Kunstgeschichtlichen Gesellschaft, 20 Mai bis 3 Juli 1898*, Berlin, 1899.

1898   LONDON Sale. - T.M. Whitehead Sale, London, 3 May, 1898.

1899-1900 LONDON Exhib. - [WEALE, W.H.J.], *Exhibition of Pictures by Masters of the Flemish and British Schools including a Selection from the Works of Sir Peter Paul Rubens. The New Gallery, Regent Street, [London], 1899-1900*, [s.l.], 1899.

1901   BRUSSELS Sale. - *Catalogue des tapisseries, antiquités grecques et faïences italiennes faisant partie de la collection de Somzée et dont la vente publique aura lieu à Bruxelles [...], du lundi 20 au samedi 25 mai 1901 [...]*, [s.l.], 1901.

1901   LONDON Sale. - Earl of Ashburnham. Sale, London, 1901.

1902   BRUGES Exhib. - *Exposition des Primitifs flamands et d'art ancien. Catalogue. Bruges, hôtel Gruuthuuse, 15 juin au 15 septembre 1902*, Bruges, 1902.

1902   BRUGES Exhib. - H[ULIN] DE LOO, G., *Bruges 1902. Exposition de tableaux flamands des XIVe, XVe et XVI siècles. Catalogue critique précédé d'une introduction sur l'identité de certains maîtres anonymes*, Ghent, 1902.

1902   LONDON Sale. - H. Yates Thompson Sale, London, 14 May, 1902.

1902   LONDON Sale. - *Catalogue of a Choice Collection of Pictures and other Works of Art, chiefly Italian of Medieval and Renaissance Times, the Property of Signor Stephano Bardini of Florence, which will be sold by Auction by Messrs. Christie, Manson and Woods, 8 Kings Street, St. James's Square, London, on Monday May 26, 1902 and four Following Days*, [s.l.], 1902.

1902   LONDON Sale. - Catalogue 211. Quaritch, London, 1902.

1903   PARIS Sale. - *Collection Emile Pacully. Tableaux anciens et modernes des écoles allemande, espagnole, flamande, française, hollandaise, italienne, dont la vente aura lieu galerie Georges Petit, 8 rue de Sèze, le lundi 4 mai 1903*, [s.l.], 1903.

1904   LONDON Sale. - Catalogue 235. Quaritch, London, 1904, Nov.

1904   PARIS Exhib. - *Exposition des Primitifs français au Palais du Louvre (Pavillon de Marsan) et à la Bibliothèque nationale. Catalogue. Paris [...], avril 1904*, [Paris], 1904.

1905   BRUGES Exhib. - *Exposition d'art ancien. Guide du visiteur. Hôtel de Gruuthuuse, [Bruges 1905]*, Bruges, 1905.

1905   BRUSSELS Exhib. - *Exposition d'art ancien bruxellois. Royaume de Belgique. 75e anniversaire de l'Indépendance nationale. Cercle artistique et littéraire de Bruxelles (Waux-Hall), 19 juillet - fin septembre 1905*, Brussels, 1905.

1905   LIÈGE Exhib. - *Exposition de l'art ancien au pays de Liège. Catalogue général, 1905*, Liège, 1905.

1906   LONDON Exhib. - TEMPLE, A.G., *Illustrated Catalogue of the Exhibition of Works by the Early Flemish Painters. Art Gallery of the Corporation of London (Guildhall Gallery)*, (London), 1906.

1907   BRUGES Exhib. - *Exposition de la Toison d'Or (et de l'art néerlandais sous les ducs de Bourgogne) à Bruges, juin - octobre 1907. Catalogue*, Brussels, 1907.

1907   SAINT-TROND Exhib. - *Catalogue des objets exposés au palais de l'art ancien. Exposition provinciale du Limbourg, Saint-Trond, 1907*, (Saint-Trond), 1907.

1908   VIENNA Museum. - LEHRS, M., *Geschichte und kritischer Katalog des deutschen, niederländischen und französischen Kupferstichs im XV. Jahrhundert*, Vienna, 1908.

1909   CAMBRIDGE Exhib. - *A loan Exhibition of Flemish Art. The Fogg Art Museum, Harvard University, Cambridge, Mass., May 13th - August 20th, 1909*, [s.l.], 1909.

1909   LONDON Sale. - Sotheby Sale, London, 6 May 1909.

1909   NEW YORK Collection. - Robert Hoe Collection. Catalogue, 1909.

1910   BRUSSELS Museum. - DESTRÉE, Joseph and VAN DEN VEN, P., *Les Tapisseries [des] Musées royaux du Cinquantenaire*, Brussels, 1910.

1910   STUTTGART Sale. - *Katalog der berühmten Sammlung des Herrn Barons Adalbert von Lanna in Prag. 2. Teil, Handzeichnungen alter Meister und Kupferstiches Letztere umfassend die Dubletten des 1. Teils die Ornamentstich-Sammlung, die Englische und Französische Schule [...] Versteigerung zu Stuttgart 6. bis 11. Mai 1910 [...], im Saale des Königshaus durch die Kunsthandlung H.G. Gutekunst in Stuttgart*, [s.l.], 1910.

1911   MALINES Exhib. - *Exposition des anciens métiers d'art malinois, d'art religieux de la province d'Anvers et de folklore local. Catalogue*, Malines, 1911.

1911   TOURNAI Exhib. - SOIL DE MORIAME, E.J., *Exposition des anciennes industries d'art tournaisiennes. Catalogue. Ville de Tournai, juillet - octobre 1911*, [s.l.], 1911.

1912   BERLIN Sale. - [WOERMANN, K.], *Galerie Weber, Hamburg, Versteigerung: Dienstag, den 20., Mittwoch den 21. und Donnerstag, den 22. Februar*

446

1912. Rudolph Lepke's Kunst. Auctions-Haus, Berlin, [s.l.], 1912.

1912   Bruges Exhib.*

1912   London Sale. - Robert Blathwayt Collection, Dyrham Park, Chippenham. Sale, London, Nov. 20, 1912.

1912   New York Sale. - *Catalogue of the Library of Robert Hoe of New York: illuminated Manuscripts, Incunabula, Historical Bindings, [...] to be sold by [...]. The Anderson Auction Company*, 6 vol., New York, 1911-12.

1912   Paris Sale. - *Catalogue des tableaux anciens des écoles primitives et de la renaissance. Oeuvres importantes des écoles allemande, flamande, hollandaise et italienne des XIVe, XVe et XVIe siècles. Objets d'art et de curiosité. Enluminures, émaux [...], sculptures [...], tapisseries [...] dépendant des collections de M. Jean Dollfus et dont la vente [...] aura lieu à Paris, galerie Georges Petit, les lundi 1 et mardi 2 avril 1912 [...]*, [s.l.], 1912.

1913   Ghent Exhib. - *Exposition universelle et internationale de Gand. L'art ancien dans les Flandres (région de l'Escaut). Exposition rétrospective. Gand 1913, juin - octobre. Catalogue*, Ghent, 1913.

1914   Berlin Exhib. - *Ausstellung von Werken alter Kunst aus dem Privatbesitz von Mitgliedern des Kaiser Friedrich-Museums-Vereins, Mai 1914, in der königlichen Akademie der Künste, Pariser Platz 4. Katalog mit 25 Tafeln*, [s.l.], 1914.

1914   ... Collection. - Catalogue de la collection Lebœuf de Montgermont.

1915   Amsterdam Museum. - *Catalogus van de beeldhouwwerken in het Nederlandsch museum voor geschiedenis en kunst te Amsterdam.**

1915   Cleveland Exhib. - Gage Gallery, Cleveland, 1915.*

1915   Philadelphia Exhib. - *Loan Exhibition of Tapestries, Pennsylvania Museum and School of Industrial Art, Philadelphia, Pa., 1915*, [s.l.], 1915.

1917   Berlin Sale. - Friedländer, M.J., *Die Sammlung Richard von Kaufmann, Berlin. Gemälde. Versteigerung Dienstag den 4. Dezember 1917 und die folgenden Tage, unter der Leitung der Unterzeichneten P. Cassirer, Berlin und H. Helbing, München*, (Berlin), 1917.

1918   London Sale. - *Frederick Locker-Lampson (1821-1895), Rowfant, Sussex. Sold at Christie's, Dec. 20, 1918.**

1919   Brussels Sale. - *Catalogue de tableaux anciens et modernes et copies modernes d'après des maîtres anciens dont la vente publique aura lieu place du Congrès, 2, à Bruxelles les 15, 16, 17 mai, 2, 3 et 4 juin 1919 par le ministère de Me de Ro, notaire, 14 avenue de l'astronomie, Bruxelles*, [s.l.], 1919.

1919   New York Exhib. - New York Public Library. New York, 1919.*

1920   Amsterdam Sale. - *Catalogue d'une vente importante de tableaux anciens dépendant des collections I.P.... et N... à Paris, II. L... à Amsterdam, III. Diverses provenances, Amsterdam, 13 avril 1920, sous la dir. de Fr. Muller et Cie, (Art. W. M. Mensing), [s.l.], 1920.*

1920 BRUSSELS Exhib. - *Le polyptique de l'Agneau des frères van Eyck et le retable du St-Sacrement de Dieric Bouts [...]. Exposition du 14 août au 26 septembre 1920. Musée royal des beaux-arts de Belgique,* (Brussels), 1920.

1921-22 LONDON Exhib. - Burlington Fine Arts Club.*

1923 BRUSSELS Exhib. - *Exposition des Primitifs septentrionaux, mai-juin 1923* (Typewritten catalogue).

1923 PARIS Exhib. - *Exposition de l'art belge ancien et moderne [...], au Musée du Jeu de Paume à Paris, du 10 mai au 10 juillet 1923,* Brussels - Paris, 1923.

1924 LÉAU Exhib. - *Exposition d'art, d'archéologie, d'histoire et de folklore. Ville de Léau. Du 6 au 21 juillet 1924,* Léau, 1924.

1924 PARIS Exhib. - *Exposition de l'art ancien au pays de Liège [...]. (Catalogue, avant-propos par* M. LAURENT), *Palais du Louvre, Musée des arts décoratifs, Pavillon de Marsan, 20 mai - 30 juin 1924,* [s.l.], 1924.

1924-25 BRUGES Exhib. - *Tentoonstelling van oude stadsgezichten, in de groote zaal der halle, Brugge, dec. 1924 - feb. 1925.**

1926 AMSTERDAM Sale. - *Tableaux anciens XVe-XVIIe siècles. Vente publique à Amsterdam le 13 juillet 1926. Direction Ant. Mensing (Frederick Muller et Cie),* [s.l.], 1926.

1926 BERNE Exhib. - *Exposition de l'art belge ancien et moderne. Catalogue des œuvres exposées (au Musée des beaux-arts et à la Kunsthalle de Berne. 27 mars - 7 juin 1926),* (Brussels, 1926).

1926 TOLEDO Exhib. - Toledo Museum of Art, 1926.*

1927 BRUGES Exhib. - *Tentoonstelling van miniaturen en boekbanden. Geïllustreerde catalogus, Brugge, juli en augustus 1927,* [s.l.], (1927).

1927 LONDON Exhib. - *Exhibition of Flemish and Belgian Art 1300-1900, organized by the Anglo-Belgian Union, 1927. Royal Academy of Arts, London,* London, 1927.

1927 LONDON Exhib. - CONWAY, M., *Catalogue of the Loan Exhibition of Flemish and Belgian Art, Burlington House, London, 1927. A Memorial Volume,* London, 1927.

1928 DETROIT Exhib. - *The Seventh Loan Exhibition. French Gothic Art of the Thirteenth to Fifteenth Century. The Detroit Institute of Arts. November 16 to December 6, 1928,* [s.l.], 1928.

1928 LONDON Sale. - *Catalogue of Ancient and Modern pictures and Drawings Renoved from Beenham Court, Newbury, also Old Pictures, the Property of Sir Felix Clay Bart, the Property of Major G. Cornwallis. West and*

448

from Other Sources, London, Christie, Manson and Woods, May 11, 1928, [s.l.], 1928.

1928 New York Exhib. - *Exhibition of Flemish Primitives from the Collection of the Prince of Hohenzollern-Sigmaringen. Exhibition Catalogue. A.S. Drey Galleries, New York, 1928,* [s.l.], 1928.

1928 New York Exhib. - *Loan Exhibition of Paintings from Memling, Holbein and Titian to Renoir and Picasso at the Reinhard Galleries [...], in Aid of the Greenwich House Health Center. Feb. 17 - March 17, 1928,* New York, 1928.

1928 Vienna Museum. - Benesch, O., *Die Zeichnungen der niederländischen Schulen des XV. und XVI. Jahrhunderts (Beschreibender Katalog der Handzeichnungen in der graphischen Sammlung Albertina,* herausgegeben von A. Six, Bd. II), Vienna, 1928.

1929 New York Exhib. - *Catalogue of a loan Exhibition of Flemish Primitives in Aid of the Free Milk Fund for Babies, Inc. (Preface by Dr* M.J. Friedländer, *Director of the Berlin Museum), F. Kleinberger Galleries, Inc. 12 East 54th Street, New York, October - November 1929,* [s.d.], 1929.

1930 Antwerp Exhib. - *Exposition internationale, coloniale, maritime et d'art flamand [...], Anvers 1930. Section d'art flamand ancien [...]. Catalogue. Juin - septembre,* 4 vol., (Brussels, 1930).

1930 Antwerp Exhib. - *Trésor de l'art flamand du moyen âge au XVIIIe siècle. Mémorial de l'exposition d'art flamand ancien à Anvers, 1930,* par un groupe de spécialistes, 2 vol., Brussels, 1932.

1930 Detroit Museum. - Heil, W., *Catalogue of Paintings in the Permanent Collection of the Detroit Institute of Arts: European Paintings,* [Detroit], 1925.

1930 Vienna Sale. - Demmler, Th., *Die Sammlung Dr. Albert Figdor. Wien. Erster Teil, IV. Italienische Skulpturen und Plastiken in Stein, Holz, Stucco. Deutsche, niederländische, französische Skulpturen,* herausgegeben von O. von Falke, Berlin, 1930.

1931 Boston Museum. - Hendy, Ph., *The Isabella Stewart Gardner Museum. Catalogue of Paintings,* Boston, 1931.

1931 Cleveland Exhib. - *Art Through the Ages. The Cleveland Museum of Art, 1931.**

1931 Copenhagen Exhib. - *Udstillinge naf Belgisk Kunst fra XV. - XX. Aarhundrede, København, Ny Carlsberg Glyptotek, 26. April - 25. Maj 1931,* [s.l.], 1931.

1931 New York Exhib. - *Loan Exhibition of Arms and Armor. Metropolitan Museum of Art, New York, 1931.**

1932   LONDON Exhib. - *Exhibition of French Art 1200-1900. Royal Academy of Arts, Burlington House, Piccadilly, London, 1932*, [s.l.], 1932.

1932   LONDON Exhib. - *Exposition d'œuvres de la collection Auspitz, organisée par W. Bachstitz chez Thomas Agnew et fils, Londres, 1932*, [s.l.], 1932.

1932   LONDON Museum. - POPHAM, A.E., *Catalogue of Drawings by Dutch and Flemish Artists preserved in the Department of Prints and Drawings in the British Museum, V, Dutch and Flemish Drawings of the XV and XVI Centuries,* (London), 1932.

1933   CHICAGO Exhib. - *Catalogue of a Century of Progress Exhibition of Paintings and Sculpture Lent from American Collections, The Art Institute of Chicago, June 1 to November 1, 1933,* 2nd ed., [s.l.], 1933.

1933-34   NEW YORK Exhib. - *The Pierpont Morgan Library. Exhibition of Illuminated Manuscripts held at the New York Public Library, New York, 1933-34,* (New York), 1933.

1934   CHICAGO Exhib. - *Exhibition of Paintings and Sculpture. French - English - German - Dutch and Flemish - Italian - Spanish - American, Fourteenth to the Twentieth Century, The Art Institute of Chicago, Chicago, Ill., 1934,* [s.l.], 1934.

1934   NEW YORK Exhib. - New York Public Library. New York, 1934.*

1935   BRUSSELS Exhib. - *Exposition universelle et internationale de Bruxelles 1935 [...]. Cinq Siècles d'art [...] 24 mai - 13 octobre. Catalogue,* 5 vol., Brussels, 1935.

1935   PARIS Exhib. - *De van Eyck à Bruegel. Préface de* P. LAMBOTTE. *Introduction de* P. JAMOT. *Musée de l'Orangerie, [Paris], 1935,* [s.l.], 1935.

1935   TOLEDO Exhib. - *The Toledo Museum of Art, founded by Edward Drummond Libbey. Catalogue. French and Flemish Primitive Exhibition, November 3 to December 15 Nineteen Hundred and Thirty-Five,* [s.l.], 1935.

1936   BROOKLYN Exhib. - *European Art, 1450-1500. Brooklyn Museum, Brooklyn, N.Y., 1936.*

1936   CLEVELAND Exhib. - *Catalogue of the Twentieth Anniversary Exhibition of the Cleveland Museum of Art. The Official Art Exhibit of the Great Lakes, 1936,* [s.l.], 1936.

1936   LONDON Museum. - RACKHAM, B., *Victoria and Albert Museum, Department of Ceramics. A Guide to the Collections of Stained Glass,* London, 1936.

1936   LONDON Sale. - *Catalogue of the Famous Collection of old Master Drawings formed by the late Henry Oppenheimer [...] which [...] will be sold at Auction by Messrs. Christie, Manson and Woods [...], London [...] on Friday July 10, 1936, Monday, July 13 [...],* [s.l.], [1936].

1936   ROTTERDAM Exhib. - [HANNEMA, D. and VAN GELDER, J.G.], *Museum*

Boymans, Rotterdam 1936, Jeroen Bosch, Noord-Nederlandsche Primitieven, 10 Juli - 15 October, [s.l.], 1936.

1937 PARIS Exhib. - *Chefs-d'œuvre de l'art français. Palais national des arts, Paris, 1937*, [s.l.], 1937.

1937 PRINCETON Exhib. - *Exhibition of Belgian Medieval Art. Princeton University, 1937.**

1938 BRUGES Museum. - HOSTEN, E. and STRUBBE, E.I., *Geïllustreerde catalogus. Stedelijke Museum van Schoone Kunsten, Brugge*, 2nd revised and enlarged ed., Bruges, 1938.

1938 HARTFORD Exhib. - *Wadsworth Atheneum. Hartford, 1938.**

1938 MILWAUKEE Exhib. - *Milwaukee Art Institute, September 1938. Thirteen Paintings from the Seligman Galleries in New York*, [s.l.], 1938.

1938 PARIS Sale. - *Tableaux, aquarelle, pastel. Ecole française, Ecoles étrangères [...] Dépendant de la succession de M.E. Pacully, Hôtel Drouot, 5 juillet 1938*, [s.l.], 1938.

1939 BRUGES Exhib. - *Exposition Memling organisée par la ville de Bruges au Musée communal (22 juin - 1 octobre 1939). Catalogue*, Bruges, 1939.

1939 BRUGES Exhib. - Saint John's Hospital.*

1939 NEW YORK Exhib. - *Masterpieces of Art. New York World's Fair, May to October 1939. Catalogue of European Paintings and Sculpture from 1300-1800*, compiled by George Henry McCALL under the Editorship of William R. VALENTINER, [s.l.], 1939.

1939 WORCESTER-PHILADELPHIA Exhib. - *The Worcester - Philadelphia Exhibition of Flemish Painting organized by The Worcester Art Museum, Worcester, Massachusetts and The John G. Johnson Collection, Philadelphia. Worcester Art Museum, February 23 - March 12. John G. Johnson Collection at the Philadelphia Museum of Art, March 25 - April 26, 1939*, [s.l.], 1939.

1939-40 ROTTERDAM Exhib. - ...*

1940 BOSTON Exhib. - *Exhibition of Medieval Art. Boston, Museum of Fine Arts, Feb. 17 through March 24, 1940.**

1940 CLEVELAND Exhib. - *Masterpieces of Art from New York and San Francisco World's Fairs, The Cleveland Museum of Art, 1940*, [s.l.], 1940.

1940 GRAND RAPIDS Exhib. - Grand Rapids Art Gallery, May, 1940.*

1940 SAN FRANCISCO Exhib. - *Golden Gate International Exposition, San Francisco, June-Sept. 1940. Art Official Catalogue. Palace of Fine Arts.**

1940-41 KANSAS CITY Exhib. - *Seventh Anniversary Exhibition of German, Flemish, and Dutch Paintings. December, 1940 - January, 1941. William Rokhill Nelson Gallery of Art, Atkins Museum of Fine Arts, Kansas City, Missouri*, [s.l.], 1940.

1941   CAMBRIDGE Mass. Exhib. - *Netherlandish Art. Fogg Art Museum, December 1-26, 1941.**

1941   DETROIT Exhib. - *Masterpieces of Art from European and American Collections. Twenty-Second Loan Exhibition of Old Masters. Catalogue of the Exhibition. The Detroit Institute of Arts. April 1 through May 31, 1941,* Detroit, 1941.

1941   MUSKEGON Exhib. - *Hackley Art Gallery, Muskegon, October - November, 1941.**

1942   CLEVELAND Exhib. - *Exhibition of the John L. Severance Collection. The Cleveland Museum of Art, 1942,* [s.l.], 1942.

1942   CLEVELAND Museum. - *Catalogue of the John L. Severance Collection. Bequest of John L. Severance 1936,* Cleveland, 1942.

1942   NEW YORK Exhib. - *Flemish Primitives. An Exhibition organized by the Belgian Government through the Belgian Information Center, New York. April 13, 1942 to May 9, 1942. At the Gallery of M. Knoedler and Company, Inc.* [...], *New York City,* [s.l.], 1942.

1944   DETROIT Museum. - [RICHARDSON, E.P.], *The Detroit Institute of Arts. Catalogue of Paintings,* 2nd ed., Detroit, 1944.

1944   LOS ANGELES Exhib. - *Balch Collection and Old Masters from Los Angeles Collections, Los Angeles County Museum, 1944.**

1944   MONTREAL Exhib. - *Five Centuries of Dutch Art Association of Montreal. March 9 - April 9, 1944.**

1945   HOUSTON Collection. - *Catalogue of the Edith A. and Percy S. Straus Collection. Museum of Fine Arts of Houston. April, 1945.**

1945   LOUVAIN Exhib. - *Herwordend Leuven. Tentoonstelling van kunstwerken gered uit de Leuvensche kerken die geteisterd werden door oorlogs feiten in het jaar o.h. 1944. Universiteitshalle, Leuven, 2 tot 23 september 1945.* Louvain, 1945.

1945   THE HAGUE Exhib. - *Nederlandsche Kunst van de XVde en XVIde eeuw. Koninklijk Kabinet van Schilderijen, Mauritshuis, 1 september tot 21 october 1945, 's-Gravenhage,* [s.l.], 1945.

1946   AMSTERDAM Exhib. - *Van Jan van Eyck tot Rubens. Tentoonstelling van meesterwerken uit de Belgische musea en kerken. Rijksmuseum, Amsterdam, 23 maart - 19 mei. Museum Boymans, Rotterdam, 25 mei - 16 juni 1946,* (Amsterdam), 1946.

1946   NEW YORK Exhib. - *Loan Exhibition. 24 Masterpieces to Commemorate the hundreth Anniversary of the Knoedler Gallery and the Seventy-fifth Anniversary of the Metropolitan Museum of Art, Nov. 4 to 23, 1946, M. Knoedler and Co,* [s.l.], 1946.

1946   ROTTERDAM Exhib. - *Van Jan van Eyck tot Rubens. Tentoonstelling van meesterwerken uit de Belgische musea en kerken. Rijksmuseum, Amster-*

dam, *23 maart - 19 mei. Museum Boymans, Rotterdam, 25 mei - 16 juni 1946,* (Amsterdam), 1946.

1947   BRUSSELS Exhib. - *La Tapisserie française du moyen âge à nos jours. (Introduction de* P. VERLET), *Bruxelles, Palais des beaux-arts, janvier - février 1947,* [Brussels], 1947.

1947   NEW YORK Museum. - WEHLE, H.B. and SALINGER, M., *The Metropolitan Museum of Art. A Catalogue of Early Flemish, Dutch and German Paintings,* New York, 1947.

1947   PARIS Exhib. - VAN PUYVELDE, L., *Les Primitifs flamands. Catalogue. Musée de l'Orangerie, Paris, 5 juin - 7 juillet 1947,* Brussels, 1947.

1947-48   CLEVELAND Exhib. - *Exhibition of Gold. The Cleveland Museum of Art, 1947-48.*[*]

1948   ANTWERP Exhib. - *Tentoonstelling kerkelijke kunst. Catalogus. Stedelijke feestzaal, 16 oct. - 15 nov. 1948,* [s.l.], 1948.

1948   BALTIMORE Exhib. - *Themes and Variations. Baltimore, Museum of Art, Md., 1948.*[*]

1948   BRUSSELS Exhib. - *Chefs-d'œuvre récupérés en Allemagne. Palais des beaux-arts, Bruxelles, novembre - décembre 1948,* (Brussels), 1948.

1948   CAMBRIDGE Mass. Exhib. - *Early Flemish Paintings. Fogg Museum of Art, Cambridge, Mass., 1948*[*]

1948   's-HERTOGENBOSCH Exhib. - *Belgische kant van de 16de eeuw tot heden. 's-Hertogenbosch, 1948.*[*]

1948-49   CAMBRIDGE Mass. Exhib. - *Seventy Master Drawings. Fogg Art Museum, Nov. 27, 1948 - Jan. 6, 1949.*[*]

1948-49   ROTTERDAM Exhib. - *Tekeningen van Jan van Eyck tot Rubens. Museum Boymans, Rotterdam, Kersttentoonstelling, 17 december 1948 - 1 februari 1949,* [s.l.], 1948.

1949   BALTIMORE Exhib. - *Illuminated Books of the Middle Ages and Renaissance,* Baltimore, 1949.

1949   BRUGES Exhib. - *Gérard David. Musée communal, Bruges, 18 juin - 21 août 1949,* Brussels, 1949.

1949   BRUSSELS Exhib. - *De van Eyck à Rubens. Dessins de maîtres flamands. Palais des beaux-arts, Bruxelles, mars - avril 1949,* Brussels, 1948.

1949   LONDON Exhib. - *Gérard David. London, Wildenstein & Co.*[*]

1949   PARIS Exhib. - *De van Eyck à Rubens. Les maîtres flamands du dessin. Paris, Bibliothèque nationale, 1949,* (Paris), 1949.

1949   TOURNAI Exhib. - *Exposition des arts religieux,* [s.l.], 1949.

1950   BRUGES Exhib. - *Orfèvrerie à Bruges. Musée communal, Bruges, 1 juillet - 3 septembre 1950,* Brussels, 1950.

1950   BUFFALO Exhib. - *Bosch to Beckmann Exhibition, Albright Art Gallery,*

Buffalo, New York, April 15 to May 14, 1950, [s.l.], 1950.

1950 INDIANAPOLIS Exhib. - *Holbein and his Contemporaries. A Loan Exhibition of Painting in France, the Netherlands, Germany and England. October 22 - December 24, 1950, The Art Association of Indianapolis, Indiana. The John Herron Art Museum,* Indianapolis, 1950.

1950-51 PHILADELPHIA Exhib. - *Masterpieces of Drawing. Diamond Jubilee Exhibition. Philadelphia Museum of Art, November 4, 1950 - February 11, 1951,* [s.l.], 1950.

1951 AMSTERDAM Exhib. - *Bourgondische pracht van Philips de Stoute tot Philips de Schone. Catalogus* [...], *Rijksmuseum, Amsterdam, 28 juli - 1 october 1951,* [Amsterdam], 1951.

1951 ARRAS Exhib. - *L'Art du moyen âge en Artois. Tapisseries d'Arras, 15 avril - 15 mai. Manuscrits à peintures, sceaux, 15 avril - 2 septembre. Orfèvrerie, 1 - 30 juin. Catalogue de l'exposition. Musée d'Arras, palais Saint-Vaast, 1951,* (Arras), 1951.

1951 BRUGES Exhib. - *Fiamminghi e Italia. Chefs-d'œuvre de maîtres anciens italiens et flamands du XVe au XVIIe siècle. Musée communal, Bruges, juillet - août 1951,* Brussels, 1951.

1951 BRUSSELS Exhib. - *Le Siècle de Bourgogne. Palais des beaux-arts, Bruxelles, 13 octobre - 16 décembre 1951. Catalogue* [...], [s.l.], 1951.

1951 DETROIT Exhib. - *French Drawings of Five Centuries from the Collection of the Fogg Museum of Art, Harvard University. The Detroit Institute of Arts. May 15th - September 30th, 1951,* [s.l.], 1951.

1951 DIJON Exhib. - *Le grand siècle des ducs de Bourgogne, Musée de Dijon, Palais des ducs de Bourgogne, 1951,* [s.l.], 1951.

1951 IOWA Exhib. - *Six Centuries of Master Drawings. State University of Iowa, 1951.**

1951 LIÈGE Exhib. - *Art mosan et arts anciens du pays de Liège. Exposition internationale,* [Liège, 1951].

1951 LONDON Museum. - DAVIES, M., *The Earlier Italian Schools. National Gallery Catalogues,* London, 1951.

1951 PITTSBURG Exhib. - *French Painting 1100-1900. October eighteenth-December second 1951. Department of Fine Arts, Carnegie Institute (Pittsburg),* [s.l.], 1951.

1951 ROMA Exhib. - *I Fiamminghi e l'Italia. Pittori italiani e fiamminghi dal XV al XVIII secolo. Bruges, Museo communale, luglio - agosto 1951; Venezia, Palazzo Ducale, settembre 1951; Roma, ottobre - novembre 1951,* Venice, 1951.

1951 TIRLEMONT Exhib. - *Historische stand der Franciscaanse stichtingen te Tienen, op de missietentoonstelling van 8 - 15 Juli 1951, in Tienen, Franciscaanse stede. Franciscaanse stichtingen in Tienen,* [s.l.], 1951.

454

1951   Venice Exhib. - *I Fiamminghi et l'Italia. Pittori italiani e fiamminghi dal XV al XVIII secolo. Bruges, Museo communale, luglio - agosto 1951; Venezia, Palazzo Ducale, settembre 1951; Roma, ottobre - novembre 1951,* Venice, 1951.

1951   Worcester Exhib. - *Condition: Excellent. Exhibition, Worcester Art Museum, 1951,* (Worcester), 1951.

1951-52   Hartford-Baltimore Exhib. - *2.000 Years of Tapestry Weaving, Wadsworth Atheneum, Hartford and Baltimore Museum of Art.**

1951-52   Worcester Exhib. - *The Practice of Drawing. Worcester Art Museum, Nov. 17, 1951 - Jan. 6, 1952.**

1952-53   Brussels Exhib. - *Exposition héraldique, 29 décembre MCMLII - 31 janvier MCMLIII, sous le haut patronage de S.A.R. la princesse Joséphine-Charlotte de Belgique, organisée par l'Office généalogique et héraldique de Belgique,* Brussels, 1952.

1952-53   Paris Exhib. - *Le Portrait dans l'art flamand de Memling à Van Dijck. Orangerie des Tuileries, Paris, 21 octobre 1952 - 4 janvier 1953,* (Brussels, 1952).

1953   Bruges Exhib. - *Le Portrait dans les anciens Pays-Bas. Bruges, Musée communal (Exposition. 27 juin - 31 août 1953),* Brussels, 1953.

1953   Brussels Exhib. - *Chefs-d'œuvre de l'art ancien dans les musées et collections belges. Palais des beaux-arts, Bruxelles, XXVe anniversaire, 29 mai- 24 juin 1953,* (Brussels), 1953.

1953   Brussels Exhib. - *Exposition Bruxelles au XVe siècle, 9 octobre - 22 novembre 1953, Musée communal, Bruxelles,* (Brussels), 1953.

1953   Duisburg Exhib. - ...*

1953   Mons Exhib. - *Trésors d'art du Hainaut. Mons, chapelle Saint-Georges, cloître des Visitandines, du 17 mai au 31 juillet 1953,* 2nd ed., [s.l.], 1953.

1953   Montreal Exhib. - *Five Centuries of Drawings. Montreal Museum of Art, Oct. - Nov. 1953.**

1953   Ostende Exhib. - *Art fantastique. Kursaal, Ostende, 5 juillet - 31 août 1953,* Brussels, 1953.

1953-54   London Exhib. - [Brockwell, M.W.], *Flemish Art 1300-1700. Winter Exhibition, 1953-54, Royal Academy of Arts, London,* [s.l.], 1953.

1953-54   Los Angeles Exhib. - *Mediaeval and Renaissance Illuminated Manuscripts. A Loan Exhibition. Los Angeles County Museum, November 25, 1953 - January 9, 1954,* (Los Angeles), 1953.

1954   Antwerp Exhib. - *De Madonna in de kunst. Stad Antwerpen, Kon. Museum voor Schone Kunsten, catalogus [...] 28 augustus - 30 november 1954,* (Antwerp), 1954.

1954   BORDEAUX Exhib. - (MARTIN-MÉRY, G.), *Flandres - Espagne - Portugal du XVe au XVIIe siècle, Bordeaux, 19 mai - 31 juillet 1954*, (Bordeaux), 1954.

1954   BRUSSELS Exhib. - *Trésors d'art du Brabant. Exposition organisée sous l'égide de la députation permanente du Conseil provincial du Brabant. Catalogue, Bruxelles, Musées royaux d'art et d'histoire, juin - juillet 1954*, (Brussels), 1954.

1954   DETROIT Museum. - [RICHARDSON, E.P.], *Catalogue of the Paintings and Sculpture Given by Edgar B. Whitcomb and Anna Scripps Whitcomb to the Detroit Institute of Arts*, Detroit, 1954.

1954   LOS ANGELES Museum. - *A Catalogue of Flemish, German, Dutch and English Paintings XV - XVIII Century, Los Angeles County Museum*, Los Angeles, Calif., 1954.

1954   NEW YORK Exhib. - *Paintings and Drawings from the Smith College Collection. M. Knoedler & Co, New York, March 30 - April 11, 1954.*[*]

1955   BRUSSELS Exhib. - *Tentoonstelling. Zilveren kunstwerken. Catalogus. Provinciaal Museum Sterckshof, Deurne-Antwerpen, 2 april - 5 juni 1955. Koninklijke Musea voor Kunst en Geschiedenis, Brussel, 11 juni - 10 juli 1955*, (Antwerp), 1955.

1955   DEURNE (ANTWERP) Exhib. - *Tentoonstelling. Zilveren kunstwerken. Catalogus. Provinciaal Museum Sterckshof, Deurne-Antwerpen, 2 april - 5 juni 1955. Koninklijke Musea voor Kunst en Geschiedenis, Brussels, 11 juni - 10 juli, 1955*, (Antwerp), 1955.

1955   GHENT Exhib. - *Charles-Quint et son temps. Exposition organisée par l'Administration communale de Gand en collaboration avec le Ministère de l'Instruction publique, 3 avril - 30 juin 1955, Musée des beaux-arts, Gand*, (Brussels), 1955.

1955   LONDON Museum. - DAVIES, M., *Early Netherlandish School. National Gallery Catalogues*, 2nd revised ed., London, 1955.

1955   MINNEAPOLIS Exhib. - *Fortieth Anniversary Exhibition of Forty Masterpieces. Minneapolis Institute of Arts, Jan. 12 through Feb. 27, 1955.*[*]

1955   NEW YORK Exhib. - *An Exhibition of Paintings. E. and A. Silberman Galleries, Oct. 12 to Nov. 1, 1955*, [s.l.]. 1955.

1955   SCHAFFHAUSEN Exhib. - *Meisterwerke Flämischer Malerei. Hundert Gemälde aus der Blütezeit der Malerei in Flandern von Van Eyck bis Rubens. Stadt Schaffhausen, Museum zu Allerheiligen, 17 September bis 3 Dezember 1955*, Schaffhausen, 1955.

1956   BROOKLYN Exhib. - *"Thine Eyes Shall See". Brooklyn Museum, Brooklyn, N.Y.*, [s.l.], 1956.[*]

1956   BRUSSELS Museum. - CRICK-KUNTZIGER, M., *Catalogue des tapisseries*

(XIVe au XVIIIe siècle). Musées royaux d'art et d'histoire de Bruxelles, [s.l., 1956].

1956 GHENT Exhib. - *Tentoonstelling Scaldis. Provincie Oostvlaanderen. Gent, 16 juli - 23 september 1956. Oude kunst en kultuur in de Aloude St.-Pietersabdij. Moderne kunst in het Museum voor Schone Kunsten,* (Ghent), 1956.

1956 NEW HAVEN Exhib. - *Yale University Art Gallery. Pictures collected by Yale Alumni, May 8 - June 18, 1956,* [s.l.], 1956.

1956 NEW YORK Exhib. - *For the Connoisseur. New York, Wildenstein and Co., Sept. 24 - Oct. 31, 1956.**

1956 TOURNAI Exhib. - *Scaldis - Escaut - Schelde. (Art et civilisation). Tournai, halle aux draps, Casino communal, Musée d'histoire et d'archéologie, Musée des beaux-arts, du 15 juillet au 10 septembre 1956,* [s.l.], 1956.

1957 BALTIMORE Exhib. - *History of Bookbinding, Baltimore, 1957.*

1957 BRUSSELS Exhib. - *Exposition art, histoire et sciences. Catalogue. Bruxelles, Musées royaux d'art et d'histoire, 26 avril - 30 mai 1957* [...] (Brussels), 1957.

1957 BRUSSELS Exhib. - *Tentoonstelling. Koper en brons. Catalogus. Het Sterckshof, Provinciaal Museum voor Kunstambachten, Deurne-Antwerpen, 13 april - 10 juni 1957. Koninklijke Musea voor Kunst en Geschiedenis, Brussel, 15 juni - 29 juli 1957,* [s.l.], 1957.

1957 DEURNE (ANTWERP) Exhib. - *Tentoonstelling. Koper en brons. Catalogus. Het Sterckshof, provinciaal Museum voor Kunstambachten, Deurne - Antwerpen, 13 april - 10 juni 1957. Koninklijke Musea voor Kunst en Geschiedenis, Brussel, 15 juni - 29 juli 1957,* [s.l.], 1957.

1957 GHENT Exhib. - *Juste de Gand, Berruguete et la cour d'Urbino. Exposition agréée par la Commission internationale de l'I.C.O.M., organisée par la ville de Gand* [...]. *Musée des beaux-arts, Gand, 12 octobre - 15 décembre 1957,* (Brussels), 1957.

1957 SAN DIEGO Exhib. - *The Madonna in Art. December 6 - 29, 1957. The Fine Arts Gallery of San Diego, Balboa Park, San Diego, California,* [s.l.], 1957.

1957-58 BRUSSELS Exhib. - (BAUDOUIN, F. and BOON, K.G.), *Dieric Bouts. Palais des beaux-arts, Bruxelles, 1957-1958, Museum Prinsenhof, Delft,* Brussels, 1957.

1957-58 DELFT Exhib. - (BAUDOUIN, F. and BOON, K.G.), *Dieric Bouts, Palais des beaux-arts, Bruxelles 1957-1958, Museum Prinsenhof, Delft,* Brussels, 1957.

1958 AMSTERDAM Exhib. - *150 Jaar Rijksmuseum. Jubileumtentoonstelling. Middeleeuwse Kunst der Noordelijke Nederlanden, Amsterdam, 28 juni - 28 september 1958,* [Amsterdam], 1958.

1958 ANTWERP Museum. - (DELEN, A.J.J.), *Catalogue descriptif. Maîtres anciens. Musée royal des beaux-arts, Anvers*, 2nd ed. (revised and enlarged by M.J.J. BROECKX and G. GEPTS-BUYSAERT), [s.l.], 1958.

1958 BRUSSELS Exhib. - *Le Maître de Flémalle. L'Annonciation dite de Mérode. Catalogue. Musées royaux des beaux-arts de Belgique à Bruxelles, 5 - 20 janvier 1958*, [s.l.], 1958.

1958 LIÈGE Exhib. - *Trois millénaires d'art verrier à travers les collections publiques et privées de Belgique. Catalogue général de l'exposition, Liège, Musée Curtius, 1958*, [s.l.], 1958.

1958 MADRID Exhib. - *Arte Flamenco en las Colecciones Españolas. Octubre-diciembre 1958. Sociedad Española de Amigos del Arte*, [Madrid], 1958.

1958 MALINES Exhib. - *Margareta van Oostenrijk en haar hof. Tentoonstelling, 26 juli - 15 september 1958*, Malines, 1958.

1958 NEW YORK Exhib. - *The Taste of Connoisseurs. French and Company, Inc., New York, September 1958.*[*]

1958 TOURNAI Exhib. - *Arts religieux. Tournai, cathédrale, du 18 mai au 30 september*, [s.l.], 1958.

1958 TOURNAI Exhib. - *Tapisseries d'Occident. Tournai, halle aux draps, du 19 juillet au 31 août 1958*, [s.l.], 1958.

1959 AMSTERDAM Exhib. - *Le Siècle d'or de la miniature flamande. Le mécénat de Philippe le Bon. Exposition organisée à l'occasion du 400e anniversaire de la fondation de la Bibliothèque royale de Philippe II à Bruxelles, le 12 avril 1599. Palais des beaux-arts, Bruxelles. Rijksmuseum, Amsterdam, 26 juin - 13 septembre 1959. (Catalogue par* L.M.J. DELAISSÉ), 1959.

1959 ANTWERP Exhib. - *Derde eeuwfeest Sint-Laurentiusparochie 1659-1959. Catalogus. Tentoonstelling "Laus Laurentio". Kerkschat en beeld van de parochie vroeger en nu. Religieuze kunstvoorwerpen tot de 18e eeuw (uit privaat bezit). Feestzaal, A. Goemaerelei, 18, Antwerpen. Van 18 oktober tot 1 november 1959*, [s.l.], 1959.

1959 BRUGES Exhib. - *Schilderijen geschonken door de vrienden der Musea (1903 - 1914). Catalogus. Stad Brugge. Groeningemuseum, 21 maart - 5 april 1959*, [s.l.], 1959.

1959 BRUSSELS Exhib. - *La Miniature flamande. Le mécénat de Philippe le Bon. Exposition organisée à l'occasion du 400e anniversaire de la fondation de la Bibliothèque royale de Philippe II, le 12 avril 1559 (Catalogue de* L.M.J. DELAISSÉ). *Palais des beaux-arts, Bruxelles, avril - juin 1959*, [Brussels], 1959.

1959 INDIANAPOLIS Exhib. - *Paintings from the Collection of George Henry Alexander Clowes, Indianapolis, October 2nd to November 1st, 1959*, [s.l.], 1959.

1959   LIÈGE Exhib. - *La Nativité dans l'art. Catalogue de l'exposition organisée au Musée Curtius, Liège, 1959*, [s.l.], 1959.

1959   LOUVAIN Exhib. - (VAN MOLLE, F.), *St. Gertrudis. Tentoonstelling, St.-Gertrudiskerk te Leuven, 16 augustus - 13 september 1959*, (Heverlee), 1959.

1959   NEW YORK Exhib. - *Great Master Drawings of Seven Centuries. Benefit Exhibition of Columbia University for the Scholarship Fund of the Department of Fine Arts and Archaeology. New York, Knoedler & Co, October 13 - November 7, 1959.**

1959   RALEIGH Exhib. - *W.R. Valentiner Memorial Exhibition. The North Carolina Museum of Art, Raleigh, North Carolina, April 6 through May 17, 1959.**

1959   ROEULX (LE) Exhib. - *Neuf siècles de l'histoire du Hainaut au Roeulx, du 26 avril au 30 juin 1959*, [s.l.], 1959.

1959   VERVIERS Exhib. - *Les Collections du Musée diocésain de Liège. Préface de L. Dewez. Musée communal de Verviers (Les Amis du Musée, VIII)*, (Verviers), 1959.

1960   BRUGES Exhib. - *Le Siècle des Primitifs flamands. Exposition organisée par l'Administration communale de Bruges et The Detroit Institute of Arts, Detroit, Michigan, USA, au Musée communal des beaux-arts (Musée Groeninge), 26 juin - 11 septembre 1960. Catalogue*, Bruges, 1960.

1960   GHENT Exhib. - *Fleurs et jardins dans l'art flamand. Musée des beaux-arts, Gand, avril - juin 1960*, Brussels, 1960.

1960   MONTREAL Museum. - *Montreal Museum of Fine Arts. Catalogue of Fine Arts. Catalogue of Paintings, Montreal, Canada, 1960*, (Montreal), 1960.

Addenda :

GANS, E., *The Cambyses Justice Medal*, dans *The Art Bulletin*, XXIX, 1947, pp. 121-122.

VAN DE WALLE DE GHELCKE, TH., *Propos sur l'Exposition Gérard David et son catalogue*, dans *Annales de la Société d'Emulation de Bruges*, LXXXVI, 1949, pp. 219-224.

INDEX OF ARTISTS

460

Metalwork

van Thienen, Renier: nos. 103-104
Brabant: nos. 101-102, 105, 106
Brabant or Dinant: nos. 109-112
Bruges: nos. 107, 121-122, 123
Dinant or Brabant: nos. 109-112
Flanders: nos. 124-126
France: no. 108
Southern Netherlands: nos. 113, 114, 117-120
Ypres: nos. 115-116

Goldsmith's Work

the Gufkenses: no. 127
Loyet, Gérard: no. 133
Pauwels the Younger, Joos: no. 138
Master Henri: no. 127
Brabant: nos. 132, 134
Brussels: no. 135
Flemish - Burgundian: no. 131
Franco - Burgundian: no. 128
Netherlands: no. 130
Southern Netherlands: nos. 136, 137
Tournai: no. 129

Arms and Armor

Southern Netherlands: nos. 139-142, 143, 144, 145, 146, 147

Textiles

Feré, Pierre (Arras): no. 148
Grenier, Pasquier (Tournai): nos. 150, 151
Bruges or Tournai: no. 153
English: no. 160
Franco - Flemish: nos. 154-155
Southern Netherlands: nos. 156, 157, 158, 159
Tournai: nos. 149, 152
Tournai or Bruges: no. 153

Furniture

Brabant: nos. 161, 163
Bruges: nos. 162, 164

Glass and Stained-Glass

van de Voorde, Chrétien: nos. 165-168
Liège: no. 169

LIST OF LENDERS

Amsterdam, Rijksmuseum: nos. 101-102

Antwerp, Musée Royal des Beaux-Arts: nos. 3, 18, 38, 43

Antwerp, Oudheidkundige Musea, Vleeshuis: no. 159

Antwerp, Jan Van Herck Collection: no. 91

Baltimore, Md., The Walters Art Gallery: nos. 2, 22, 109-112, 196 , 197, 202, 203, 204, 208, 213

Boston, Mass., Museum of Fine Arts: nos. 7, 131, 153

Blankenberge, Church of Saint-Roch: no. 158

Bruges, Cathedral of Saint-Sauveur: nos. 1, 19, 164

Bruges, Church of Jerusalem: no. 136

Bruges, Church of Notre-Dame: no. 157

Bruges, City Hall: no. 123

Bruges, Commissie van Openbare Onderstand: nos. 94-95

Bruges, Convent of the Black Sisters: no. 39

Bruges, Gruuthuse-Museum: nos. 68, 72, 90, 121-122, 162, 165-168

Bruges, Noble Brotherhood of the Holy Blood: no. 25

Bruges, Saint John's Hospital, Memlinc Museum: nos. 30, 31, 107

Bruges, Stadsarchief: nos. 172, 173, 174, 175, 176, 177, 178, 179, 180, 181, 182, 183, 184, 185, 186, 187, 188, 189

Bruges, Stedelijk Museum voor Schone Kunsten (Groeningemuseum): nos. 4, 13, 33, 44, 45, 54

Brussels, Archives Générales du Royaume: no. 170

Brussels, Musées Royaux d'Art et d'Histoire: nos. 80, 86-89, 97, 99, 138, 139-142, 143, 144, 145, 146, 147, 152

Brussels, Musées Royaux des Beaux-Arts: no. 21

Brussels, Private Collection: no. 16

Cambridge, Mass., Fogg Art Museum, Harvard University: no. 62

Cincinnati, Ohio, The Cincinnati Art Museum: no. 32

Cleveland, Ohio, The Cleveland Museum of Art: nos. 28, 47, 128

Detroit, Mich., The Detroit Institute of Arts: nos. 5, 9, 24, 40, 41, 46, 52, 53, 154-155

Diest, Church of Saint-Sulpice: nos. 81-84

Etterbeek (Brussels), Church of Sainte-Gertrude: no. 85

Furnes, Museum of the City Hall: nos. 124-126

Geel, Church of Sainte-Dymphne: nos. 74-77

Ghent, Museum voor Oudheden der Bijloke: nos. 71, 115-116

Ghent, Private Collection: no. 66

Ghent, Stadsarchief: nos. 108, 190, 191, 192, 193, 194, 195

CONCORDANCE

of the catalogue numbers in this Exhibition with those of the Bruges Exhibition "Le Siècle des Primitifs Flamands", June 25 to September 11, 1960

DETROIT	BRUGES	DETROIT	BRUGES	DETROIT	BRUGES
1	1	29	33	57	68
2	—	30	38	58	—
3	2	31	45	59	73
4	5	32	47	60	—
5	3	33	36	61	74
6	10	34	37	62	—
7	13	35	35	63	71
8	16	36	44	64	76
9	15	37	42	65	72
10	11	38	34	66	75
11	12	39	48	67	70
12	17	40	50	68	78
13	18	41	53	69-70	—
14	—	42	—	71	100
15	6	43	55	72	82
16	8	44	57	73	101
17	—	45	59	74-77	96
18	23	46	56	78-79	89-90
19	21	47	—	80	86
20	25	48	60	81-84	102
21	26	49	58	85	91
22	27	50	61	86-89	97
23	28	51	63	90	84
24	24	52	65	91	85
25	30	53	64	92	94
26	31	54	67	93	88
27	54	55	69	94-95	87
28	32	56	66	96	92

DETROIT	BRUGES	DETROIT	BRUGES	DETROIT	BRUGES
97	95/bis	136	107	170	—
98	93	137	—	171	—
99	95	138	106	172	169
100	98	139-142	146-149	173	152
101-102	121	143	—	174	153
103-104	118-119	144	144	175	154
105	120	145	143	176	155
106	125	146	145	177	156
107	126	147	150-151	178	157
108	133	148	—	179	158
109-112	122	149	—	180	159
113	123	150	135	181	160
114	124	151	—	182	161
115-116	128-129	152	134	183	162
117-120	—	153	136	184	163
121-122	131-132	154-155	137	185	164
123	130	156	139	186	165
124-126	127	157	140	187	166
127	—	158	141	188	167
128	113	159	142	189	168
129	114	160	138	190	170
130	112	161	—	191	171
131	115	162	—	192	172
132	108	163	104	193	173
133	109	164	103	194	174
134	110	165-168	77	195	175
135	111	169	116	196-213	—

466

TABLE OF CONTENTS

Printed in Belgium by N.V. Drukkerij L. Blondé, Antwerp.
Color and half-tones plates engraved by Photogravure De
Schutter, Antwerp, except for the color plates of the Master
of the Saint Ursula Legend, which are by the Wayne Color-
plate Company, Detroit, Mich.

The color transparencies were supplied by the Institut Royal
du Patrimoine Artistique, Brussels (Louis Loose, photographer),
except for that of the van der Weyden, which was supplied
by the Museum of Fine Arts, Boston; that of the Petrus
Christus and that of the Master of the Saint Ursula Legend,
by The Detroit Institute of Arts (Joseph Klima, photographer),
and that of the van der Goes, by The Walters Art Gallery,
Baltimore.

The reproductions of the American loans are from photographs supplied through the courtesy of the lending institutions and collectors. The Belgian loans are reproduced from
photographs copyrighted by A.C.L., Brussels, Institut Royal du
Patrimoine Artistique.